SAGE Readings for Introductory Sociology

Third Edition

For first-year students, who never fail to inspire me.

SAGE Readings for Introductory Sociology

Third Edition

Kimberly McGann

Editor

Nazareth College

Los Angeles | London | New Delhi
Singapore | Washington DC | Melbourne

FOR INFORMATION:

SAGE Publications, Inc.
2455 Teller Road
Thousand Oaks, California 91320
E-mail: order@sagepub.com

SAGE Publications Ltd.
1 Oliver's Yard
55 City Road
London EC1Y 1SP
United Kingdom

SAGE Publications India Pvt. Ltd.
B 1/I 1 Mohan Cooperative Industrial Area
Mathura Road, New Delhi 110 044
India

SAGE Publications Asia-Pacific Pte. Ltd.
18 Cross Street #10-10/11/12
China Square Central
Singapore 048423

Printed in Canada

Library of Congress Cataloging-in-Publication Data

Names: McGann, Kimberly, editor.

Title: SAGE readings for introductory sociology / [edited by] Kimberly McGann.

Description: Third Edition. | Thousand Oaks : SAGE Publishing, 2021. | Revised edition of SAGE readings for introductory sociology, [2017] |

Identifiers: LCCN 2020048098 | ISBN 9781071834282 (paperback) | ISBN 9781071834268 (epub) | ISBN 9781071834275 (epub) | ISBN 9781071834251 (pdf)

Subjects: LCSH: Sociology.

Classification: LCC HM585 .S24 2021 | DDC 301—dc23
LC record available at https://lccn.loc.gov/2020048098

This book is printed on acid-free paper.

Acquisitions Editor: Jeff Lasser
Editorial Assistant: Tiara Beatty
Production Editor: Astha Jaiswal
Copy Editor: Integra
Typesetter: C&M Digitals (P) Ltd.
Proofreader: Lawrence W. Baker
Cover Designer: Dally Verghese
Marketing Manager: Jennifer Jones

21 22 23 24 25 10 9 8 7 6 5 4 3 2 1

Contents

Preface ix

PART I THINKING SOCIOLOGICALLY 1

Reading 1 The Sociological Imagination: The Promise 3
C. Wright Mills

Reading 2 "Not Your Typical Student": The Social Construction of the "First-Generation" College Student 11
Tina Wildhagen

Reading 3 W. E. B. Du Bois and Black Heterogeneity: How *The Philadelphia Negro* Shaped American Sociology 29
Marcus Anthony Hunter

Reading 4 Sense and Nonsense About Surveys 39
Howard Schuman

PART II CULTURE, SOCIALIZATION, AND INTERACTION 49

Reading 5 The Presentation of Self 51
Erving Goffman

Reading 6 American Hookup 61
Lisa Wade

Reading 7 Disciplined Preferences: Explaining the (Re)Production of Latino Endogamy 77
Jessica M. Vasquez

Reading 8 Rethinking Colorblindness: How Role Conflict Shapes Administrators' Responses to Racial Inequality at a Predominantly White University 99
Cedrick-Michael Simmons

Reading 9 Neither Clear Nor Present: The Social Construction of Safety and Danger 117
Ruth Simpson

PART III CONSTRUCTING DEVIANCE AND NORMALITY 127

Reading 10 Situational Ethics and College Student Cheating 129
Emily E. LaBeff, Robert E. Clark, Valerie J. Haines, and George M. Diekhoff

Reading 11 The New Jim Crow 141
Michelle Alexander

Reading 12 Calling the Shots: Why Parents Reject Vaccines 147
Jennifer A. Reich

Reading 13 American Policing and the Danger Imperative 161
Michael Sierra-Arévalo

PART IV GENDER 189

Reading 14 Doing Gender 191
Candace West and Don H. Zimmerman

Reading 15 Doing, Undoing, or Redoing Gender?: Learning From Transpeople in the Workplace 207
Catherine Connell

Reading 16 "Out" in the Club: The Down Low, Hip-Hop, and the Architexture of Black Masculinity 221
Jeffrey Q. McCune Jr.

Reading 17 Masculine Norms and Infectious Disease: The Case of COVID-19 233
Tyler Reny

PART V RACE 247

Reading 18 The Code of the Streets 249
Elijah Anderson

Reading 19 She's Not a Low-Class Dirty Girl 265
Kimberly Kay Hoang

Reading 20 America for Americans: A history of Xenophobia 285
Erika Lee

Reading 21 The Political Bind of Oil vs. Tribes 305
Yvonne P. Sherwood

PART VI SOCIAL CLASS 315

Reading 22 Unequal Childhoods: Class, Race, and Family Life 317
Annette Lareau

Reading 23 Social Class Differences in College Student Participation in Peace Corps, Teach for America, and Other Service Programs 329
Alanna Gillis

Reading 24 Strangers in Their Own Land: Anger and Mourning on the American Right 349
Arlie Russell Hochschild

Reading 25 Uberland: How Algorithms Are Rewriting the Rules of Work 367
Alex Rosenblat

Preface

How Should I Read This Book?

This book was designed to be appropriate for use either in conjunction with a traditional textbook or as a stand-alone text for an introduction to sociology course. Whether your instructor has assigned this book as a supplement or your only text, there are additional materials included to help you get the most from each article. Each reading has a brief introduction that places it in perspective for you and suggests an approach to reading the piece. There are also discussion questions and/or activities to accompany each piece that may be used as the basis of class discussion by your teacher or simply as thought-provoking exercises for you to do on your own. The writing styles of the readings vary widely, and you will likely find many of the pieces accessible and enjoyable to read. However, there are some that are likely to present more of a challenge, and I encourage you not to give up on these! Think of writing like wrapping paper: Just because you don't think it's attractive or it's hard to take apart doesn't mean that what's inside isn't really enjoyable! All these articles have something important and interesting to say about the social world we live in. Just as we shouldn't judge a book by its cover, I encourage you not to judge an article's ideas by its writing style!

I Like This! What Do I Do Now?

If you find yourself intrigued with some of the ideas you encounter in this book, you might consider majoring or minoring in sociology if you aren't already. Many students over the years have found a sociological perspective to be a compelling, useful, and meaningful way to understand the world around them but are unsure what exactly to do with those skills and ideas once they graduate. Your professor and the chair of the sociology department should be your first stop. They will have a good idea of the types of jobs that majors and minors from your school have found. The American Sociological Association also has an excellent set of resources for those interested in using a sociology major or minor on the job market. Just visit asanet.org and type *sociology major* into the search box (or visit directly at http://www.asanet.org/teaching-learning/undergraduate-student-resources).

Finally, remember that you don't have to major or minor in sociology to put the ideas from these readings to work in your own life and the world around you. A sociological perspective is a valuable tool for understanding how the context of the social world has consequences (good and bad) for what happens to individuals. Not only can this help you make informed decisions about your own life choices, but you'll be able to see how social forces also influence your life chances and plan accordingly.

Acknowledgments

I was lucky enough to have Donileen Loseke and Spencer Cahill introduce me to sociology at Skidmore College when I was an undergraduate, and I am still grateful for their dedication and talent as both sociologists and teachers. My experiences with them set the standard that I still aspire to as a teacher and scholar. My former classmate at Rutgers, Wayne Brekhus, inspires me with his ability to be an outstanding teacher and prolific scholar, and taking on this project in the middle of a pandemic and while planning for an uncertain fall was in part inspired by seeing how he balances such undertakings. My colleagues at Nazareth and elsewhere—Devparna Roy and Cedrick Michael Simmons in particular—were extremely helpful in sharing ideas and helping me think about the kinds of issues that were important to include in this edition.

I'd like to thank Jeff Lasser at SAGE Publications for offering me the chance to do a third edition and for having a wonderfully collaborative and straightforward approach to this process. This has again been a thoroughly enjoyable project to work on.

I am most grateful to all of the students who have taken classes with me over the past 13 years. Their insights and feedback have vastly improved my teaching, and I have learned as much from them as they have from me. Their goodwill and willingness to put up with (and often embrace) my wacky analogies, stick figure drawings, and bad jokes always amaze me. College students are interesting people at an interesting time in their lives, and I feel lucky to have a job that lets me be a part of that.

PART

I

Thinking Sociologically

The Sociological Imagination

The Promise

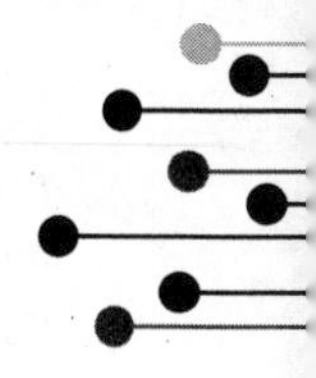

C. Wright Mills

Students often enroll in an introduction to sociology course without having any idea what sociology is. Oftentimes, the course description sounded interesting or the class fulfilled a requirement or a friend recommended the class. And sometimes, students leave class at the end of the semester having learned a great deal about poverty, social norms, culture, race, and gender but perhaps still a little fuzzy on what makes sociology "sociology." This is not just understandable, but it also should be of no great surprise given that many of the topics that sociologists study are also studied by other disciplines. Social workers and economists also study the distribution of wealth and the effects of poverty. Psychologists are interested in how social norms affect people's behavior. Anthropologists study culture. Historians look at how gender roles and race relations have changed over time. If there's so much overlap in what different disciplines study, what is it that makes sociology unique as a discipline?

The answer lies not in what *sociologists study but in* how *they study the world around them. This unique sociological perspective is described in this classic piece by C. Wright Mills. He uses the term* sociological imagination *to describe a way of studying the world that connects what happens to individuals to larger social, cultural, political, and economic forces. Or as he puts it, "Neither the life of an individual nor the history of a society can be understood without understanding both" (p. 3). What Mills is arguing is that sociology provides a perspective that lets people see how what happens to them is influenced by events, policies, and interactions that make up the social structure of a society. It's important to note that he's not at all arguing that we as individuals have no autonomy and that our own individual actions and efforts don't matter in what happens to us. Instead, he's urging us to be aware of the social and historical context in which our lives unfold and to think about how those social and historical forces shape our individual life chances. (Life chances are the odds that some opportunity or obstacle will present itself to you.) To give one example—college students who graduated between 2008 and 2014 are much*

---

more likely to be unemployed or underemployed than students who graduated before 2008. Why might this be? From an individual perspective, we might argue that these particular students are less motivated or not as smart or qualified as those who graduated before 2008. Perhaps they just didn't try as hard to get jobs. These are all individual-level explanations, and none of them explain why these graduates were so much less likely to find good jobs. But if we employ Mills's sociological imagination, it immediately becomes clear that the number of jobs available in the U.S. economy shrank drastically in 2008 due to the financial crisis. It certainly mattered for students graduating in that time period if they were smart, qualified, and motivated to find a job. But it also mattered that there weren't enough jobs in the economy for all the qualified candidates. This is an example of linking what's happening at the social and historical level (the economy shrank and had fewer jobs available) to what happens to individuals (the 2008–2014 cohort of college graduates were less likely to find good jobs). And it will be a similar case for those who graduated in May of 2020 in the middle of the COVID-19 pandemic. Their job prospects will not be the same as for those who graduated just a year earlier in 2019. Seeing this link between the conditions in the broader society and what happens to individuals is the underpinning of sociological imagination, and it is this way of thinking about the world that defines sociology.

As you read this article, think about what aspects of your life are shaped by where and when you are living. The sociological imagination is the underpinning of sociology as a discipline, but it's also incredibly useful in understanding how and why life unfolds the way it does for you and those around you. Once you start to be able to see the connections between what happens to individuals and larger social forces, you're well on your way to having a better understanding of the social world and being able to see the world from a sociological perspective.

Nowadays men often feel that their private lives are a series of traps. They sense that within their everyday worlds, they cannot overcome their troubles, and in this feeling, they are often quite correct: What ordinary men are directly aware of and what they try to do are bounded by the private orbits in which they live; their visions and their powers are limited to the close-up scenes of job, family, neighborhood; in other milieux, they move vicariously and remain spectators. And the more aware they become, however vaguely, of ambitions and of threats which transcend their immediate locales, the more trapped they seem to feel.

Underlying this sense of being trapped are seemingly impersonal changes in the very structure of continent-wide societies. The facts of contemporary history are also facts about the success and the failure of individual men and women. When a society is industrialized, a peasant becomes a worker; a feudal lord is liquidated or becomes a businessman. When classes rise or fall, a man is employed or unemployed; when the rate of investment goes up or down, a man takes new heart or goes broke. When wars happen, an insurance salesman becomes a rocket launcher; a store clerk, a radar man; a wife lives alone; a child grows up without a father. Neither the life of an individual nor the history of a society can be understood without understanding both.

Yet men do not usually define the troubles they endure in terms of historical change and institutional contradiction. The well-being they enjoy, they do not usually impute to the big ups and downs of the societies in which they live. Seldom aware of the intricate connection between the patterns of their own lives and the course of world history, ordinary men do not usually know what this connection means for the kinds of men they are becoming and for the kinds of history-making in which they might take part. They do not possess the quality of mind essential to grasp the interplay of man and society, of biography and history, of self and world. They cannot cope with their personal troubles in such ways as to control the structural transformations that usually lie behind them.

What they need, and what they feel they need, is a quality of mind that will help them to use information and to develop reason in order to achieve lucid summations of what is going on in the world and of what may be happening within themselves. It is this quality, I am going to contend, that journalists and scholars, artists and publics, scientists and editors are coming to expect of what may be called the sociological imagination.

1

The sociological imagination enables its possessor to understand the larger historical scene in terms of its meaning for the inner life and the external career of a variety of individuals. It enables him to take into account how individuals, in the welter of their daily experience, often become falsely conscious of their social positions. Within that welter, the framework of modern society is sought, and within that framework the psychologies of a variety of men and women are formulated. By such means the personal uneasiness of individuals is focused upon explicit troubles and the indifference of publics is transformed into involvement with public issues.

The first fruit of this imagination—and the first lesson of the social science that embodies it—is the idea that the individual can understand his own experience and gauge his own fate only by locating himself within his period, that he can know his own chances in life only by becoming aware of those of all individuals in his circumstances. In many ways it is a terrible lesson; in many ways a magnificent one. We do not know the limits of man's capacities for supreme effort or willing degradation, for agony or glee, for pleasurable brutality or the sweetness of reason. But in our time we have come to know that the limits of "human nature" are frighteningly broad. We have come to know that every individual lives, from one generation to the next, in some society; that he lives out a biography, and that he lives it out within some historical sequence. By the fact of his living he contributes, however minutely, to the shaping of this society and to the course of its history, even as he is made by society and by its historical push and shove.

The sociological imagination enables us to grasp history and biography and the relations between the two within society. That is its task and its promise. To recognize this task and this promise is the mark of the classic social analyst. It is characteristic of Herbert Spencer—turgid, polysyllabic, comprehensive; of E. A. Ross—graceful, muckraking, upright; of Auguste Comte and Emile Durkheim; of the intricate and subtle Karl Mannheim. It is the quality of all that is intellectually excellent in Karl Marx; it is the clue to Thorstein Veblen's brilliant and ironic insight, to Joseph Schumpeter's many-sided constructions of reality; it is the basis of the psychological sweep of W. E. H. Lecky no less than of the profundity and clarity of Max Weber. And it is the signal of what is best in contemporary studies of man and society.

No social study that does not come back to the problems of biography, of history and of their intersections within a society has completed its intellectual journey. Whatever the specific problems of the classic social analysts, however limited or however broad the features of social reality they have examined, those who have been imaginatively aware of the promise of their work have consistently asked three sorts of questions:

1) What is the structure of this particular society as a whole? What are its essential components, and how are they related to one another? How does it differ from other varieties of social order? Within it, what is the meaning of any particular feature for its continuance and for its change?

2) Where does this society stand in human history? What are the mechanics by which it is changing? What is its place within and its meaning for the development of humanity as a whole? How does any particular feature we are examining affect, and how is it affected by, the historical period in which it moves? And this period—what are its essential features? How does it differ from other periods? What are its characteristic ways of history-making?

3) What varieties of men and women now prevail in this society and in this period? And what varieties are coming to prevail? In what ways are they selected and formed, liberated and repressed,

made sensitive and blunted? What kinds of "human nature" are revealed in the conduct and character we observe in this society in this period? And what is the meaning for "human nature" of each and every feature of the society we are examining?

Whether the point of interest is a great power state or a minor literary mood, a family, a prison, a creed—these are the kinds of questions the best social analysts have asked. They are the intellectual pivots of classic studies of man in society—and they are the questions inevitably raised by any mind possessing the sociological imagination. For that imagination is the capacity to shift from one perspective to another—from the political to the psychological from examination of a single family to comparative assessment of the national budgets of the world; from the theological school to the military establishment; from considerations of an oil industry to studies of contemporary poetry. It is the capacity to range from the most impersonal and remote transformations to the most intimate features of the human self—and to see the relations between the two. Back of its use there is always the urge to know the social and historical meaning of the individual in the society and in the period in which he has his quality and his being.

That, in brief, is why it is by means of the sociological imagination that men now hope to grasp what is going on in the world, and to understand what is happening in themselves as minute points of the intersections of biography and history within society. In large part contemporary man's self-conscious view of himself as at least an outsider, if not a permanent stranger, rests upon an absorbed realization of social relativity and of the transformative power of history. The sociological imagination is the most fruitful form of this self-consciousness. By its use men whose mentalities have swept only a series of limited orbits often come to feel as if suddenly awakened in a house with which they had only supposed themselves to be familiar. Correctly or incorrectly, they often come to feel that they can now provide themselves with adequate summations, cohesive assessments, comprehensive orientations. Older decisions that once appeared sound now seem to them products of a mind unaccountably dense. Their capacity for astonishment is made lively again. They acquire a new way of thinking, they experience a transvaluation of values: in a word, by their reflection and by their sensibility, they realize the cultural meaning of the social sciences.

2

Perhaps the most fruitful distinction with which the sociological imagination works is between "the personal troubles of milieu" and "the public issues of social structure." This distinction is an essential tool of the sociological imagination and a feature of all classic work in social science.

Troubles occur within the character of the individual and within the range of his immediate relations with others; they have to do with his self and with those limited areas of social life of which he is directly and personally aware. Accordingly, the statement and the resolution of troubles properly lie within the individual as a biographical entity and within the scope of his immediate milieu—the social setting that is directly open to his personal experience and to some extent his willful activity. A trouble is a private matter: values cherished by an individual are felt by him to be threatened.

Issues have to do with matters that transcend these local environments of the individual and the range of his inner life. They have to do with the organization of many such milieux into the institutions of a historical society as a whole, with the ways in which various milieux overlap and interpenetrate to form the larger structure of social and historical life. An issue is a public matter: some value cherished by publics is felt to be threatened. Often there is a debate about what that value really is and about what it is that really threatens it. This debate is often without focus if only because it is the very nature of an issue, unlike even widespread trouble, that it cannot very well be defined in terms of the immediate and everyday environments of ordinary men. An issue, in fact, often involves a crisis in institutional arrangements, and often too it involves what Marxists call "contradictions" or "antagonisms."

In these terms, consider unemployment. When, in a city of 100,000, only one man is unemployed, that is his personal trouble, and for its relief we properly look to the character of the man, his skills, and his immediate opportunities. But when in a nation of 50 million employees, 15 million men are unemployed, that is an issue, and we may not hope to find its solution within the range of opportunities open to any one individual. The very structure of opportunities has collapsed. Both the correct statement of the problem and the range of possible solutions require us to consider the economic and political institutions of the society, and not merely the personal situation and character of a scatter of individuals.

Consider war. The personal problem of war, when it occurs, may be how to survive it or how to die in it with honor; how to make money out of it; how to climb into the higher safety of the military apparatus; or how to contribute to the war's termination. In short, according to one's values, to find a set of milieux and within it to survive the war or make one's death in it meaningful. But the structural issues of war have to do with its causes; with what types of men it throws up into command; with its effects upon economic and political, family and religious institutions, with the unorganized irresponsibility of a world of nation-states.

Consider marriage. Inside a marriage a man and a woman may experience personal troubles, but when the divorce rate during the first four years of marriage is 250 out of every 1,000 attempts, this is an indication of a structural issue having to do with the institutions of marriage and the family and other institutions that bear upon them.

In so far as an economy is so arranged that slumps occur, the problem of unemployment becomes incapable of personal solution. In so far as war is inherent in the nation-state system and in the uneven industrialization of the world, the ordinary individual in his restricted milieu will be powerless—with or without psychiatric aid—to solve the troubles this system or lack of system imposes upon him. In so far as the family as an institution turns women into darling little slaves and men into their chief providers and unweaned dependents, the problem of a satisfactory marriage remains incapable of purely private solution.

What we experience in various and specific milieux, I have noted, is often caused by structural changes. Accordingly, to understand the changes of many personal milieux we are required to look beyond them. And the number and variety of such structural changes increase as the institutions within which we live become more embracing and more intricately connected with one another. To be aware of the idea of social structure and to use it with sensibility is to be capable of tracing such linkages among a great variety of milieux. To be able to do that is to possess the sociological imagination.

DISCUSSION QUESTIONS

1. Make a list of three to four important goals you would like to accomplish sometime in the future. What larger social forces will either facilitate you achieving these goals or make them more difficult to attain?
2. How do you think your life would be different if you had been born 100 years ago? What do you think would have been different about your childhood? Your diet and exercise habits? Your life expectancy? Your educational opportunities? Your career choices? Your fashion sense?
3. Friendship seems like a natural, freely chosen relationship that is based entirely on individual preferences. People who meet and enjoy each other's company often become friends. How do larger social forces influence our "choice" of friends? Does when and where you grow up affect who you might become friends with? Does your gender, race, or social class? What role do you think technology and social media might play in how people go about getting and maintaining friendships?

READING 2

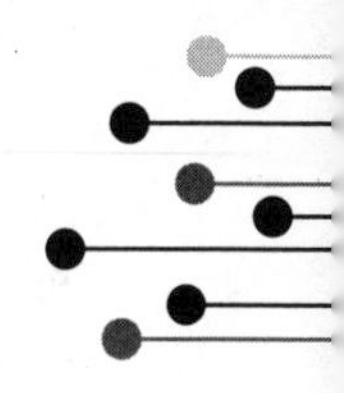

"Not Your Typical Student"

The Social Construction of the "First-Generation" College Student

Tina Wildhagen

About a third of students enrolled in higher education are first-generation students—*students whose parents do not have a four-year college degree. While these students have represented a significant proportion of those attending college for many years, it was not until the early 2000s that the label "first generation" was created by schools and applied to such students. Like all identities, the category of first-generation student is socially constructed. It is a label whose meaning is shaped by those who use it and those to whom it is applied.*

In this research, Tina Wildhagen shows how one elite school ("Cabot College") uses the first-generation label to serve the school's institutional interests rather than the interests of the students. This is an intriguing finding, as membership in the first-generation student category generally brings more support (academic, financial, and social) from schools. She also finds that the first-generation label is used as a proxy for social class, and that the staff at Cabot that work with first-generation students assume that they are academically and socially less prepared than their peers because of presumed lower social class, even though at Cabot first-generation students are very near their peers in terms of financial resources and academic strength. Wildhagen interviewed first-generation students and found that while some embraced the first-generation label, others found Cabot's programs for the group to be offensive and unrealistic. But her most significant sociological finding is that the ideology that underlies the first-generation label encourages students to focus on their own individual upward mobility and not to think about how colleges like Cabot might reproduce social class inequality. Identifying with others of your social class and realizing that you share similar life chances is what sociologists call class consciousness, and it tends to be one of the prerequisites to social movements, whether at a particular school across a nation, that demand true equality of opportunity.

Excerpt from "'Not Your Typical Student': The Social Construction of the 'First-Generation' College Student" by Wildhagen, T. *Qualitative Sociology* (2015) 38, pp. 285–303. Reprinted with permission.

As you read, think about the other ways that schools categorize students, and how those categories benefit the institutional interests of the schools.

Sociologists have long argued that classifying people into groups lies at the heart of inequality (e.g., Massey 2007; Tilly 1999). As Massey (2007, 5–6) writes, "All stratification processes boil down to a combination of two simple but powerful mechanisms: the allocation of people to social categories, and the institutionalization of practices that allocate resources across these categories." To the extent that cultural communities and social identities cohere around these social categories, categorization also matters for inequality because it can shape peoples' behaviors and social identities. Moreover, the categorization of people by institutions often serves institutional interests by increasing institutional capacities to monitor and control the behavior and subjectivities of individuals (Scott 1998; Weber 1978).

In this study, I analyze the social construction of one such social category—first-generation college students—at a selective college. I examine how the institutional discourse about first-generation students benefits the school in ways that are at odds with the interests of the students themselves. First-generation college students are typically defined as students without a parent who has graduated from a 4-year college. Although there have always been college students without college-going parents, it was not until the early 2000s that colleges and universities began to socially construct this category—that is, create a decision rule for membership in this category, classify students according to the rule, construct a discourse that defines what it means to belong to this category, and assume that individuals who are assigned to this category find that assignation to be meaningful in some way. In so doing, the category moves from being defined solely in terms of its decision rule (i.e., whether one has a parent who has obtained a college degree) to being defined in terms of the particular social meanings that colleges attach to it.[1] As Armstrong and Massé (2014, 807) write in a review of sociological scholarship on higher education, "Schools not only produce classification systems but also play a salient role in the instantiation of them—that is in the production of persons to fill categories."

While abundant research on first-generation college students exists, many researchers and higher education professionals tend to take the category for granted, assuming that it is a sensible way of grouping students, and that students themselves see the category as meaningful. Taking a different approach, this study positions the first-generation category itself as the object of analysis. The questions raised by this study revolve around the tension between the external classification of individuals using a nascent social category—the category of first-generation college student—and the reactions of the classified to that assignation. First, I seek to understand the particular discursive meanings that a selective college ("Cabot College")[2] has attached to this category, paying close attention to the ways in which these meanings benefit the college's interests.

The Power of Classification

Sociologists view classification as an essential element of how power operates in the social world. Bourdieu (1984) focuses on the power to classify certain cultural practices and world views as legitimate as key to understanding how social class inequality works. For example, schools are primary arbiters of class inequality because they evaluate students according to purportedly neutral standards that are actually reflective of middle-class cultural practices and world views. Not only is power exercised by classifying cultural practices, expectations, and narratives as legitimate, but also through the classification of *people* (Bourdieu 1987). Writing about the consequences of being classified, Jenkins (2000, 21–22) notes that "The effective categorization of a group of people by a more powerful Other is thus never just a matter of classification. . . . As an intervention in that group's social world it will . . . change that world and the experience of living in it; in other words, it has consequences." That is, classification matters for the people being classified.

From this perspective, classifying students as first generation is not a power-neutral process that follows from an inevitable and logical classification of students, but rather an attempt to group students in a way that benefits institutional interests. Moreover, some of the institutional interests served by classifying students as first generation may conflict with students' own interests.

Data and Methods

Drawing on data from a larger study of the construction of the first-generation college student category and first-generation identity at multiple colleges, the current study focuses on these processes at one selective liberal arts college ("Cabot College").[3] I collected data at Cabot over a 2-year period, between 2012 and 2014, attending events and conducting interviews with students and staff.

Selective colleges serve as instructive sites for research on the construction of the first-generation category because they sit near the top of the hierarchy of higher education institutions in terms of resources, prestige, and student outcomes. As such, they offer students without a familial heritage of college-going the possibility of more dramatic upward social mobility compared to less selective and open-access schools.[4] This possibility of steep upward ascent means that first-generation students at selective colleges may encounter cultural environments that differ more markedly from their home environments compared to the differences that may be experienced at less selective institutions (Davis 2010).

The first part of the analysis focuses on the discourse about first-generation college students at Cabot and the ways in which this discourse serves institutional interests. I trace the contours of this discourse through in-depth interviews with professional staff working in admissions and student affairs and attendance at events and programs aimed at first-generation students. I conducted interviews with ten staff members (six in admissions and four in student affairs), each lasting between 45 and 60 minutes. All interviews were semi-structured, beginning with a common schedule of questions and topics but open to pursuing additional topics that were relevant to each participant. Interviews with staff members covered the following topics: staff members' work with first-generation students (both direct and indirect), their perceptions of first-generation students compared to their peers, and their opinions on the usefulness of categorizing students as first generation at Cabot. I also attended four official college events held specifically for first-generation students over the course of two years, including two programs for entering students and two formal dinners.

The second part of the analysis focuses on how students who are categorized as first generation make sense of this categorization. I draw on semi-structured interviews with 30 first-generation students to investigate how students react to being categorized as such by Cabot. Each of the interviews lasted between 50 and 90 minutes. The interviews covered the following topics: family background, family's perceptions of the purpose of college, family encouragement for college, high school academic preparation and social experiences, the transition to college, knowledge of the first-generation category, identification with the first-generation category, and connections with other first-generation students. Although all student participants are first generation, the sample suggests the heterogeneity that exists within that group. The sample includes 18 students from minority racial or ethnic groups (10 Latinas, six African Americans, and two Asians) and 12 who identified as white.[5] While none of the students' parents had direct experience with a selective college or university, about half of them (16) had parents who had either attended a postsecondary institution before dropping out or obtained an Associate's degree during the student's childhood. Most of the students' parents held working class jobs, such as factory worker, clerical worker, and food-service worker. A minority of students (eight) had at least one parent who held a lower middle-class job, such as bank teller and computer repair technician.

Results

Institutional Discourse about First-Generation Students

First-Generation Discourse: Not Your Typical Student

The starting point for the analysis of the institutional discourse about first-generation college students at Cabot is that these students are seen as separate from the typical college student. According to my participants in the admissions office, which is responsible for marking prospective Cabot students as first generation at their point of first formal contact with the school, this categorization is a necessary and legitimate way of grouping students. Admissions staff saw the first-generation category as having inherent meaning, with the possibility that the meaning of the category was constructed at least in part by the institution going largely unacknowledged. All six of the admissions staff members whom I interviewed indicated that they saw first-generation students as different from other students in consequential ways, despite the fact that they have little if any direct contact with students either before or after they arrive on campus. One admissions worker related how those who read admissions files could assume certain things about an applicant from knowing the educational background of the student's parents: "We know that when we see that a student is first generation, that student isn't your typical student. We have to look at that student differently."

All six of the participants working in the admissions office made comments that similarly distinguished first-generation students from other students, with this marker of difference typically focusing on first-generation students' presumed deficiencies relative to their peers. For instance, when I asked another admissions worker how she thought first-generation applicants differed from other students, her response suggested academic deficiency: "They [first-generation students] haven't had the preparation that our other applicants have. They've gone to high schools with limited resources. They often can't write as well." Another admissions worker referenced cultural differences between first-generation and other students, stating that first-generation students are "coming from different worlds" and "aren't familiar with the culture of college." Admissions staff members thus transform students whose parents have limited direct experience with higher education into an abstraction that focuses on their assumed disadvantages and deficits.

However, according to survey data from a pooled sample of first-year students at Cabot between 2010 and 2014, first-generation Cabot students as a group may not differ as widely from their continuing-generation peers as admissions staff believe they do.[6] On average, first-generation students at Cabot reported strong GPAs (3.31, the equivalent of a B-plus average), only slightly lower than the GPA (3.46) reported by their continuing-generation peers. Additionally, 20% of first-generation students reported a GPA of 3.7 (an A-minus average) or higher (compared to about 30% for continuing-generation students). While first-generation Cabot students do report lower average family incomes than their continuing-generation peers, the average reported family income of first-generation respondents ($100,000) exceeds the national median income for married couples in 2013: $76,500 (DeNavas-Walt and Proctor 2014). Twenty percent of first-generation students also reported family incomes that exceeded the sample mean (58% for continuing-generation students).

These data show that there are a non-trivial number of students at Cabot who are categorized as first generation, perform quite well academically, and whose families are not economically disadvantaged (at least according to family income), conflicting with the monolithic construction of the group as disadvantaged and underperforming. While first-generation students both at Cabot and nationally (Saenz et al. 2007) do report slightly lower grades than their peers, first-generation Cabot students perform well academically, with many excellent students among them.[7, 8]

First-Generation Discourse: Becoming Caboters

Once students are admitted, the admissions office provides lists of those students who have been categorized as first generation to various programs administered by student affairs. Among these programs are an orientation and formal dinners held specifically for first-generation students. I conducted interviews with four student affairs workers and attended four of these events.

My interviews with student affairs staff and observations of events for first-generation students indicated that once these students are marked as atypical during the admissions process, they are discursively constructed as conditionally worthy of the institutional resources that are bestowed upon them. This worthiness hinges on students' amenability to socioeconomic and cultural transformation. Earning Cabot's continued support requires recognizing one's family as presenting barriers to success. Students also must be willing to learn about middle-class culture and appreciate its values and aesthetics.

The analysis revealed two ways in which encouraging first-generation students to distance themselves from their families and acculturate to the middle class benefit the institution. First, encouraging separation from families provides Cabot with the space it needs to instill in these students a strong common identity as "Caboters." Cabot staff actively draw upon some of the same qualities that are associated with the discursive construction of the first-generation category—being intrepid explorers of the world who are dedicated to self-improvement—in order to accomplish this. The very term itself—*first generation*—connotes someone who is on the vanguard, exploring unknown terrain that one's parents were unable or unwilling to confront. Second, encouraging first-generation students' movement away from their families and toward middle-class acculturation provides them with a hybrid social class identity that lessens the possibility of recognizing or engaging in class conflict at Cabot.

Each of the four student affairs workers whom I interviewed characterized first-generation students' parents as unfamiliar with life at a selective college and, therefore, unable to assist them with making informed decisions about any aspect of college life. For example, when asked how first-generation parents' involvement figures into their adjustment to Cabot, one staff member described these parents as unhelpful at best:

Staff Member: These students can't call their parents and ask them which classes to take, which clubs to join. Their parents just have no idea about how a school like this works. That's one of the main difficulties for these students in adjusting to life here. They watch their peers call their parents to consult with them about various things, and they just can't do it. I knew a [first-generation] student who was talking to her mom about taking an art history course, and her mom just blew up at her. She didn't understand why a student would want to take a course like that. This particular student decided that it was time to stop talking with her mom about her courses.

Interviewer: What about the art history course upset the student's mother?

Staff Member: I guess she thought that art history was useless in terms of securing a job after college. She just didn't seem to get what we're trying to do here, to broaden students' horizons, to make them see things in a new way.

In this case, the parent of the first-generation college student is characterized not only as unhelpful, but also as contesting Cabot's efforts to educate students in the liberal arts tradition. The staff member sees this student's mother as obstructing Cabot's attempt to "make [students] see things in a new way," which the school sees as an important component of what it means to be a Caboter.

Students are warned that their families may act as barriers to their progress, and, as such, they are cautioned that they should be wary of familial interference. They must "blaze their own trails," as one staff member put it.

Another staff member indicates potential for Cabot to use the first-generation identity to instill a strong Caboter identity in first-generation students:

Staff member: We want all students to feel a sense of belonging to this place. We want them all to wear that Cabot badge loud and proud, to be a Caboter—and hopefully to return year after year, long after they've graduated. In order for them to do that, they need to be a part of things here on campus. They can't be stuck in the world they knew back home. They have to be present here.

Interviewer: Does that mean that first-generation students have trouble also identifying as authentic Cabot students, as Caboters?

Staff member: No, I don't think it *has* to mean that. Cabot students are strong and driven, they want to explore themselves and what the world has to offer, and first-generation students have that, too. So that's a good fit, but we want [first-generation] students to have the opportunity to embrace all that it means to be a Caboter.

From this perspective, encouragement to break from one's family and focus on one's life at Cabot creates space for the school to instill a strong sense of institutional identity among first-generation students. This staff member alludes to alumni allegiance, with students "return[ing] year after year," as one reason why fostering an institutional identity is in the interest of the college. Scott (1998, 346) notes that states tend to plan interventions not for individuals with specific tastes and needs, but instead for "generic subjects," "standardized citizens [who] were uniform in their needs and even interchangeable." In the same way, transforming all students into Caboters simplifies the school's work of planning for students' needs and designing ways to produce loyal graduates.

First-Generation Discourse: Embracing the Middle Class

In order to achieve the upward mobility that a selective college offers them, first-generation students also receive the message from Cabot that they must learn to appreciate and affect middle-class cultural values and norms. The invitation to a dinner held for first-generation students, for example, advised students to wear "business casual" attire, explicitly stating that this excludes pajamas and hats. Many of my student participants referred to this dinner during our interviews, describing the "strange atmosphere" of the event. One student described her reaction to the dinner:

> Yeah, I walked in, and there were like all of these musicians just playing there. I was like what am I supposed to do? Stand right here and listen to it? Or am I supposed to try to talk to people while I'm there. It just seemed really artificial, like, here, listen to this fancy music, first-generation college students. It was really awkward.

This student's comment points to the part of the discourse about first-generation students that focuses on the need to acculturate to the middle class. Many scholars have shown how middle-class cultural capital is valued by gateway institutions like schools and workplaces (Lareau 2003; Bourdieu and Passeron 1990). As such, one could make the argument that it is useful for students to become familiar with middle-class cultural norms and tastes. However, given that this emphasis on middle-class socialization is embedded within a discourse that frames first-generation students' families and communities as liabilities, and their own academic preparation as lacking, middle-class socialization becomes framed in terms of learning the *proper* way of behaving and thinking, rather than as a classed set of behaviors that may be valued arbitrarily.

As Armstrong and Massé (2014, 808) note, a "central task" of colleges and universities is "the production of individuals identified with the professional and managerial classes." The first-generation category may help schools, particularly selective schools, to accomplish that task by providing students with a hybrid social class identity defined by upward mobility and individuality. This hybrid identity potentially diverts students' attention away from antagonistic class relations both on and off campus. The first-generation identity may serve to discipline students to think about social class in individualistic and personal terms rather than in collective terms, lessening the possibility of overt class conflict on campus and paving the way for Cabot, as a selective college, to fulfill expectations of producing upper middle-class managers and professionals. As Russell writes, "Today's vocabulary of class defines the landscape of social relations in terms of politically, socially and historically unencumbered individuals whose liberties are given free expression in the market place" (1995, 36). First-generation students become "unencumbered individuals" who can compete in the free market only once they break from their families of origin. Here, first-generation students are encouraged to adopt a "neoliberal subjectivity," a view of actively constructing oneself and one's future, which Weis et al. (2014, 202) also found among students at elite secondary schools. One student described this as Cabot's attempt to turn first-generation students into "good little Caboters."

Students' Responses to the First-Generation Category

In this second half of the analysis, I present students' reactions to being categorized as first generation and to the specific discursive construction of first-generation students at Cabot. While the first-generation category benefits the institution in a number of ways, not all students readily accepted this categorization, with some even pushing back against the first-generation discourse.

Students on Being Categorized as First Generation

Student participants varied by their familiarity with the term "first generation" before they arrived at Cabot. While 40% of my student participants reported having never heard the term before becoming a Cabot student, the other 60% had already heard this term applied to themselves during their participation as high school students in various programs designed to prepare disadvantaged students for college. Students who had not been identified previously as first generation tended to express discomfort with this categorization, while those who had already been classified as such tended to accept the categorization.

A number (seven) of students explained how their pre-college programs had taught them to embrace their first-generation status as a strategic advantage in college admissions. For instance, after noting that she had first learned the term "first generation" in a college preparation program called Reaching High, one student went on to explain how the program had taught students that colleges valued first-generation applicants:

> [Reaching High] used it when it regarded [college] applications. So when I first applied [to college], [Reaching High] told me to say I was first generation. You know, they said colleges like to see that, that it could help your application.

Whereas first-generation students who had been categorized as such before arriving at Cabot expressed familiarity with the first-generation category, with many viewing it as a strategic advantage in college admissions, the students who had not participated in pre-college programming aimed at first-generation students were unfamiliar with the term before entering Cabot. While these students were aware that their parents had either not attended or not completed college, none had ever been explicitly categorized according to that fact, nor had many of them given much thought to the implications for them of their parents' educational attainment.

When asked whether she had thought of herself as first generation prior to arriving at Cabot, one such student said that while she knew that her parents had not gone to college, she "didn't really identify like that." She went on, "Most of my friends at home were that [first generation] too, so it was nothing special." Another student described herself as "still figuring out the first-generation thing" because it had been new to her when she arrived at Cabot. Yet another said that she had not known that first generation "existed as an identity" before coming to Cabot. Nine of these students expressed apprehension at being newly categorized as first generation. As one student told me:

Student: Yeah, so I hadn't even encountered that term until I came to Cabot. The first encounter that I had [with the term] is that Cabot has this great peer mentoring program for students in the sciences and so they pick up students who are first generation.

Interviewer: So how did it feel to learn that Cabot was now defining you as a member of this group that you'd never heard of?

Student: I like the mentoring program that I'm a part of. I think that's really cool. But I do feel a little uncomfortable about being put into this first-generation box when I'm not necessarily sure what that's supposed to mean. It's not necessarily negative, but it does make me feel uncomfortable sometimes.

The extent to which Cabot students accepted their classification as first generation varied by students' previous experiences with this classification. On the one hand, first-generation students who had been classified as such prior to attending Cabot tended to view this classification as legitimate and meaningful. Students who had not previously encountered this category, on the other hand, were more likely to question the legitimacy of their personal categorization as first generation.

Students on Becoming Caboters

Although the institutional discourse about the need for first-generation students to break from their families of origin was presented as a universal truth for all first-generation students at Cabot, there was a disparate impact of that piece of the discourse on the students. Some students expressed and displayed a great deal of emotional turmoil about disconnecting from their parents, often crying when describing the changing nature of their relationships with their parents since arriving at Cabot. This separation from one's parents, held up by Cabot as a necessary condition of first-generation students' success, amounted to a rejection of one's parents for these students. Other students seemed to be less emotionally affected by this process, tending to describe separation from parents as a "normal" part of growing up. The following two students' responses to a program for entering first-generation students, where students were advised to limit contact with their families back home and focus on the resources available at Cabot, illustrate these disparate responses:

Student 1: There's no way. I can't go that long without talking to my parents. . . . I need to see how they're doing, too. Like my little sister and brother. I need to see how they're doing in school.

Interviewer: How did you feel when they said that you shouldn't talk to your parents that often?

Student 1: (through tears) It was upsetting. I can't just leave my family behind like that. . . . Maybe I don't want to be a good little Caboter. Maybe I want to hold on to who I am. They can't take that from me.

Student 2: Oh, believe me, I don't plan to talk to my parents very often. I mean I love them, don't get me wrong, but I need to focus on me here. That's why I'm here.

Interviewer: Do you think that they will call you very often?

Student 2: Maybe like once a week or something. Not too much. No, I think they understand. I need to have some space to figure out life here.

Here, both students perceive the school's directive to avoid familial intrusions as a way to transform them into Caboters. However, while the first student questions whether she "wants to be a good little Caboter," viewing the adoption of a Cabot identity as potentially inconsistent with maintaining who she really is, the second student says that she "does need some space to figure out life here," suggesting that becoming a Caboter might be an important part of who she wants to be.

Students on Adopting a New Social Class Identity

While there were differences in students' willingness and ability to limit contact with their families back home during their time at Cabot, all first-generation students reported feeling culturally out of place at Cabot. Some of the students linked their discomfort with what they perceived as Cabot's efforts to encourage first-generation students to adopt a new social class identity.

As described earlier, a number of my participants (eight) had attended dinners for first-generation college students at Cabot, two of which I also attended. The dinners were formal, with servers bustling around the room and a string quartet playing in the corner. According to my field notes, during the period before the actual dinner when guests were expected to socialize, many of the students stood along the walls clustered into groups of two or three, glancing from the floor to the string quartet, unsure of what to do. One student described receiving the invitation to this event:

> I didn't know what to say [when I received the invitation] because they sent the rudest emails out, like you need to wear formal clothes. That means not pajamas, and not this and this. And it had really patronizing pictures, like *really* patronizing pictures of a suit, or a dress.

Offended by the implication that first-generation students would wear pajamas to a formal event, this student perceived this push to adopt middle-class cultural styles of professional dress as patronizing.

Another student recognized the potential for the first-generation category to dampen the social class awareness of those who are categorized as such by seeing events such as the dinner for first-generation students as lacking solidarity:

Student: In our discussions on campus most of the time, things like class get lost. I mean, I guess when you finally realize you're a minority of some group, you really understand that there's [class] oppression going on. But I feel like the [class] minority here is so low, and there's not a lot of resistance going on here. I'm just looking for more people I can relate to based on class.

Interviewer: Have you attended any of the campus events or programs for first-generation students?

Student: I mean, yeah, like I went to the first-generation dinner, but there was *no solidarity* there. I hated it.

In her negative reaction to the dinner for first-generation students, this student displays a nascent criticism of Cabot's use of the first-generation category to portray social class as an individual achievement rather than relational groups engaged in conflict.

There were, however, a small number of students (three) who had come to embrace the first-generation category for its provision of a classed identity that allowed them to avoid discussing their social class backgrounds in more overt terms. One student's comments typify these sentiments:

Interviewer: Has it been meaningful for you to be a first-generation student at Cabot?

Student:	I would say it's probably one of the most meaningful things I've gotten out of Cabot thus far. Part of my culture shock coming in was I didn't know it was common to have parents with Ph.D.'s or with Master's Degrees. I just thought everyone sort of worked blue collar. That's what I was used to. But being first generation, that's a very positive thing. I'm doing something that my parents haven't done. And I can talk about my background in a positive way that people respect.
Interviewer:	So do you talk about being first generation more than other aspects of your background?
Student:	It's pretty much all I say about myself if I'm talking about my background. I don't want to get into all of that social class stuff, because it can put people off. I don't want to talk about money or anything. But first generation, that's cool. It's like I've achieved something to be here, not like I have this thing going against me.

This student saw the first-generation identity as offering her an opportunity to frame herself as an individual who had earned her place at Cabot, as opposed to someone from a disadvantaged class background whom Cabot had helped. Her comments illustrate how the discourse about first-generation students at Cabot can lead students away from developing a critical class consciousness, which I have argued is in the interest of the institution. Thus, some students avoided claiming an associational class identity by adopting the first-generation identity, which focuses on their accomplishments as individuals rather than their membership in a particular social class.

Discussion and Conclusions

Selective colleges and universities increasingly tout the size of their first-generation populations as markers of social class diversity. Some research even focuses on the benefits of being labeled "first generation" for students. For example, Stephens et al. (2014) found that acknowledging the implications of social class differences for students' college experiences eliminated the GPA gap between first- and continuing-generation students at a private university at the end of their first year of college. However, this study demonstrated how the discursive construction of first-generation students at a selective college can have negative consequences for students who are categorized as such, pushing them to reject their social origins in the quest for upward mobility and obfuscating antagonistic class relations. At the same time, the school benefits from the way in which the first-generation category is constructed, with the category creating space for Cabot to instill a strong institutional identity in first-generation students and minimizing potential class conflict by diverting students' attention away from developing a critical awareness of social class.

Although I found that some students resented the way in which Cabot discursively constructed first-generation students, there was little evidence that students had attempted to collectively challenge this discourse. Four of the student participants were engaged in an effort to start a student organization for first-generation students, but their plans for the group revolved around providing information to other first-generation students about how to apply for financial aid and access other institutional resources. While they were organizing around the first-generation identity in some sense, these students' efforts were not aimed at disputing the discursive construction of the first-generation category as analyzed in this study.

In fact, the discursive construction of the first-generation category at Cabot probably lessens the likelihood that students would be able to mount any organized resistance using the first-generation category as constructed at Cabot. Some students embraced the first-generation identity as a way to define themselves in terms of individual achievement over associational memberships, a stance that may prove antithetical to engaging in collective action that would challenge the institution. For these students, celebrating their first-generation status discouraged them from developing a critical class consciousness, instead pushing them along an individualist pathway embedded in the meritocratic ideal of individual achievement and neoliberal discouragement of collective action.

Thus, one of the contributions of the present study is that it identifies the following two unrecognized functions of the first-generation category: quelling class conflict on campus and mitigating the internal struggles caused by upward social mobility for many students. The first-generation category provides students with a prefabricated identity that eases the sting of assimilation—and even encourages it—by constructing them as people who possess a high degree of individual merit that differentiates them from their families and communities. The common strategy of conflating first-generation status with social class obscures the fact that the first-generation category as constructed at Cabot has the potential to dampen students' awareness of social classes as relational groups with antagonistic interests.

DISCUSSION QUESTIONS

1. How different are the first-generation students from the continuing-education students at Cabot College? Do the differences merit the assumptions about deficiency that the staff at Cabot assume exists among first-generation students?

2. How are first-generation students encouraged to "become Caboters"? How do the students feel about this message from the school?
3. Why does the process of classification matter in general? How come categories are something that sociologists are interested in studying?
4. What are the upsides and downsides to the first-generation label?
5. At nonelite colleges and universities, the gap in academic achievement and financial resources between first-generation and continuing-education students is much wider than at Cabot, and they often have more first-generation students. Do you think the label is likely to be problematic in the same ways at less prestigious schools? What research design would you use if you wanted to investigate this question?
6. Look at the study by Pew Research, "A majority of U.S. colleges admit most students who apply," available at https://www.pewresearch.org/fact-tank/2019/04/09/a-majority-of-u-s-colleges-admit-most-students-who-apply/, about how selective American colleges and universities are. What is likely different at less prestigious schools than at places like Cabot? Do you think the findings of the Pew study are good news or bad news for first-generation students?

NOTES

1. It is important to note that the discursive meanings applied to this category by colleges are not invented from whole cloth. For example, research indicates that first-generation students have lower graduation rates (Chen 2005; Engle and Tinto 2008; Lohfink and Paulsen 2005), lower college grades (Aspelmeier et al. 2012; Billson and Terry 1982), and weaker integration with campus life (Pascarella et al. 2004) than do their continuing-generation peers. However, discursive constructions of the first-generation category shape students' perceptions about the sources and magnitudes of these differences, the meanings of these differences, and how to respond to these differences.
2. The name of the college has been changed.
3. I omit identifying information about all interview participants. In some cases, details have been changed to protect confidentiality.
4. In fact, research suggests that for students whose parents have less education, attending a selective college may yield greater returns than for those whose parents have more education (Hout 2012).
5. I interviewed three international students but omit them from this analysis because their experiences and perceptions as first-generation students were heavily informed by the cultural, economic, and political contexts of their countries of origin.

6. These data were culled from a survey administered annually to the entire first-year class at Cabot between 2010 and 2014. Response rates averaged 33% over the five years of data collection. Each year's sample closely resembled the population of the first-year class for that year in terms of racial/ethnic and first-generation composition.
7. For other outcomes and experiences, however, there appear to be wider discrepancies between first- and continuing-generation students. For example, research suggests that graduation rates for first-generation college students are roughly half those for continuing-generation students (Chen 2005; Nuñez and Cuccaro-Alamin 1998). Some research using national samples of students also finds that first-generation students are less engaged socially and academically at college than are continuing-generation students (e.g., Pike and Kuh 2005; Strayhorn 2006).
8. As a selective college, Cabot likely chooses from a pool of first-generation applicants that is less economically disadvantaged than the pool of first-generation applicants at less selective schools. Thus, at less selective schools, there may be larger gaps in academic achievement between first- and continuing-generation students.

READING 3

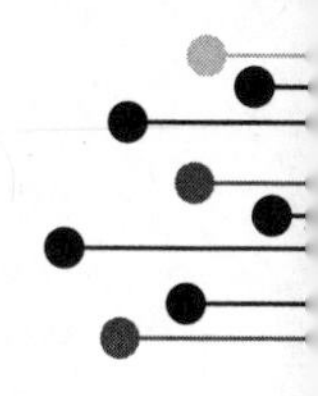

W. E. B. Du Bois and Black Heterogeneity

How *The Philadelphia Negro* Shaped American Sociology

Marcus Anthony Hunter

W. E. B. Du Bois was a pioneering African American scholar whose prolific research and writing in the late 1800s and well into the 20th century was central to the establishment of sociology as a scholarly discipline. His wide-ranging research on race set forth some of the key methodological practices and theoretical principles that are used throughout sociology today to study a wide range of topics. In his famous study The Philadelphia Negro,[1] *Du Bois sought to link the day-to-day lived experiences of African Americans in Philadelphia with the larger social, economic, and historical forces of the time. He was rigorous in his methods, interviewing thousands of people and keeping organized notes over the span of his study. In this endeavor, he epitomized both the methods and perspective of the still relatively new discipline of sociology.*

In this reading, contemporary sociologist Marcus Anthony Hunter highlights one of Du Bois's key sociological contributions—the concept of heterogeneity. Heterogeneity in a general sense simply means that there is difference among those within a category. Du Bois's research challenged the idea widely held by many social scientists at the time that all African Americans were essentially the same in terms of social class, politics, and religion. His research methods and compelling writing helped shift sociology as a discipline toward a more nuanced, and accurate, way of thinking about the social groups that they studied.

The idea of heterogeneity among social groups has widespread applications today, and the tendency for members of stigmatized or less powerful groups to be assumed to be all the same remains stubbornly stuck in many cultural beliefs. When Hillary Clinton ran for president, many commentators openly posited that women would vote for her just because she was also a woman—which was a view that assumed that all 150 million plus women in the United States

---

Excerpt from "W. E. B. Du Bois and Black Heterogeneity: How the Philadelphia Negro Shaped American Sociology" by Hunter, M.A. *The American Sociologist* (2015) 46, pp. 219–233. Reprinted with permission.

were essentially the same in their political concerns and priorities. Heterogeneity is also assumed by college staff in Reading 2 in how they view first-generation college students. It is to W. E. B. Du Bois that we owe a meticulous and convincing reminder that we should never assume that all members of a given group are the same.

As you read, consider what other groups in society vary in ways similar to the African Americans that Du Bois studied in Philadelphia.

Introduction

"From the Fall of 1894 to the Spring of 1910," wrote W. E. B. Du Bois in his autobiography (1968: 205), "I was a teacher and a student of social science." Reflecting on the foundation and motivation of his sociological approach, Du Bois continued (1968: 206): "I determined to put science into sociology through a study of the conditions and problems of my own group. I was going to study the facts, any and all facts, concerning the American Negro and his plight, and by measurement and comparison and research, work up to any valid generalizations which I could." As a result, for 16 years, Du Bois endeavored to apprehend and convey the sociological theories and knowledge embedded within the broader Black American experience.

Here, the commissioned study later dubbed *The Philadelphia Negro: A Social Study* (1899) offers a unique window into this important juncture in Du Bois's sociological approach. As the first monograph of its kind, *The Philadelphia Negro* offers insights into Du Bois's use of the urban Black experience from 1603 to 1895 in Philadelphia to develop broader social theories. To do so, Du Bois took inventory and stock of the existing scholarship of the time finding great use in the notion of *heterogeneity*—an emergent sociological concept rooted in the work of his contemporaries Franklin Giddings (1896), Herbert Spencer (1896), and Georg Simmel (1895, 1898a, b, c, 1903).

For his part, Du Bois affords a notion of heterogeneity tied to the production and understanding of urban space that necessarily intervened in the development and discourse on the concept. As a result, Du Bois's efforts to provide generalizable theories about race, space, and place at dawn of the 20th Century center on his analysis and observations of the significant lines of variation and distinction amongst and between urban Black Americans.

In this article, I distill Du Bois's emphasis on *Black heterogeneity* regarding 1) *class*, 2) *politics*, and 3) *religion*, to illustrate the corrective, descriptive and prescriptive virtues of his sociological approach as provided in his masterwork *The Philadelphia Negro: A Social Study* (1899).

The Philadelphia Negro in Context (1885–1899)

Despite the emphasis and interests in science and sociology, Du Bois acknowledged that there was great difficulty in "applying scientific law and discovering cause and effect in a world of living persons" (1968: 205). Indeed, Du Bois lamented such difficulties alongside what he observed as a knowledge gap in the newfangled discipline of sociology. For Du Bois (1968: 205): "Social thinkers were engaged in vague statements and were seeking to lay down the methods by which, in some not too distant future, social law analogous to physical law would be discovered. . . . The biological analogy, the vast generalizations, were striking, but actual scientific accomplishment lagged."

Looking to produce work that would gather "the facts," Du Bois sought to challenge what he saw as the convention of "armchair" and "car-window" sociology. Du Bois believed that the common practice within American social science was to make generalizations from faint impressions of the social world, and not from experiencing the field or gathering data from actual people (Du Bois 1940).

Du Bois began his research in Philadelphia's Black Seventh Ward with little guidance and somewhat unsure about how to start:

> I counted my task here as simple and clear-cut; I proposed to find out what was the matter with this area and why. I started with no "research methods" and I asked little advice as to procedure. The problem lay before me. Study it. I studied it personally and not by proxy. I sent out no canvassers. I went myself. Personally I visited and talked with 5000 persons. What I could, I set down in orderly sequence on schedules which I made out and submitted to the University for criticism. Other information I stored in my memory or wrote out as memoranda. I went through the Philadelphia libraries for data, gained access in many instances to private libraries of colored folk and got individual information. I mapped the district, classifying it by conditions; I compiled two centuries of the history of the Negro in Philadelphia and the Seventh Ward. (Du Bois, [1968] 2007: 197–198)

The Philadelphia that Du Bois sought to understand and study was one that had emerged as an industrial urban giant, and center for Black migration north, an ideal setting to examine the socio-economic conditions of the Black community (Du Bois 1899; Katz and Sugrue 1998; Deegan 2002). Furthermore, Du Bois saw in these works an analysis of an emergent modern phenomenon—the industrial city. Hence, Du Bois divided his "scientific study" of the "Negro problem" in Philadelphia into "two parts: the social group and his peculiar social environment" (Du Bois 1968: 201).

Stated differently, Du Bois held that a study of Black life in Philadelphia and a study of the "peculiar environment" were equally important to articulating any general facts about Black life and the larger "Negro problem" (Hunter 2013a, b).

Although his time as an assistant instructor never manifested into anything more than being allowed "once to pilot a pack of idiots through the Negro slums," Du Bois after much labor, completed the study which he aptly titled "The Philadelphia Negro" (Du Bois 1968: 197). Du Bois believed that this work would earn him a more permanent post at the University, and open up the field of sociology to him. Aware of similar research emerging in other cities, Du Bois saw his efforts as being at the forefront of new sociological inquiry. Convinced that the innovation of his approach, data, and sociological imagination would serve as evidence to his claim, Du Bois asserted that "years of research" had been "able to return" that "the phenomena of society" such as the industrial city and the lifeworld of Black Americans "are worth the most careful systematic study" (Du Bois 1898: 1).

Du Boisian Heterogeneity

At the dawn of the 20th Century, sociologists were endeavoring to situate the concerns and problems of the newly emergent discipline. Heterogeneity, in particular, proved especially pregnant with possibility for sociologists across specialties and interests. "Sociology," wrote Max Weber (1978: 4) in *Economy and Society*, "is a science concerning itself with the interpretive understanding of social action and thereby with casual explanation of its course and consequences." Much like Weber, Emile Durkheim underscored the role of sociology as an interpretive science concerned with observing and analyzing "laws, customs, religions, etc." Inserting Montesquieu and Rousseau as forerunners of the philosophical and epistemological tradition undergirding the discipline, Durkheim (1975: 13, emphasis added) offered that "[t]he phenomena [sociology] deals with are so *diverse* that what they have in common seems to be hidden from view. They are so fluid that they seem to elude the observer. Causes and effects are so interwoven that the utmost care must disentangle them." In this way, both Weber and Durkheim promote a sociology concerned with variation, particularly as it occurred and appeared in social phenomena such as human attitudes and behaviors.

The importance of variance for the production of sociological knowledge was not lost on their American counterparts. Indeed, *heterogeneity* and the history of American sociology are intertwined. Encompassing the idea of variation, heterogeneity has been an operating principle in American sociology. In part, this connection is likely due to the fact that most of the peoples of the United States come from many regions, tribes, clans, and ethnicities drawn from the broader global community.

Du Bois drew on the idea of heterogeneity, specifically within the urban context, to illustrate Black communities as complex and organized arrangements of a diverse though marginalized population. As Du Bois sought to show, the Black community was diverse despite being otherwise thought of as homogeneous. Using the examples of Philadelphia Negroes, Du Bois demonstrated that the Black community is comprised of varying arrangements of diverse though equally racialized constituents and practices.

In so doing, Du Bois's analysis points to an idea of *Black heterogeneity*—the varied distinctions, perspectives, and peoples that constitute the Black community; thus Du Boisian heterogeneity theorizes the concept as imbued with a consequential mix of racial tensions and intraracial distinctions. Such factors give rise to complex civil racialized societies that are compelled to live alongside one another within and across urban America. In what follows, I uncover the contours of Du Bois's Black heterogeneity, with especial focus on his analysis of Black class, politics, and religion.

Black Heterogeneity & *The Philadelphia Negro*

Class Heterogeneity

Of the many areas of heterogeneity found in Philadelphia, Du Bois's discussion of intraracial class differences among the Philadelphia Negroes is perhaps most instructive. Offering an unprecedented account of class diversity, arrangements and cultural differences among Black Philadelphians, Du Bois (1899: 309–310) takes to task existing paradigms that considered urban Blacks as homogenous:

> There is always a strong tendency on the part of the community to consider the Negros as composing one practically homogeneous mass. This view has of course a certain justification: the people of Negro descent in this land have a common history, suffer to-day common disabilities, and contribute to one general set of social problems. And yet if the foregoing statistics have emphasized any one fact it is that wide variations in antecedents, wealth, intelligence and general efficiency have already been differentiated within this group. These differences are not, to be sure, so great or so patent as those among the whites of to-day, and yet they undoubtedly equal the difference among the masses of the people in certain sections of the land fifty or 100 years ago; and there is no surer way of misunderstanding the Negro than by

> ignoring manifest differences. . . . And yet well-meaning people continually do this.

In this discussion, Du Bois illustrates the importance of class heterogeneity for drawing out causation and correlation with racial disparities and in-group cultural differences and perspectives. Here, Du Bois seeks to supplant the monolithic conceptions of Black Philadelphians with a variegated illustration wherein the Philadelphia Negro is constitutive of differential levels of elitism, social class, wealth, and education.

Animating the importance of heterogeneity methodologically, Du Bois suggests that a sociological imagination without a diverse conception of urban Black Americans functions as an impediment to both understanding and gaining access to this population. Consider his takeaway regarding middle-class and well-to-do Philadelphia Negroes: "Nothing more exasperates the better class of Negroes than this tendency to ignore utterly their existence. The law-abiding, hard-working inhabitants of the Thirtieth Ward are aroused to righteous indignation when they see that the word Negro carries most Philadelphians' minds to the alleys of the Fifth Ward or the police courts." Highlighting the personal offense taken by members of this class, Du Bois reveals that ignoring the variation of and within Black Philadelphia damages the social scientific endeavor to understand urban America and its residents. Further, Du Bois demonstrates that such variation organizes the behavior and attitudes of urban Black residents.

That variation exists among urban Black Americans is only part of what Du Bois means to convey, as he also uses heterogeneity to distill the major social classes among Philadelphia Negroes (1899: 310–311):

> Since so much misunderstanding or rather forgetfulness and carelessness on this point is common, let us endeavor to try and fix with some definiteness the different social classes which are clearly defined among Negroes to deserve attention. . . .
>
> Grade 1 Families of undoubted respectability earning sufficient income to live well; not engaged in menial service of any kind; the wife engaged in no occupation save that of housewife, except in a few cases where she had special employment at home. The children not compelled to be bread-winners, but found in school; the family living in a well-kept home.
>
> Grade 2 The respectable working-class; in comfortable circumstances, with a good home, and having steady remunerative work. The younger children in school.
>
> Grade 3 The poor; persons not earning enough to keep them at all times above want; honest, although not always energetic or thrifty, and with no touch of gross immorality or crime. Including the very poor, and the poor.

Grade 4 The lowest class of criminals, prostitutes and loafers; the "submerged tenth."

Thus we have in these four grades the criminals, the poor, the laborers, and the well-to-do. The last class represents the ordinary middle-class folk of most modern countries, and contains the germs of other social classes which the Negro has not yet clearly differentiated.

In so doing, Du Bois demonstrates that heterogeneity contextualized through urbanism provides new sociological knowledge pertaining to the class and economic attitudes and behaviors of urbanites. Employing heterogeneity to challenge conventional wisdom, Du Bois offers a conceptualization of social class and intraracial differences we find in contemporary debates and research on the Black middle class

Political Heterogeneity

Du Bois's uncovering of and exposition on heterogeneity extends to his analysis of urban Black politics as well. "The experiment of Negro suffrage in Philadelphia," wrote Du Bois (1899: 373), "has developed three classes of Negro voters: a large majority of voters who vote blindly at the dictates of the party and, while not open to direct bribery, accept the indirect emoluments of office or influence in return for party loyalty; a considerable group, centering in the slum districts, which casts a corrupt purchasable vote for the highest bidder; lastly, a very small group of independent voters who seek to use their vote to better present conditions of municipal life." Here, Du Bois suggests that the variation in the Black voter reflects the relationships such voters share with political power and public officials.

Asserting that cultural and regional intraracial heterogeneity influences voting behavior and political beliefs, Du Bois (1899: 373) observes:

The political morality of the first group of voters, that is to say, of the great mass of Negro voters, corresponds roughly to that of the mass of white voters, but with this difference: the ignorance of the Negro in matters of government is greater and his devotion to party blinder and more unreasoning. Add to this the mass of recent immigrants from the South, with the political training of reconstruction and post-bellum days, and one can easily see how poorly trained this body of electors has been.

Focusing on the notion of "political morality," Du Bois illustrates that within group heterogeneity facilitates racial disparities as differential experiences have led to a varied Black political community with limited power and access. By animating the influence of cultural and regional differences, Du Bois shows that a seemingly homogenous voting bloc is comprised of a series of interest networks with differing perspectives and relationships to political outcomes.

Religious Heterogeneity

Though class and political heterogeneity may be powerful tools for disaggregating the urban Black experience, Du Bois also locates the variation in religious affiliation and belief as also important. "The Negro is a religious creature," Du Bois (1899: 201) observed. To this Du Bois (1899: 201) adds: "[h]is rapid and even extraordinary founding of churches is not due to this fact alone, but is rather a measure of his development, and indication of the increasing intricacy of his social life and the consequent multiplication of the organ which is the function of his group life—the church."

Du Bois's discussion of religion heterogeneity occurs at two levels: individual religious affiliations and organizational makeup of Black churches. Fusing a combination of religious and cultural traditions, Du Bois found that the churches of Black Philadelphians often incorporated traditional denominations with African cultural practices. These Black churches included St. Thomas Presbyterian Episcopal, Mother Bethel African Methodist Episcopal, Zoar Methodist Episcopal, First African Baptist and Union African Methodist Episcopal. Meant to amplify religious differences across and within race, Du Bois's identification of these Black religious organizations further underscores the heterogeneity previously explored along class and political lines.

More than just an exploration of the varied religious practices and beliefs of Philadelphia Negroes, Du Bois also hones in on the variegated purposes and organization within these Black churches. In Du Bois's discussion of the Black church, such institutions are not just born out of the disenfranchisement of Black Americans, but are also a cultural phenomenon that helps to fix individuals within urban space. Du Bois (1899: 205) argues that the "church is, to be sure, a social institution first, and religious afterwards."

As Du Bois (1899: 207) observes: "Negro churches were the birthplaces of Negro schools and of all agencies which seek to promote the intelligence of the masses; and even to-day no agency serves to disseminate news or information so quickly and effectively among Negroes as the church." Du Bois, through this observation, shows that cultural and indigenous institutions within cities such as Philadelphia have a proximal relationship with residents and, most often, determine how and in what ways residents migrate into and move within the larger city. Indeed, Du Bois (1899: 204) asserts: "Each church forms its own social circle, and not many stray beyond its bounds. Introductions into that circle come through the church and thus the stranger becomes known"; thus Du Bois uses religious heterogeneity to highlight the dialectical relationship between people and indigenous institutions in urban space.

Black Heterogeneity Matters

> [T]here is no surer way of misunderstanding the Negro or being misunderstood by him than by ignoring manifest differences of condition and power in the 40,000 Black people of Philadelphia.
>
> —W. E. B. Du Bois, *The Philadelphia Negro* (1899: 310)

Over the last 50 years, scholars across disciplines have reexamined the work of W. E. B. Du Bois pointing to myriad frameworks emergent in his work. Endeavoring to assert and uncover Du Bois's place as a central figure in sociology in particular, and the social sciences and humanities more generally, scholarship has centered on issues of race and racism (Aptheker 2000; Broderick 1974; Fields 2002; Hancock 2003; Marable 1986; Morris 2006; Morris and Ghaziani 2005; Rudwick 1974; Watts 1983; Wright 2002, 2005, 2006; Young and Deskins 2001; Zuckerman 2002). Of particular importance in the social sciences has been *The Philadelphia Negro*, as it perhaps stands as Du Bois's most comprehensive social scientific work.

As this paper demonstrates, we needn't travel into the 1930s to discover this pillar of American sociology. We can and should look to W. E. B. Du Bois's *The Philadelphia Negro: A Social Study* (1899) to locate this important entanglement of urban America, heterogeneity, sociology and knowledge production as well as its significance in uncovering empirical truths and realities fostering the production of new knowledge. Moving the discussion of Du Bois, particularly as it pertains to a reading of *The Philadelphia Negro*, beyond his analysis of the "race problem" brings to the fore the import of heterogeneity to sociological knowledge production on urban growth and change; thus we are closer to fully employing the resources and ideas Du Bois provides within and between the lines of *The Philadelphia Negro*. Explicating such Du Boisian ideas provides a significant intellectual and historical bridge, foundation, and perspective for understanding the roots of American sociological thought and knowledge production and the place of heterogeneity in such disciplinary history.

Acknowledgments The research presented in this article benefited from the generous financial support of Yale University, the American Sociological Association's Minority Fellowship Program, and UCLA. The author would like to thank and acknowledge Zandria F. Robinson, Charles Camic, Jean Beaman, Christopher Wildeman, ASA's History of Sociology section, and the reviewers for their encouraging and thoughtful feedback.

DISCUSSION QUESTIONS

1. In his research for *The Philadelphia Negro*, Du Bois was trying to avoid some early pitfalls of social science research. What were those pitfalls and what did Du Bois try to do to avoid them in his study?
2. How is Du Bois's work an example of sociological imagination?
3. What are the three social class classifications that Du Bois came up with? Do you think these classifications might apply to whites or other races as well?
4. How might ideas from *The Philadelphia Negro* help us understand the issues brought up by the #Black Lives Matter movement?
5. Sociology is defined much more by its perspective than its subject matter, and W. E. B. Du Bois's work exemplified the sociological lens used to study the world. Watch the brief video "W. E. B. Du Bois, the Historic Man and Founder of the NAACP," available at https://www.youtube.com/watch?v=u2fR5AnIckA, from the University of Pennsylvania to learn more about Du Bois and the impact he had on disciplines other than sociology.

NOTE

1. The title of Du Bois's book is jarring by contemporary standards, but at the time his book was published in 1899, *negro* was the term that was used for those who today might be described as African American, black, or people of color.

Sense and Nonsense About Surveys

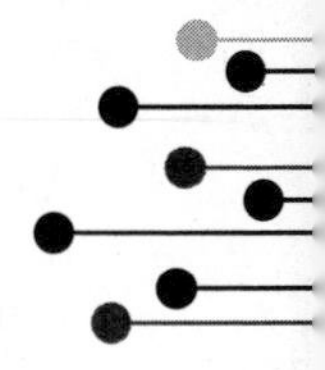

Howard Schuman

As American society becomes more and more divided politically, polls and their results are increasingly used in debates about public policies and Americans' beliefs. But how polls are designed and administered (i.e., the research methods used) makes an immense difference in whether the results have any scientific validity whatsoever. Media outlets are notoriously bad at providing the details of the research methods of polls that they cite so that readers can determine how much credibility the numbers deserve, but even if they regularly provided such information, you first need to know what aspects of how the poll was conducted influence how valid the results will be.

In this reading, Howard Schuman provides a summary of the types of things we should consider when deciding how much we should trust the results of polls. Interestingly, the most likely detail about a poll that journalists report is how many people were surveyed. While this does matter, it doesn't matter nearly as much as other considerations like who was surveyed and how the questions were asked. Use the information in this reading to equip your critical thinking cap for the next time you see a headline announcing the result of a poll about the issue of the day.

Understanding surveys is critical to being an informed citizen, but popular media often report surveys without any guidance on how to interpret and evaluate the results. Some basic guidelines can promote more sophisticated readings of survey results and help teach when to trust the polls.

Surveys draw on two human propensities that have served us well from ancient times. One is to gather information by asking questions. The first use of language around 100,000 years ago may have been to utter commands such as "Come here!" or "Wait!" Questions must have followed soon after: "Why?" or "What for?" From that point, it would have been only a short step to the use of interrogatives to learn where a fellow hominid had seen potential food, a dangerous animal, or something else of importance.

Excerpt from "Sense and Nonsense About Surveys," by H. Schuman. *Contexts* (2002), 1(2), pp. 40–47. Reprinted with permission.

Asking questions continues to be an effective way of acquiring information of all kinds, assuming of course that the person answering is able and willing to respond accurately.

The other inclination, learning about one's environment by examining a small part of it, is the sampling aspect of surveys. A taste of something may or may not point to appetizing food. A first inquiry to a stranger, a first glance around a room, a first date—each is a sample of sorts, often used to decide whether it is wise to proceed further. As with questions, however, one must always be aware of the possibility that the sample may not prove adequate to the task.

Sampling: How Gallup Achieved Fame

Only within the past century—and especially in the 1930s and 1940s—were major improvements made in the sampling process that allowed the modern survey to develop and flourish. A crucial change involved recognition that the value of a sample comes not simply from its size but also from the way it is obtained. Every serious pursuit likes to have a morality tale that supports its basic beliefs: witness Eve and the apple in the Bible or Newton and his apple in legends about scientific discovery. Representative sampling has a marvelous morality tale also, with the additional advantage of its being true.

The story concerns the infamous *Literary Digest* poll prediction—based on 10 million questionnaires sent out and more than two million received back—that Roosevelt would lose decisively in the 1936 presidential election. At the same time, George Gallup, using many fewer cases but a much better method, made the more accurate prediction that FDR would win. Gallup used quotas in choosing respondents in order to represent different economic strata, whereas the *Literary Digest* had worked mainly from telephone and automobile ownership lists, which in 1936 were biased toward wealthy people apt to be opposed to Roosevelt. (There were other sources of bias as well.) As a result, the *Literary Digest* poll disappeared from the scene, and Gallup was on his way to becoming a household name.

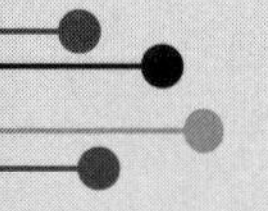

The percentage of people who refuse to take part in a survey is particularly important. In some federal surveys, the percentage is small, within the range of 5–10 percent. For even the best nongovernment surveys, the refusal rate can reach 25 percent or more, and it can be far larger in the case of poorly executed surveys.

Yet despite their intuitive grasp of the importance of representing the electorate accurately, Gallup and other commercial pollsters did not use the probability sampling methods that were being developed in the same decades and that are fundamental to social science surveys today. Probability sampling in its simplest form calls for each person in the population to have an equal chance of being selected. It can also be used in more complex applications where the chances are deliberately made to be unequal, for example, when oversampling a minority group in order to study it more closely; however, the chances of being selected must still be known so that they can later be equalized when considering the entire population.

Intuitions and Counterintuitions About Sample Size

Probability sampling theory reveals a crucial but counterintuitive point about sample size: the size of a sample needed to accurately estimate a value for a population depends very little on the size of the population. For example, almost the same size sample is needed to estimate, with a given degree of precision, the proportion of left-handed people in the United States as is needed to make the same estimate for, say, Peoria, Illinois. In both cases a reasonably accurate estimate can be obtained with a sample size of around 1,000. (More cases are needed when extraordinary precision is called for, for example, in calculating unemployment rates, where even a tenth of a percent change may be regarded as important.)

The link between population size and sample size cuts both ways. Although huge samples are not needed for huge populations like those of the United States or China, a handful of cases is not sufficient simply because one's interest is limited to Peoria. This implication is often missed by those trying to save time and money when sampling a small community.

Moreover, all of these statements depend on restricting your interest to overall population values. If you are concerned about, say, left-handedness among African Americans, then African Americans become your population, and you need much the same sample size as for Peoria or the United States.

Who Is Missing?

A good sample depends on more than probability sampling theory. Surveys vary greatly in their quality of implementation, and this variation is not captured by the "margin of error" plus/minus percentage figures that accompany most media reports of polls. Such percentages reflect the size of the final sample, but they do not reveal the sampling method or the extent to which the targeted individuals or households were actually included in the final sample. These details are at least as important as the sample size.

When targeted members of a population are not interviewed or do not respond to particular questions, the omissions are a serious problem if they are numerous and if those missed differ from those who are interviewed on the matters being studied. The latter difference can seldom be known with great confidence, so it is usually desirable to keep omissions to a minimum. For example, sampling from telephone directories is undesirable because it leaves out those with unlisted telephones, as well as those with no telephones at all. Many survey reports are based on such poor sampling procedures that they may not deserve to be taken seriously. This is especially true of reports based on "focus groups," which offer lots of human interest but are subject to vast amounts of error. Internet surveys also cannot represent the general population adequately at present, though this is an area where some serious attempts are being made to compensate for the inherent difficulties.

The percentage of people who refuse to take part in a survey is particularly important. In some federal surveys, the percentage is small, within the range of 5–10 percent. For even the best non-government surveys, the refusal rate can reach 25 percent or more, and it can be far larger in the case of poorly executed surveys. Refusals have risen substantially from earlier days, becoming a major cause for concern among serious survey practitioners. Fortunately, in recent years research has shown that moderate amounts of nonresponse in an otherwise careful survey seem in most cases not to have a major effect on results. Indeed, even the *Literary Digest*, with its abysmal sampling and massive nonresponse rate, did well predicting elections before the dramatic realignment of the electorate in 1936. The problem is that one can never be certain as to the effects of refusals and other forms of nonresponse, so obtaining a high response rate remains an important goal.

Questions About Questions

Since survey questions resemble the questions we ask in ordinary social interaction, they may seem less problematic than the counterintuitive and technical aspects of sampling. Yet survey results are every bit as dependent on the form, wording and context of the questions asked as they are on the sample of people who answer them.

No classic morality tale like the *Literary Digest* fiasco highlights the question–answer process, but an example from the early days of surveys illustrates both the potential challenges of question writing and the practical solutions.

In 1940 Donald Rugg asked two slightly different questions to equivalent national samples about the general issue of freedom of speech:

- Do you think the United States should forbid public speeches against democracy?
- Do you think the United States should allow public speeches against democracy?

Taken literally, forbidding something and not allowing something have the same effect, but clearly the public did not view the questions as identical. Whereas 75 percent of the public would not allow such speeches, only 54 percent would forbid them, a difference of 21 percentage points. This finding was replicated several times in later years, not only in the United States but also (with appropriate translations) in Germany and the Netherlands. Such "survey-based experiments" call for administering different versions of a question to random subsamples of a larger sample. If the results between the subsamples differ by more than can be easily explained by chance, we infer that the difference is due to the variation in wording.

In addition, answers to survey questions always depend on the form in which a question is asked. If the interviewer presents a limited set of alternatives, most respondents will choose one, rather than offering a different alternative of their own. In one survey-based experiment, for example, we asked a national sample of Americans to name the most important problem facing the country. Then we asked a comparable sample a parallel question that provided a list of four problems from which to choose the most important; this list included none of the four problems mentioned most often by the first sample but instead provided four problems that had been mentioned by fewer than 3 percent of the earlier respondents. The list question also invited respondents to substitute a different problem if they wished (see Table 1). Despite the invitation, the majority of respondents (60 percent) chose one of the rare problems offered, reflecting their reluctance to go outside the frame of reference provided by the question. The form of a question provides the "rules of the game" for respondents, and this must always be kept in mind when interpreting results.

Other difficulties occur with survey questions when issues are discussed quite generally, as though there is a single way of framing them and just two sides to the debate. For example, what is called "the abortion issue" really consists of different issues: the reasons for an abortion, the trimester involved and so forth. In a recent General Social Survey, nearly 80 percent of the national sample supported legal abortion in the case of "a serious defect in the baby," but only 44 percent supported it "if the family has a low income and cannot afford any more children." Often what is thought to be a conflict in findings between two surveys is actually a difference in

Table 1 Experimental Variation Between Open and Closed Questions

A. Open Question	B. Closed Question
"What do you think is the most important problem facing this country today [1986]?"	"Which of the following do you think is the most important problem facing this country today [1986]—the energy shortage, the quality of public schools, legalized abortion, or pollution—or, if you prefer, you may name a different problem as most important." 1. Energy shortage 2. Quality of public schools 3. Legalized abortion 4. Pollution

Adapted from: H. Schuman and J. Scott, "Problems in the Use of Survey Questions to Measure Public Opinion," *Science* v. 236, pp. 957–959, May 22, 1987.

In a survey experiment, less than 3% of the 171 respondents asked the question on the left volunteered one of the four problems listed on the right. Yet, 60% of the 178 respondents asked the question on the right picked one of those four answers.

the aspects of the general issue that they queried. In still other cases an inconsistency reflects a type of illogical wish fulfillment in the public itself, as when majorities favor both a decrease in taxes and an increase in government services if the questions are asked separately.

Solutions to the Question Wording Problem

All these and still other difficulties (including the order in which questions are asked) suggest that responses to single survey questions on complex issues should be viewed with considerable skepticism. What to do then, other than to reject all survey data as unusable for serious purposes? One answer can be found from the replications of the forbid/allow experiment above: Although there was a 21 percentage point difference based on question wording in 1940 and a slightly larger difference (24 percentage points) when the experiment was repeated some 35 years later, both the forbid and the allow wordings registered similar declines in Americans' intolerance of speeches against democracy (see Figure 1). No matter which question was used—as long as it was the same one at both times—the conclusion about the increase in civil libertarian sentiments was the same.

Figure 1 Attitudes Toward Free Speech Against Democracy

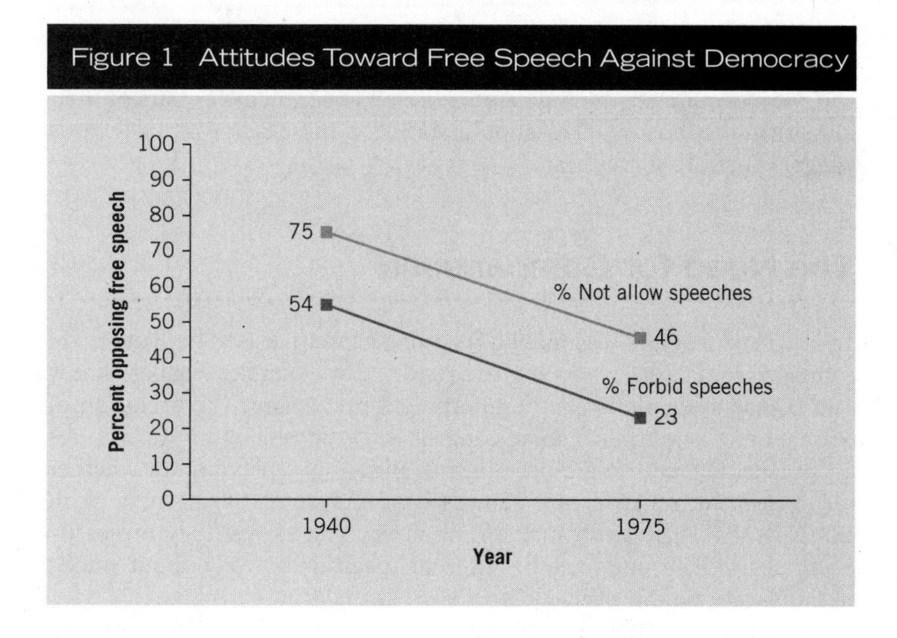

More generally, what has been called the "principle of form-resistant correlations" holds in most cases: if question wording (and meaning) is kept constant, differences over time, differences across educational levels, and most other careful comparisons are not seriously affected by specific question wording. Indeed, the distinction between results for single questions and results based on comparisons or associations holds even for simple factual inquiries. Consider, for example, a study of the number of rooms in American houses. No God-given rule states what to include when counting the rooms in a house (bathrooms? basements? hallways?); hence the average number reported for a particular place and time should not be treated as an absolute truth. What we can do, however, is try to apply the same definitions over time, across social divisions, even across nations. That way, we gain confidence in the comparisons we make—who has more rooms than who, for example.

Survey researchers should also ask several different questions about any important issue. In addition to combining questions to increase reliability, the different answers can be synthesized rather than depending on the angle of vision provided by any single question. A further safeguard is to carry out frequent experiments like that on the forbid/allow wordings. By varying the form, wording, and context of questions, researchers can gain insight into both the questions and the relevant issues. Sometimes variations turn out to make no difference, and that is also useful to learn. For example, I once expected support for legalized abortion to increase when a question substituted *end pregnancy* for the word *abortion* in the phrasing. Yet no difference was found. Today, more and more researchers include survey-based experiments as part of their investigations, and readers should look for these sorts of safeguards when evaluating survey results.

The Need for Comparisons

To interpret surveys accurately, it's important to use a framework of comparative data in evaluating the results. For example, teachers know that course evaluations can be interpreted best against the backdrop of evaluations from other similar courses: a 75 percent rating of lectures as "excellent" takes on a quite different meaning depending on whether the average for other lecture courses is 50 percent or 90 percent. Such comparisons are fundamental for all survey results, yet they are easily overlooked when one feels the urge to speak definitively about public reactions to a unique event.

Comparative analysis over time, along with survey-based experiments, can also help us understand responses to questions about socially sensitive subjects. Experiments have shown that expressions of racial attitudes can change substantially for both black and white Americans depending on the interviewer's race. White respondents, for instance, are more likely to support racial intermarriage when speaking to a black than to a white interviewer. Such self-censoring mirrors variations in cross-race conversations outside of surveys, reflecting not a methodological artifact of surveys but rather a fact of life about race relations in America. Still, if we consider time trends, with the race of interviewer kept constant, we can also see that white responses supporting intermarriage have clearly increased over the past half century, that actual intermarriage rates have also risen (though from a much lower level) over recent years, and that the public visibility of cross-race marriage and dating has also increased. It would be foolish to assume that the survey data on racial attitudes reflect actions in any literal sense, but they do capture important *trends* in both norms and behavior.

Surveys remain our best tool for learning about large populations. One remarkable advantage surveys have over some other methods is the ability to identify their own limitations, as illustrated by the development of both probability theory in sampling and experiments in questioning. In the end, however, with surveys as with all research methods, there is no substitute for both care and intelligence in the way evidence is gathered and interpreted. What we learn about society is always mediated by the instruments we use, including our own eyes and ears. As Isaac Newton wrote long ago, error is not in the art but in the artificers.

DISCUSSION QUESTIONS

1. One of the leading polling organizations in the country is Gallup. How did it become a prominent polling company after the 1930s?
2. What is probability sampling? Why is it important when conducting polls?
3. What is counterintuitive about the sample sizes needed to generalize about a population?
4. Why does who is left out (i.e., doesn't respond or isn't asked to respond) of a survey important?
5. How does the construction of the actual questions being asked in a poll potentially shape how people respond? Think of an issue you would like to know people's opinion about, and write a survey question in two different forms that would likely elicit different responses from the same person.
6. Random sampling is the key to being able to generalize to a population even though you only polled a sample of the larger group. Watch the excellent video "Methods 101 Video: Random Sampling," available at https://www.pewresearch.org/methods/2017/05/12/methods-101-video-random-sampling/, from Pew Research to learn how random sampling works and why we generalize from relatively small samples to find out things about large groups of people.

PART

II

Culture, Socialization, and Interaction

The Presentation of Self

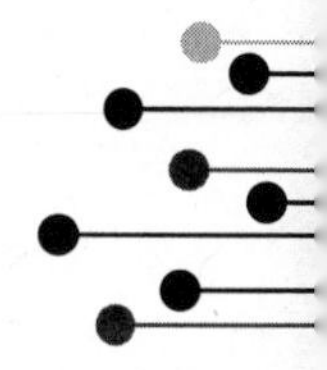

Erving Goffman

Most of us enter, participate in, and leave countless interactions each day without giving much thought to any of them. In fact, one of the most remarkable things about social interactions is how often they go smoothly. Simply getting to class, buying dinner, or spending time watching TV with friends involves an impressive amount of information gathering, decision making, action, and response. These mundane, often repeated, daily interactions wouldn't seem like they could have anything significant to tell us about the nature of social interaction, but in fact they do.

In this reading, Erving Goffman introduces us to dramaturgy, which illuminates the underlying principles that govern just such mundane face-to-face interactions. Dramaturgy is a theoretical perspective based on the analogy that face-to-face social interactions are like a theatrical performance. Goffman argues that in any face-to-face encounter, the participants engage in "the presentation of self," performing a role (student, employee, friend, significant other, etc.) just as a performer in a stage production would. Successful social actors look the part (appearance), act in a way that matches their role (manner), and play their role in the appropriate place (setting). These are referred to as sign vehicles.

For Goffman, we use sign vehicles to answer the question "what's going on here?" in every face-to-face interaction we have. The agreed upon answer to this question is what he refers to as the definition of the situation, which must be determined every time we enter into an interaction. We tend to only consciously notice this when things don't go as we expected. You probably didn't think too much about class the last time you arrived at your classroom. But imagine instead that you had arrived at your classroom to find all of the chairs pushed to the edges of the room, a disco ball hanging from the ceiling, your professor moonwalking, and 80s music playing from the computer. You would be very likely to ask or at least think, "What's going on here?" In Goffman's terms, the definition of the situation has been called into question. Your teacher's presentation of self does not match what we expect of a teacher in terms of appearance and manner and the setting has changed significantly.

Importantly, from a dramaturgical perspective, we go through the same process of using sign vehicles to figure out the definition of the situation even when an interaction unfolds exactly as expected and we don't consciously think, "What's going on here." It's a bit like driving on a long stretch of boring road. You may have had the experience of zoning out while driving and suddenly realizing that 20 minutes had passed.[1] *It wasn't that you stopped driving; you probably passed a few cars, tapped the brake a few times, and maybe even changed the radio station. But just because you weren't actively attending to the task of driving (as you might when you notice a police officer following behind you) doesn't mean you weren't paying attention and making decisions that are necessary to drive safely. Similarly, just because we don't actively attend to the assumptions and decisions we make about what's going on in most face-to-face interactions doesn't mean we're not still doing the cognitive work to arrive at a definition of the situation based on the sign vehicles we see.*

Goffman's dramaturgical ideas are wonderfully easy to apply to your day-to-day life since dramaturgy is a microlevel theory. As you read, think about examples from your own life of the types of behaviors and interactional strategies that he describes.

Preface

The perspective employed in this report is that of the theatrical performances; the principles derived are dramaturgical ones. I shall consider the way in which the individual in ordinary work situations presents himself and his activity to others, the ways in which he guides and controls the impression they form of him, and the kinds of things he may and may not do while sustaining his performance before them.

Introduction

When an individual enters the presence of others, they commonly seek to acquire information about him or to bring into play information about him already possessed. They will be interested in his general socio-economic status, his conception of self, his attitude toward them, his competence, his trustworthiness, etc. Although some of this information seems to be sought almost as an end in itself, there are usually quite practical reasons for acquiring it. Information about the individual helps to define the situation, enabling others to know in advance what he will expect of them and what they may expect of him. Informed in these ways, the others will know how best to act in order to call forth a desired response from him.

For those present, many sources of information become accessible and many carriers (or "sign-vehicles") become available for conveying this information. If unacquainted with the individual, observers can glean clues from his conduct and appearance which allow them to apply their previous experience with individuals roughly similar to the one before them or, more important, to apply untested stereotypes at him. They can also assume from past experience that only individuals of a particular kind are likely to be found in a given social setting. They can rely on what the individual says about himself or on documentary evidence he provides as to who and what he is. If they know, or know of, the individual by virtue of experience prior to the interaction, they can rely on assumptions as to the persistence and generality of psychological traits as a means of predicting his present and future behavior.

Taking communication in both its narrow and broad sense, one finds that when the individual is in the immediate presence of others, his activity will have a promissory character. The others are likely to find that they must accept the individual on faith, offering him a just return while he is present before them in exchange for something whose true value will not be established until after he has left their presence. (Of course, the others also live by inference in their dealings with the physical world, but it is only in the world of social interaction that the objects about which they make inferences will purposely facilitate and hinder this inferential process.) The security that they justifiably feel in making inferences about the individual will vary, of course, depending on such factors as the amount of information they already possess about him, but no amount of such past evidence can entirely obviate the necessity of acting on the basis of inferences.

I have said that when an individual appears before others his actions will influence the definition of the situation which they come to have. Sometimes the individual will act in a thoroughly calculating manner, expressing himself in a given way solely in order to give the kind of impression to others that is likely to evoke from them a specific response he is concerned to obtain. Sometimes the individual will be calculating in his activity but be relatively unaware that this is the case. Sometimes he will intentionally and consciously express himself in a particular way, but chiefly because the tradition of his group or social status require this kind of expression and not because of any particular response (other than vague acceptance or approval) that is likely to be evoked from those impressed by the expression. Sometimes the traditions of an individual's role will lead him to give a well-designed impression of a particular kind and yet he may be neither consciously nor unconsciously disposed to create such an impression. The others, in their turn, may be suitably impressed by the individual's efforts to convey something, or may misunderstand the situation and come to conclusions that are warranted neither by the individual's intent nor by the facts. In any case, in so far as the others act *as if* the individual had conveyed a particular impression, we may take a functional or pragmatic view and say that the individual has "effectively" projected a given definition of the situation and "effectively" fostered the understanding that a given state of affairs obtains.

When we allow that the individual projects a definition of the situation when he appears before others, we must also see that the others, however passive their role may seem to be, will themselves effectively project a definition of the situation by virtue of their response to the individual and by virtue of any lines of action that initiate to him. Ordinarily, the definitions of the situation projected by the several different participants are sufficiently attuned to one another so that open contradiction will not occur. I do not mean that there will be the kind of consensus that arises when each individual present candidly expresses what he really feels and honestly agrees with the expressed feelings of the others present. This kind of harmony is an optimistic ideal and in any case not necessary for the smooth working of society. Rather, each participant is expected to suppress his immediate heartfelt feelings, conveying a view of the situation which he feels the others will be able to find at least temporarily acceptable. The maintenance of this surface of agreement, this veneer of consensus, is facilitated by each participant concealing his own wants behind statements which assert values to which everyone present feels obliged to give lip service. Further, there is usually a kind of division of definitional labor. Each participant is allowed to establish the tentative official ruling regarding matters which are vital to him but not immediately important to others, e.g., the rationalizations and justifications by which he accounts for his past activity. In exchange for this courtesy he remains silent or noncommittal on matters important to others but not immediately important to him. We have then a kind of interactional *modus vivendi.* Together the participants contribute to a single overall definition of the situation which involves not so much a real agreement as to what exists but rather a real agreement as to whose claims concerning what issues will be temporarily honored. Real agreement will also exist concerning the desirability of avoiding an open conflict of definitions of the situation.[2] I will refer to this level of agreement as a "working consensus." It is to be understood that the working consensus established in one interaction setting will be quite different in content from the working consensus established in a different type of setting.

For the purpose of this report, interaction (that is, face-to-face interaction) may be roughly defined as the reciprocal influence of individuals upon one another's actions when in one another's immediate physical presence. *An* interaction may be defined as all the interaction which occurs throughout any one occasion when a given set of individuals are in one another's continuous presence; the term "an encounter" would do as well. A "performance" may be defined as all the activity of a given participant on a given occasion which serves to influence in any way any of the other participants. Taking a particular participant and his performance as a basic point of reference, we may refer to those who contribute the other performances as the audience, observers, or co-participants. The pre-established pattern of action which is unfolded during a performance and which may be presented or played through on other occasions may be called a "part" "routine."[3] These situational terms can easily be related to conventional structural ones. When an individual or performer plays the same part to the same audience on different occasions, a social relationship is likely to arise. Defining social role as the enactment of rights and duties attached to a given status, we can say that a social role will involve one or more parts and that each of these different parts may be presented by the performer on a series of occasions to the same kinds of audience or to an audience of the same persons.

Front

I have been using the term "performance" to refer to all the activity of an individual which occurs during a period marked by his continuous presence before a particular set of observers and which has some influence on the observers. It will be convenient to label as "front" that part of the individual's performance which regularly functions in a general and fixed fashion to define the situation for those who observe the performance. Front, then, is the expressive equipment of a standard kind intentionally or unwittingly employed by the individual during his performance. For preliminary purposes, it will be convenient to distinguish and label what seem to be the standard parts of front.

First, there is the "setting," involving furniture, décor, physical layout, and other background items which supply the scenery and stage props for the spate of human action played out before, within, or upon it.

If we take the term "setting" to refer to the scenic parts of expressive equipment, one may take the term "personal front" to refer to the other items of expressive equipment, the items that we most intimately identify with the performer himself and that we naturally expect will follow the performer wherever he goes. As part of personal front we may include: insignia of office or rank; clothing; sex, age, and racial characteristics; size and looks; posture; speech patterns; facial expressions; bodily gestures; and the like. Some of these vehicles for conveying signs, such as racial characteristics, are relatively fixed and over a span of time do not vary for the individual from one situation to another. On the other hand, some of these sign vehicles are relatively mobile or transitory, such as facial expression, and can vary during a performance from one moment to the next.

It is sometimes convenient to divide the stimuli which make up personal front into "appearance" and "manner," according to the function performed by the information that these stimuli convey. "Appearance" may be taken to refer to those stimuli which function at the time to tell us of the performer's social statuses. These stimuli also tell us of the individual's temporary ritual state, that is, whether he is engaging in formal social activity, work, or informal recreation, whether or not he is celebrating a new phase in the season cycle or in his life-cycle. "Manner" may be taken to refer to those stimuli which function at the time to warn us of the interaction role the performer will expect to play in the oncoming situation. Thus a haughty, aggressive manner may give the impression that the performer expects to be the one who will initiate the verbal interaction and direct its course. A meek, apologetic manner may give the impression that the performer expects to follow the lead of others, or at least that he can be led to do so.

Regions and Region Behavior

It was suggested earlier that when one's activity occurs in the presence of other persons, some aspects of the activity are expressively accentuated and other aspects, which might discredit the fostered impression, are suppressed. It is clear that accentuated facts make their appearance in what I have called a front region; it should be just as clear that there may be another region—a "back region" or "back-stage"—where the suppressed facts make an appearance.

A back region or backstage may be defined as a place, relative to a given performance, where the impression fostered by the performance is knowingly contradicted as a matter of course. There are, of course, many characteristic functions of such places. It is here that the capacity of a performance to express something beyond itself may be painstakingly fabricated; it is here that illusions and impressions are openly constructed. Here stage props and items of personal front can be stored in a kind of compact collapsing of whole repertoires of actions and characters.[4] Here grades of ceremonial equipment, such as different types of liquor or clothes, can be hidden so that the audience will not be able to see the treatment accorded them in comparison with the treatment that could have been accorded them. Here devices such as the telephone are sequestered so that they can be used "privately." Here costumes and other parts of personal front may be adjusted and scrutinized for flaws. Here the team can run through its performance, checking for offending expressions when no audience is present to be affronted by them; here poor members of the team, who are expressively inept, can be schooled or dropped from the performance. Here the performer can relax; he can drop his front, forgo speaking his lines, and step out of character.

The Role of Expression in Conveying Impressions of Self

Perhaps a moral note can be permitted at the end. In this report the expressive component of social life has been treated as a source of impressions given to or taken by others. Impression, in turn, has been treated as a source of information about unapparent facts and as a means by which the recipients can guide their response to the informant without having to wait for the full consequences of the informant's actions to be felt. Expression, then, has been treated in terms of the communicative role it plays during social interaction and not, for example, in terms of consumatory or tension-release function it might have in expresser.[5]

Underlying all social interaction there seems to be a fundamental dialectic. When one individual enters the presence of others, he will want to discover the facts of the situation. Were he to possess this information, he could know, and make allowances for, what will come to happen and he could give the others present as much of their due as is consistent with his enlightened self-interest. To uncover fully the factual nature of the situation, it would be necessary for the individual to know all the relevant social data about the others. It would also be necessary for the individual to know the actual outcome or end product of the activity of the others during the interaction, as well as their innermost feelings concerning him. Full information of this order is rarely available; in its absence, the individual tends to employ substitutes—cues, tests, hints, expressive gestures, status symbols, etc.—as predictive devices. In short, since the reality that the individual is concerned with is unperceivable at the moment, appearances must be relied upon in its stead. And, paradoxically, the more the individual is concerned with the reality that is not available to perception, the more must he concentrate his attention on appearances.

The individual tends to treat the others present on the basis of the impression they give now about the past and the future. It is here that communicative acts are translated into moral ones. The impressions that the others give tend to be treated as claims and promises they have implicitly made, and claims and promises tend to have a moral character. In his mind the individual says: "I am using these impressions of you as a way of checking up on you and your activity, and you ought not to lead me astray." The peculiar thing about this is that the individual tends to take this stand even though he expects the others to be unconscious of many of their expressive behaviors and even though he may expect to exploit the others on the basis of the information he gleans about them. Since the sources of impression used by the observing individual involve a multitude of standards pertaining to politeness and decorum, pertaining both to social intercourse and task-performance, we can appreciate afresh how daily life is enmeshed in moral lines of discrimination.

DISCUSSION QUESTIONS

1. Goffman proposes that in every interaction we are each playing a role and that we must work to present our desired self to our audience. Is he saying that we are all being fake in all of our social interactions?
2. In what kinds of social situations are you most likely to be aware of your impression management efforts?
3. What are some of the examples of the impression management you do each time you are in class?
4. Can you think of an interaction that was either confusing or embarrassing because someone's performance did not go well? Using dramaturgical terms, explain why the interaction was uncomfortable.
5. How might Goffman's ideas help explain why suddenly doing much of our socializing via Zoom or with masks on was so profoundly disconcerting when the COVID-19 pandemic first started?
6. Give two examples from your day-to-day life of when you are front stage and when you are backstage.

NOTES

1. Note that this is VERY different from distracted driving, like texting, or talking on a cell phone when you really aren't paying attention to the fundamentals of driving. This example is about distraction-free driving when you might be described as lost in your own thoughts or just listening to music or the radio.
2. An interaction can be purposely set up as a time and place for voicing differences in opinion, but in such cases participants must be careful to agree not to disagree on the proper tone of voice, vocabulary, and degree of seriousness in which all arguments are to be phrased, and upon the mutual respect which disagreeing participants must carefully continue to express toward one another. This debaters' or academic definition of the situation may also be invoked suddenly and judiciously as a way of translating a serious conflict of views into one that can be handled within a framework acceptable to all present.
3. For comments on the importance of distinguishing between a routine of interaction and any particular instance when this routine is played through, see John von Neumann and Oskar Morgenstern. 1947. *The Theory of Games and Economic Behaviour,* 2nd ed.; Princeton: Princeton University Press, p. 49.

4. As Métraux (*op. cit.*, p. 24) suggests, even the practice of voodoo cults will require such facilities.
5. Every case of possession has its theatrical side, as shown in the matter of disguises. The rooms of the sanctuary are not unlike the wings of a theater where the possessed find the necessary accessories. Unlike the hysteric, who reveals his anguish and his desires through symptoms—a personal means of expression—the ritual of possession must conform to the classic image of a mythical personage.

American Hookup

Lisa Wade

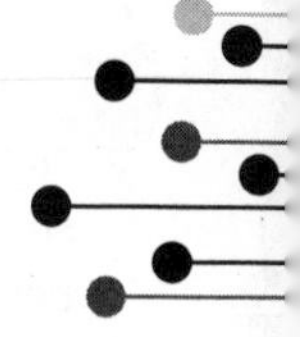

Socialization is the process of learning culture. One aspect of this is learning the expected behaviors and attitudes that go along with the different roles in that culture. We must learn what behaviors and attitudes are expected of men and women, college students, employees, friends, spouses, student athletes, or musicians, just to name a few. Many roles can simply be added to our cultural repertoires, while others require the unlearning of a previous role.

Roles often have particular cultural scripts associated with them and these are an important part of how culture guides how we behave as we interact with one another. One example of this is finding a romantic partner. In the past 20 years, technology has drastically altered the way we connect and communicate with potential partners. In the past, making a stranger aware of your existence and interest generally required being in the same physical location at some point, but dating sites like Match.com and OkCupid and dating apps like Bumble, Grindr, and Tinder have changed that. The script for meeting potential partners has changed.

Another place that the script for romantic encounters has changed over time is on college campuses. Both the media and social scientists have devoted considerable attention to the rise of "hookup culture." Hooking up is an intentionally vague phrase that refers to a physical, romantic encounter that could range anywhere from kissing to having intercourse. Much of the concern about hookup culture is focused on the belief that college students are now having drastically more sex than they used to, but in fact they aren't. Nor are they any less interested in having committed romantic relationships than in the past. As sociologist Lisa Wade points out in this excerpt from her book American Hookup, *it isn't hookup itself that's a problem, it's hookup* culture.

What hookup culture has changed is the script for finding partners. Hooking up and its required partying and drinking are often the predominant means available to meet potential partners for traditional aged college students on residential campuses. But hookup culture is also self-defeating as a means to find a committed romantic partner because the expression of any type of romantic interest,

---

and even basic kindness, are considered taboo. For this and several other reasons she outlines in this excerpt, Wade describes hookup culture as a fog that has descended on college campuses . . . "an occupying force, coercive and omnipresent" that is neither enjoyable nor beneficial to a majority of students.

As you read, think about what the cultural script for finding romantic or sexual partners looks like at your school. Does the culture she describes sound familiar or alien? If hookup culture exists on your campus, but you chose not to participate, how does this shape your options for dating or other social opportunities?

The New Culture or Sex

"I love it here," Owen said happily, a freshman in college just back from winter break. "Last semester," he told me, "was one of the most interesting, exciting, and strangest times of my life."

Owen had grown up in a farming town in central California, graduating from a high school of about sixty students. Such a small group of peers made puberty awkward. "Everyone knew everything about everyone else," he said, so sexual experimentation was rare and, when indulged in, secretive. He'd had one clandestine affair, which he remembered fondly, but despite his good looks—lean and tallish with a broad, lopsided smile and tousled dark hair—Owen's sexual activities in high school were limited.

College promised to be a whole new world. His campus offered what felt like an endless supply of potential partners and more anonymity than he'd ever dreamed of. In his first semester, he sought casual sexual encounters with what he called "gusto," and he had his fair share of good luck. "I'm shy and nerdy," he admitted, "but I clean up pretty well." It was everything he'd hoped it would be.

"I'm basically in a paradise full of girls I'm attracted to," he said, exhilarated, "everyone is fucking each other."

As his second semester progressed, though, his excitement started to waver. "A lot of the social life I've experienced," he observed wryly, "is some twisted sort of self-perpetuating vicious cycle of unrealistic expectations, boundless enthusiasm, and copious amounts of alcohol." He complained about mind games, soured friendships, and women who liked him only for his looks. "I can't expect any of the girls I'll meet on a Friday night to care about my personality or my favorite books," he grumbled. "That's just unrealistic." Some only talked to him when they wanted to share his weed. It was discouraging.

He partly blamed himself. "Oftentimes I just flat-out lack grace," he conceded. Other times he wasn't as openhearted as he wanted to be, acting distant or dismissive toward women to avoid being rejected himself. But he also felt like there was something particularly difficult about negotiating casual sex on campus. "I find it especially hard to try to smooth out a relationship with a girl whom I barely know beyond what color underwear she wears," he said, with a characteristic degree of self-deprecation.

As Owen's second semester progressed, he sounded increasingly uncertain, even morbid. "When I think about my sex life, he confessed, it feels like my insides tie themselves tight together before they boil and rot. He hated the gossip that often followed an encounter. He began doubting himself. Things got dark and he started obsessing. Worrying about it saps a lot of time and energy from my life, he said in frustration. By the end of the year, despite his initial interest, he had sworn off casual sexual encounters entirely: I can't handle another negative sexual relationship in my life. My heart might break."

On campuses across America, students are sounding an alarm. They are telling us that they are depressed, anxious, and overwhelmed. Half of first-year students express concern that they are not emotionally healthy, and one in ten say that they frequently feel depressed. The transition from teenager to young adult is rarely easy, but this is more than just youthful angst. Students are less happy and healthy than in previous generations, less so even than just ten or twenty years ago.

As Owen's transformation suggests, the sexual environment on college campuses is part of why. He anticipated an erotic and care-free life and, at first, that's what college seemed to offer. But, over the course of his first year, he became increasingly disillusioned. The reasons why are related to his specific encounters and are complicated by his personal story, but there is nothing unique about his disappointment.

The idea that college students are having a lot of sex is certainly an enthralling myth. Even students believe it. In Bogle's landmark study, students guessed that their peers were doing it fifty times a year. That's twenty-five times what the numbers actually show. In Kimmel's *Guyland*, young men figured that 80 percent of college guys were having sex any given weekend; they would have been closer to the truth if they were guessing the percent of men who had *ever* had sex. Students overestimate how much sex their peers are having, and by quite a lot.

In fact, today's students boast no more sexual partners than their parents did at their age. Scholars using the University of Chicago's General Social Survey have shown that they actually report slightly fewer sexual partners than Gen-Xers did. Millennials look more similar to the baby boomer generation than they do to the wild sexual cohort that they are frequently imagined to be.

There are students on campus with active sex lives, of course, but there are plenty with none at all and some with sexual escapades that are, at best, only "slightly less nonexistent" than they were in high school. The average graduating senior reports hooking up just eight times in four years. That amounts to one hookup per semester. Studies looking specifically at the sexual cultures at Duke, Yale, and East Carolina universities, the universities of Georgia and Tennessee, the State University of New York at Geneseo, and UC Berkeley report similar numbers. Not all students are hooking up, and those that do aren't necessarily doing so very often. Neither are students always hopping out of one bed and into another; half of those eight hookups are with someone the student has hooked up with before. Almost a third of students will graduate without hooking up a single time.

Despite the rumors, then, there is no epidemic of casual sexual encounters on college campuses. So, hookups can't be blamed. There just aren't enough of them to account for the malaise. Neither does two sexual encounters every twelve months, possibly with the same person, look like either female empowerment or male domination; if so, it's quite a tepid expression of power. There certainly is no bacchanalian Utopia, poly, queer, or otherwise. Students are too busy not having sex to be enacting the next revolution. The cause of students' unhappiness, then, can't be the hookup. But it *is* about hooking up. It's hookup *culture*.

Hookup culture is an occupying force, coercive and omnipresent. For those who love it, it's all sunshine, but it isn't for everyone else. Deep in the fog, students often feel dreary, confused, helpless. Many behave in ways they don't like, hurt other people unwillingly, and consent to sexual activity they don't desire.

Campuses of all kinds are in this fog. No matter the size of the college, how heavy a Greek or athletic presence it boasts, its exclusivity, its religious affiliation, or whether it's public or private, hookup culture is there. We find it in all regions of the country, from the Sunshine State of Florida to the sunny state of California. Students all over say so. Hookups are "part of our collegiate culture," writes a representative of the American South in the University of Florida's *Alligator*. If you don't hook up, warns a woman at the University of Georgia, then you're "failing at the college experience." A woman at Tulane puts it succinctly: "Hookup culture," she says, "it's college."

Hooking Up, a How-To

The goal is to look "fuckable," Miranda said, her voice buzzing with excitement. She and her roommate Ruby were tearing through their tiny closets, collecting a pile of "provocative" items to consider wearing to that night's party. The theme was "burlesque," so they were going for a classy stripper vibe. Bridget offered her two cents as she headed back to her own room: "Lacy bras, corsets, fishnet stockings—anything that hints at being sexy underwear!" Ruby pulled on tights, short shorts, and calf-high boots. On top she wore a bright yellow bra and a see-through white tank top.

Miranda plumped her breasts and contemplated her outfit, a black crop top and a cherry red skirt with a zipper running down the front. She unzipped it a bit from the bottom and, then, a bit more. Ruby finished her "sleepy, drowsy, sexy eye look" with a splash of yellow to match the bra, just as Bridget walked back in balancing three shots of Smirnoff. "Let's get some dick tonight, ladies!" she yelled. They tossed back their shots and headed out. It was approaching midnight.

Across campus, Levi sat down at his computer and googled "burlesque party," trying to figure out what to wear. The search returned mostly women in corsets. He turned to his friend and motioned to the screen. "It doesn't matter what you wear," his friend said sharply, "you're a guy." So, he put on a pair of "jeans and a nice green button-down shirt" that his mom had given him for Christmas. Satisfied, he looked at his reflection in the tall mirror tacked up on his dorm room closet: "I'd shaved recently, so I looked pretty sharp," he thought. His roommate smeared some gel through his dark hair, tugged on the front of his polo shirt, and swallowed the last of his beer. "Ready?"

Step 1: Pregame.

"You don't walk out of the house without your shoes on and you don't walk into a party without a couple of shots of vodka," insisted one of my students. "It's real." The first step in hooking up is to get, as Miranda put it, "shitfaced."

Party-oriented students believe that drinking enhances their experience. Destiny, for example, gushed, about how it felt to be a bit drunk at a college-sponsored concert:

> I honestly think I would not have had as much fun as
> I did if I wasn't intoxicated. . . . I couldn't care less about what
> people thought about me and felt free enough just
> to do whatever I wanted and to be bubbly and carefree.
> That night I didn't have a care in the world and it felt
> absolutely fantastic.

Students also tend to think that alcohol improves their personality. Getting drunk, they argue, brings out their "intoxicated self," one that is freer, more relaxed, less anxious, and generally more fun to be around. Destiny emphasized how alcohol made her feel carefree three times in as many sentences. Others believe that it gives them confidence. "I rely on mixed drinks and shots," wrote another female student. "They are not lying when they call it 'liquid courage.'"

Step 2: Grind.

"If you can't dirty dance," insisted one of my female students, "then you can't dance at all." Grinding is the main activity at most college parties. Women who are willing to press their backs and backsides against men's bodies and dance rhythmically. "It is a bestial rubbing of genitals reminiscent of mating zebras," Laura wrote scornfully after attending a party. "Guys were coming up behind women on the dance floor and placing their hands on their hips like two way-ward lobster claws, clamping on and pulling them close."

Because men generally come up to women from behind, sometimes the identity of the man whose penis abuts their backside is a mystery. In that case, instead of turning around—for reasons that will soon become clear—they peer over to their friends for an indication as to whether they should continue. As one of Ronen's students at Stanford observed:

It is essential that he be "cute" because the ultimate goal in hookup culture isn't just to hook up, it's to hook up with the right person. Or, more specifically, a *hot* person. Hotness, says one female student, "is the only qualification one needs to be considered for a hookup." "Average guys just don't cut it," another wrote:

> Sure, it's not a social tragedy to hook up with an average-looking guy. But hooking up with someone attractive is a social asset for sure. It raises your standing in the hierarchy of potential partners. It makes you more attractive.

Using indicators like hotness, blondness, fraternity membership, and athletic prowess, students form a working consensus about who is hookup-worthy, and that guides their decisions. "So many hookups," confirmed one student, "are dictated by how our peers view the potential partner." She admitted that she usually asked other people what they thought of guys before getting together with them. "I am unable to separate my opinion from those of my friends," she wrote frankly.

Let me be careful to distinguish this from the idea that people seek sexual contact with others they find attractive. Nominally, at least, this idea acknowledges that people have individual tastes. Beauty, they say, is in the eye of the beholder. In hookup culture, though, beauty is in the eyes of the beholders, plural. A body's value is determined by collective agreement. It's crowdsourced.

Just as hooking up with a hot student can increase one's own popularity, hooking up with one widely considered unattractive can harm it. Because of this, students who are collectively categorized as unhot are sexual hot potatoes. Students fear being burned.

Kendra, for example, quite enjoyed her hookup. "I had fun," she remembered, "and it was a learning experience, and it made me feel good about myself because I felt attractive to someone." But, when she saw him in the harsh light of the cafeteria the next morning, she was suddenly embarrassed: "He wasn't attractive to me. At all. In any way," she wrote, as if squirming with discomfort. "He was scrawny. I mean, really scrawny, with glasses, and just not stereotypically masculine." Revealing that her regret was more about what other people might think than her own experience, she explained, "He wasn't the guy you're *supposed* to hook up with."

When she told her friends later, she exaggerated her level of inebriation, wanting to make "the fact that I hooked up with a relatively unattractive guy okay." By hooking up with someone that others might not approve of, Kendra was doing hookup culture wrong. "Because the point of hookups is to get with someone hot," she insisted, "and if you don't do that, you should have a damn good excuse."

Step 3: Initiate a Hookup.

"The classic move to establish that you want to hook up with someone," Miranda's friend Ruby wrote from a woman's perspective, "is to turn around to face him, rather than dance with your back pressed against his front." Initiation can come from behind, too. He may tug on her arm or pull one hip back gently to suggest she spin. Or, he might put his face next to hers, closing the distance between them such that, with the turn of her head, there might be a kiss.

If she spins around, Miranda explained, it "seals the deal." Turning around isn't just turning around; it's an advance, an invitation to escalate. Once students are face to face, it's *on*. This is why women look to their friends when a guy approaches them from behind instead of taking a look for themselves. Turning around is tantamount to agreeing to a "difmo"—a DFMO, or "dance-floor make-out."

Back at the burlesque party, Ruby would make exactly that move. The shots of Smirnoff had loosened her inhibitions, and she wasn't alone. "All around me," she wrote, "I saw the same thing happening—female friends of mine meeting guys and flirting, dancing, and then making out." She would join the dance floor shortly and, in the midst of the throbbing crowd, end up dancing with Levi.

They danced for a while, she turned around, and eventually Levi carried her piggyback the two blocks to his dorm. They fell into his bed, laughing, and "suddenly it was happening."

Step 4: Do . . . something.

According to the Online College Social Life Survey, in 40 percent of hookups, Ruby's "it" means intercourse. Another 12 percent include only what we might call foreplay: nudity and some touching of genitals, while 13 percent proceed to oral sex, mostly performed by women on men, but don't include intercourse. A full 35 percent of hookups don't go any further than open-mouth kissing and groping.

This can be confusing. "I sometimes have a hard time distinguishing what a particular person means when mentioning a hookup," reported one of my students. Currier argues that the ambiguity is strategic, allowing students to exaggerate or downplay their encounters depending on what they want others to think. Specifically, she found that it allowed women to "protect their status as 'good girls' (sexual but not promiscuous)" and men to "protect their social status as 'real men' (heterosexual, highly sexually active)." It also has to do with how they feel about the person they hooked up with the next morning. Hookups with high-status people may be exaggerated and those with lower-status people minimized.

In any case, thanks to its ambiguity, the content of any given hookup is mysterious unless the participants get specific or it happens in public. The *purpose* of the hookup, however, is the opposite of ambiguous. Or, at least, it's supposed to be and this is where Ruby worried she might have messed up that night.

Step 5: Establish Meaninglessness.

The goal is "fast, random, no-strings-attached sex," Ruby explained, but she wasn't sure that's what had happened with Levi. In fact, they were already quite close friends. Both ran in the popular crowd and were squarely in the "hot" category. Levi had an easy way about him and, though he wasn't a member of a fraternity or an athlete, his time in high school sports had left him able to fit in with the men who were. Ruby was a favorite among the popular boys Levi hung out with. With light brown skin, a heart-shaped face, and wavy brown hair that fell to the small of her back, she had the kind of beauty that others eroticized as "exotic."

Ruby swore that she'd never thought of him as a potential hookup before that night. So, she was surprised at the turn of events. Uneasy, too. "I don't want hooking up with Levi to mean anything," she confessed nervously. "I don't think seeing someone naked should necessarily drastically change the way you think about them," she wrote, but she was concerned that it might affect their friendship.

> It's mostly me psyching myself out, telling myself that now that we've hooked up our friendship has to change. It doesn't—or at least I really don't want it to. But I can't help feeling so weird every time I see him since then. All I can think is, it didn't mean anything to me . . . but did it to you? Do you hate me now, because you cared and I didn't?

Truly, step 5 is the trickiest. How do two people establish that an intimate moment between them wasn't meaningful?

College students know, then, that the wider culture imbues sexual activity with great emotional significance, and this belief overlaps considerably with what they think characterizes loving, romantic relationships for themselves as well. So, despite the language we have for dismissing the significance of sex in practice, establishing that a hookup was meaningless is a challenging personal and interpersonal task.

If the hookup is going to be understood as meaningless, all of these implications have to be nullified.

This is how they do it.

Step 5a: Be (or claim to be) Plastered.

When students talk about meaningless sex on college campuses, they are almost always referring to drunk sex. According to the Online College Social Life Survey, most casual sex occurring on college campuses involves alcohol; men have drunk an average of six drinks and women an average of four. "People who hook-up casually are almost always drunk or have at least been drinking," a female student observed. "Thank god for vodka?" Levi asked rhetorically. "I blame it on the Cuervo," countered a student at Marist College. One University of Florida, Gainesville student half-joked, "If you don't remember the sex, it didn't count."

I was first clued into the symbolic function of alcohol in hookup culture while listening to students discuss "sober sex" when I visited campuses and talked to students in small groups. It was the hushed and reverent tone that got my attention. Sober sex is interpreted entirely differently from drunk sex. It's *heavy* with meaning. "A sober hookup indicates one that is more serious," explained a student. About sober hookups, students say things like "shit's getting real" and "it takes a lot of balls." "If you are sober," a female student described in more detail:

> It means you both are particularly attracted to each other and it's not really a one-time thing. When drunk, you can kind of just do it because it's fun and then be able to laugh about it and have it not be awkward or not mean anything.

Step 5b: Cap Your Hookups.

"We've only hooked up once," explained a male student, "so . . . it automatically is not a big deal." A second trick for dismissing the significance of hookups is to limit how many times two students hook up together. One hookup, students argue, isn't anything to get serious about. "One and done," is what they say. A female student snorted when asked if she would hook up with a guy a second time. "No way," she said gruffly. She had "no feelings for him," so he was "not a viable hookup ever again." Based on the Online College Social Life Survey, we know that most people only hook up with any given person once and very few hook up more than two or three times.

Students believe that avoiding repeat hookups helps ensure that no one gets the idea that a relationship is on the table. They think this is simply the right thing to do. One insisted that it would be "extremely rude" to hook up with someone a second time if there weren't feelings involved.

Capping hookups also reduces the possibility of someone "catching feelings." "The number one established rule of hooking up," wrote a woman enrolled at Tufts, is "don't get too attached." It's a real risk, explained a student at Bellarmine University. "Sometimes you actually catch feelings and that's what sucks." Students, then, aim to hook up with someone that they don't particularly like and, from there, retreat.

If the relationship-averse generally agree that repeat hookups with the same person are risky, they're right. The Online College Social Life Survey shows that three-quarters of seniors have been in at least one monogamous relationship lasting six months or more and, even though hookups rarely lead to relationships, most relationships start with hookups. So, one must be vigilant to ensure that expectations for a relationship don't accidentally evolve.

Step 5c: Create Emotional Distance.

After it's all over, students confirm that a hookup meant nothing by giving their relationship—whatever it was—a demotion. The rule is to be less close after a hookup than before, at least for a time. If students were good friends, they should act like acquaintances. If they were acquaintances, they should act like strangers. And if they were strangers, they shouldn't acknowledge each other's existence at all. "Unless at the beginning you've made it clear that you want more than a hookup," wrote a male student at Bowdoin, "then the expectation is . . . just to pretend it didn't happen."

The logic gets wacky, but it goes something like this: an unrequited crush will probably be more damaging to a friendship than being temporarily unfriendly. After a hookup, then, when the possibility of romance is a specter that must be eliminated, acting aloof is the best way to ensure that students remain friends. "People act very strangely," one student commented, "to make sure, almost to prove, they're keeping things casual."

Plenty of students feel uncomfortable with this proposition, but hookup culture has a way of enforcing compliance. If the rule is to be unfriendly, then even the slightest kindness—essentially, any effort to connect or reach out—can be interpreted as romantic interest. So, if students are nice after a hookup, they risk making an impression that they don't want to make. As one male student remarked with regret, "I try to stay friends with girls I've hooked up with, or at least stay on a 'don't hate me' basis [but] . . . I've found that, in doing so, you sometimes run into trouble with leading someone on." A second student struggled with how to handle a guy she liked, but not "in that way." She wrote:

> I don't want to be rude by not answering his text messages and not being friendly every time I see him. He doesn't deserve that. But I guess he also doesn't deserve to be led on. . . . I have no idea what to do.

She knew he liked her and it felt terrible to treat him dismissively, but she was advised that "being mean was the best way to handle it." "Many guys I have spoken to," confirmed another student, "admitted to . . . not being nice to the women they hook up with to 'protect' their feelings." The more students value a person's friendship, the more essential they may think it is to be unfriendly after a hookup.

Ruby thought it essential. Since she and Levi had been close friends before their hookup, she temporarily demoted him to acquaintance. A few days later, Ruby filled me in:

> I've seen and interacted with Levi a few times—definitely much less than I would have in a normal three-day span. I've only spent about ten minutes alone with him, in which we joked and made casual small talk, graciously avoiding the fact that we've had each other's genitals in our mouths.

It worked. A week later, Ruby would happily report, "It's as if it never happened and I am perfectly good with that."

Changing the Culture

Hookup culture is now part of American history, the newest way that young people have come to initiate sexual encounters and form romantic relationships. In some ways, it is a mashup of the best things about the sexual cultures of the last one hundred years. Like the gay men of the 1970s, students in hookup culture are inspired by a joyous sense of liberation and the belief that they have the right to indulge their desires and no reason to feel shame. Like the middleclass youth of the 1950s, today's college students get to explore the whole range of sexual options if they want to and, thanks to effective, accessible birth control, they get to do so with much fewer unintended pregnancies and early marriages. Like the young working people who took advantage of the dazzling new nightlife in the cities of the 1920s, students relish novelty and the opportunity to be at least a little unruly. And, like men and women throughout history, and perhaps against all odds, students fall in love. Young people break the rules, as they always have, and out of hookups come committed, lasting, emotionally supportive relationships.

But hookup culture also carries with it some of the worst things about the last hundred years. It is still gripped, for example, by the limiting gender stereotypes that emerged during the Industrial Revolution, that fissuring of love and sex that left us thinking that women's hearts are weak and men's hearts are hard, that men's desires are ablaze and women's barely flicker.

Thanks to these stereotypes, when men pursue sex on campus today it is interpreted as a sign of a healthy, red-blooded masculinity, but we still don't acknowledge a healthy, red-blooded femininity. When women of color are sexual, it's seen as a racial trait; when poor and working-class women are sexual, it's read as "trashy"; and when middle-class white women are sexual, it's interpreted, all too often, as just a proxy for relational yearning. And, since hookup culture demands that students seem uninterested in romance lest they seem desperate, this stereotype ensures that women usually lose the competition over who can care less, if only by default.

These stereotypes also warp what seems possible, making it difficult to advocate for sex that is both casual and kind. As a result, when women express a desire for a caring partner, it's almost always interpreted as desperation for a boyfriend rather than a request to be treated well. And when men stiff-arm their hookup partners after the fact, they are assumed to do so because they want to keep things casual, not because we've decided that it's okay for them to refuse to do the emotional labor that is essential to all respectful interactions.

Hookup culture also continues to uphold the particular strain of gender inequality that took hold in the 1920s, giving men the power to control both love and sex and making women into rivals for male attention. In fact, on campus things may have gotten worse. Competition among women can be especially fierce thanks to the fact that they attend college in higher numbers than men.

College today is oddly like postwar America, those years after so many men were killed in World War II, when the idea that women are greedy for boyfriends took hold.

A woman's sexiness is still held up as a measure of her worth, and men continue to be the arbiters of whether women are sufficiently sexy. It's not altogether unenjoyable for women, but it is often intimidating and emotionally harmful as well. Meanwhile, men are competing for men's approval, too. Some men seek their own orgasms to impress other men and deny them to women for the same reason, while women focus on being hot enough to get guys off in ways that undermine their own pleasure.

Hookup culture has also failed to integrate the best things about gay liberation: people and practices that are wonderfully queer. Instead, it remains hostile or indifferent to non-heterosexual desire, sometimes but rarely setting up environments in which heterosexuality isn't assumed, catered to, and celebrated.

Being sexually active on campus is still dangerous, too. When the young men and women of the 1950s abandoned public dates for private intimacy, students became more vulnerable to sexual predation. Research published in 1957—to my knowledge, the earliest study of sexual assault on campus—found that 21 percent of college women claimed to have been victims of an attempted or completed sexual assault, the same number we find today. Hookup culture continues this ominous tradition by catalyzing sexual aggression among otherwise non-aggressive men and offering camouflage to genuine predators. With pleasure comes danger, and we have yet to fully figure out how to reduce the latter without inhibiting the former.

Feminists tried to change many of these things, to ensure that women and men could engage with one another sexually as equals, but they were only successful in fixing half the problem. They opened doors for women, giving them the opportunity to embrace the part of life that had been given to men during urbanization: the right to work, to pursue male-dominated occupations, to be unabashedly ambitious, and to seek out sex just for fun. And they tried to open doors for men, too—to give them the right to pursue female-dominated occupations or to focus on the home, the right to prioritize nurturance and care and to hold sex close to their hearts—but Americans resisted the latter change more than they have the former. We are still waiting for men to embrace the part of life that was once given exclusively to women, and for the society around them to reward them for doing so.

In hookup culture, we see these dynamics play out clearly. Since the ideal that is held up is a stereotypically masculine way of engaging sexually, both men and women aim to have "meaningless sex." Expressing emotions is seen as weak. Hookup culture, strongly masculinized, demands carelessness, rewards callousness, and punishes kindness. In this scenario, both men and women have the opportunity to have sex, but neither is entirely free to love.

The majority of students would prefer more meaningful connections with others. They want an easier path toward forming committed, loving relationships. Most would also be glad if their casual relationships were a little less competitive and a lot kinder. And while heterosexual men have more orgasms than women, it is at the expense of a full range of sexual expression. Alienated from the pleasure that can come with being desired, and told that it's unmanly and pathetic to seek emotional connection with their sexual partners, men suffer in hookup culture, too.

Students wish they had more options. Some pine for the going-steady lifestyle of the 1950s. Many mourn the antiracist, feminist Utopia that their grandparents envisioned but never saw fully realized. Quite a few would like things to be a lot more queer. Some want a hookup culture that is warmer: where students aren't just poly—hooking up with multiple partners—but poly*amorous*—hooking up with multiple partners who are loving toward them. There are certainly some who would quite like something more akin to college in the 1700s: a lot more studying and whole lot less "fun."

I think in this is a hint as to what we might hope to see in the coming decades: a diversification of what is possible. We need a more complex and rich cultural life on campus, not just a different one. Students want the opportunity to choose monogamy or not; the right to be treated kindly always; freedom from the rigid constraints on what it means to be a man or woman, including whom we're allowed to desire and whether we want to be male or female at all; and the option to decide whether being sexy—or even sexual—is something one wants in the first place. We need to chip away at hookup culture's dominance and force it to compete with other, more humane sexual cultures that we can envision, and many more that we haven't envisioned yet.

We must transform hookup culture, too, because some students will always prefer hookups. We need to say yes to the opportunity for casual sexual encounters, but no to the absence of care, unfair distribution of pleasure, unrelenting pressure to be hot, and risk of sexual violence. We need to flush out and end racism, sexism, ableism, classism, and other biases. We need a new culture of hooking up, one that keeps the good and roundly rejects the bad.

A campus with lots of healthy, competing sexual cultures is full of opportunity. It requires students to really think about what they want for themselves and from one another. It also requires them to talk to one another instead of assuming (often erroneously) that they know what their peers want. Competing cultures would encourage thoughtfulness, communication, tolerance, and introspection, and all of those things are great for sex.

Seeing what's happening on campus as a culture—recognizing that it's not the hookup itself, but hookup culture that is the problem—is the first step to changing it. Because culture is a type of shared consciousness, change has to happen collectively. And it can. Especially because so many colleges qualify as total institutions, because of the sheer togetherness of the student body, a campus can transform, and faster than you might suspect.

But students need everyone else to change, too. We are all in the fog. We face an onslaught of sexualized messaging designed to make us worry that our sex lives are inadequate. There is an erotic marketplace off campus, too, and it is distorted by prejudice, a fixation on wealth, and a shallow worship of youth and beauty. For certain, there is an orgasm gap between men and women outside of college, and the practices that enhance sexual encounters—communication, creativity, tolerance, confidence, and knowledge—are scarcer than they should be. We all tend to look to men for approval while valuing women's opinions too little. Sexual violence is epidemic everywhere, and unfortunately anyone, male or female, can be cold and cruel.

The corrosive elements of hookup culture are in all of our lives: in our workplaces, in our politics and the media, within our families and friendships, and, yes, in bars and bedrooms. They're even in our marriages. It makes no sense, then, to shake our fingers at college students. They are us. If we want to fix hookup culture, we have to fix American culture. When we do, we can nurture sexualities that are kinder and safer, more pleasurable and authentic, more fun and truly free.

DISCUSSION QUESTIONS

1. What are the steps in hooking up? How do these steps maintain hookup culture?
2. Who is most likely to enjoy and benefit from hookup culture? Who is least likely? Do these differences map to the types of social traits that get privileged in society at large?
3. What role do emotions play in hookups? What strategies do people use to manage their emotions before, during, and after a hookup? How are these problematic?
4. Does the culture she describes sound familiar or alien? If hookup culture exists on your campus, but you chose not to participate, how does this shape your options for dating or other social opportunities?
5. Ask several people in their 50s or older how they went about finding romantic partners when they were younger. Pool your answers with several classmates. What was different? Is there anything that is the same?

READING 7

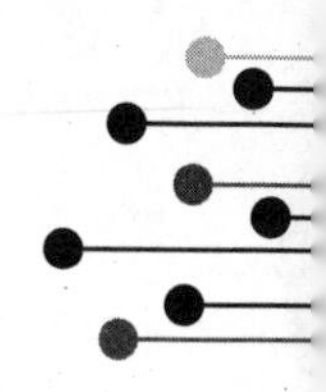

Disciplined Preferences

Explaining the (Re)Production of Latino Endogamy

Jessica M. Vasquez

As Lisa Wade demonstrated in her article "American Hookup," our choices in romantic partners and how we interact with them are shaped by our culture. But even who we find attractive or perceive as a potential partner in the first place (for a hookup or sometime more serious) is highly influenced by culture. We implicitly consider a whole host of social characteristics when considering whether someone may be a potential romantic partner; their racial and ethnic background, education level, where they live, gender, age, and religion all play a role.

An examination of dating and marriage patterns shows that we don't like to stray very far, socially speaking. Most people wind up with partners who are socially similar to them, a pattern that social scientists call endogamy. This is remarkable given that in Western culture, sexual attraction and choice of spouse are seen as the most personal and individual of experiences, and that belief is safeguarded with considerable vigor—would you let our parents pick who you married or even hooked up with? What about your sociology professor? In America, most of us want full autonomy in choosing our romantic partners, but when we have it, we overwhelmingly choose partners in socially predictable ways.

In this reading, Jessica Vasquez accounts for endogamy among Latinos by examining how location, immigrant status, gender, location, and even skin color all play a role in shaping how Latinos perceive potential partners. Even when individuals describe choosing to only date others like them, she demonstrates how those choices have been socially inscribed. As with most things, we are never far from our culture's influence on how we interpret and interact with others.

The author thanks Christopher Wetzel, Pierrette Hondagneu-Sotelo, Eileen Otis, Jill Harrison, Jiannbin Shiao, Aaron Gullickson, C.J. Pascoe, Kemi Balogun, Patricia Gwartney,

Excerpt from "Disciplined Preferences: Explaining the (Re)Production of Latino Endogamy," by Jessica M. Vasquez. *Social Problems* (2015), 62(3), pp. 455–475. Reprinted with permission from Oxford University Press, USA.

and Matthew Norton for insightful feedback on earlier drafts. Appreciation also goes to audience members of a panel at the Annual Meeting of the Pacific Sociological Association in 2014 who pushed this scholarship forward through stimulating questions and comments. This project was funded by the American Sociological Association/National Science Foundation Fund for the Advancement of the Discipline, the Ford Foundation, the Russell Sage Foundation, the University of Kansas, and the University of Oregon. Direct correspondence to: Jessica M. Vasquez, Department of Sociology, 1291 University of Oregon, Eugene, OR97403–1291. E-mail: vasquezj@uoregon .edu.

While courtship and marriage are often thought of as products of individual agency and "mythic love" (Swidler 2001), legal and social practices circumscribe personal preferences about sexual intimacy.[1] Because families are seen as the foundation of the social order (Moran 2001), their regulation has been "a primary means through which a racially divided and racist society has been maintained" (Dalmage 2000:2). Historically, the state through the legal system orchestrated the marriage and reproductive pool by excluding certain national origin groups from the country (Haney López 1996). Similarly, anti-miscegenation laws sought to prevent racial mixing and "to protect whiteness" (Root 2001:35). Although anti-miscegenation laws were struck down in 1967 (Kennedy 2003), intermarriage rates remain low, moving from "nearly nonexistent to merely atypical" (Taylor, Funk, and Craighill 2006:1).

Today, race continues to organize intimate relationships. Despite a decline in racial endogamy in the twentieth century, race persists as the most powerful division in the marriage market (Rosenfeld 2008). Endogamy (intragroup relations) is commonplace, reflected by 87 percent of people in the United States marrying within their own racial category (Bean and Stevens 2003; Lee and Bean 2010).

Persistently low intermarriage rates lead to these questions: Why does high racial endogamy persist in an era without legal proscription? And, how do groups constitute themselves and entrench racial divisions through interactional practices? By drawing on retrospective interviews from racially intermarried and intramarried couples that involve at least one Latino person, I demonstrate the social pressures that bear on intimacy and argue that what we conceive of as personal preferences are actually socially constructed and reinforce the racial hierarchy. My chief argument is that the selection of a marriage partner is circumscribed by what I call disciplined preferences. Disciplined preferences are internalized romantic tastes that are produced through racialized social practices—including violence, threats, censure, and advice—that condition Latinos to date and marry intraracially. Heather Dalmage (2000) uses the term "border patrolling" to denote how meso-level actors such as families, peers, and the community affect individual choices. I demonstrate how border-patrolling practices are internalized as self-discipline and reproduce endogamy. I also use the concepts of surveillance, punishment, and self-discipline to explain the continued high level of racial endogamy in a social system where intermarriage is legal.[2] The mechanisms that enforce endogamy include: family surveillance, violence or threats from an in-group or out-group, group stereotypes, and notions of cultural fit.

Explaining Endogamy: Border Patrolling by Third Parties

Residential segregation is strongly related to endogamy (Landale, Oropesa, and Bradatan 2006; Rosenfeld 2009; Stevens and Swicegood 1987), dividing populations by race and class, thereby limiting interracial contact and possibilities for romantic liaisons. Due to the "sheer force of propinquity" (Alba and Nee 2003:99), ethnic neighborhoods foster endogamy, whereas intermarried couples are more often located outside of ethnic neighborhoods (Alba, Jiménez, and Marrow 2014; Telles and Ortiz 2008).

Symbolic boundary literature shows that individuals and groups use moral discourses to maintain group worth, to position one group above others, and to guard against the erosion of advantage (Lamont and Molnar 2002; Roth 2012; Sherman 2009). Endogamy is a boundary that maintains social closure, prohibits others' access to valuable resources, and is encoded in representations of social life that construct interracial relations as deviant (Childs 2009). If the objective of boundary work is to differentiate a group from others (Roth 2012), intraracial sexual relations are a powerful tool to enforce social closure and visibly perpetuate, through monoracial families, group cohesion. Endogamy is the ultimate symbolic boundary enforcer in that it "support[s] the social structure by helping to fix social distances . . . between groups" (Merton [1941] 2000:483). I propose that a cogent way to explain endogamy is to link the structural argument of segregation with community-level enactments of boundaries. The question then becomes: How do people enforce and internalize the social edict of intramarriage?

Expanding on the classic explanations of residential segregation and symbolic boundaries, I demonstrate how endogamy is policed through informal, interpersonal border patrolling. "Border patrolling" is a form of discrimination that stems from "the belief that people should stick to their own, taking race and racial categories for granted" (Dalmage 2000:42). Boundary surveillance perpetuates the myth of group homogeneity, punishes boundary crossers, and may be internalized to limit transgressions.

My theoretical proposition is to explain racial endogamy by demonstrating how meso-level social forces, including family, peer, and community, construct individual subjectivities and actions. Borrowing from social psychologist Kay Deaux (2006:4), the meso level is "a point of focus that links the individual to the social system" where social interaction takes place. Family- and community-enforced surveillance as well as self-discipline—the internalization of societal power—help explain the continued high level of racial endogamy in a social system where intermarriage is legal. Violence and intimidation have been historically effective deterrents to intermarriage as "groups actively police each other to ensure that domination is maintained" by means of "threats of violence or actual violence" (Childs 2009; Collins 2008:267; Hodes 1997). Focusing on the interactional level of analysis is crucial because race is "*performative* . . . [racial and] ethnic boundaries . . . constituted by day-to-day affirmations, reinforcements, and enactments of . . . differences" (Nagel 2000:111, emphasis in original). This article fleshes out the interactional mechanisms by which third parties, such as family, peers and community, engrave racial and sexual boundaries.

In what follows I demonstrate how border-patrolling mechanisms (family surveillance and censure, violence and threats of violence, group stereotypes, and ideas about cultural fit) operating at the meso level may vary according to social location and yet produce conformity. Reacting to family and community pressures, most individuals discipline their intimacy preferences and "choose" to abide by the convention of same-race romances.

Methods

This article draws from 70 in-depth, life history interviews with heterosexual Latinos in endogamous and exogamous marriages and their adult children living independently. I include both partners in Latino intramarriages but only Latino partners of intermarriages for, while they married exogamously, their dating histories and counsel to their children concerning marriage is useful information. These data are drawn from a larger comparative project on dating and marriage histories among Latinos and their partners.

There is near parity of interviewees across field sites: 36 interviewees are located in Los Angeles County, California, and 34 are located in the northeast region of Kansas (Topeka, Lawrence, and Kansas City). More intramarried Latinos hail from California (32 of 47), whereas more Latinos intermarried with whites reside in Kansas (13 of 16). This unevenness likely reflects the distinct "marriage markets" that ensue from the concentration of Latinos in Los Angeles County and the predominance of whites in northeastern Kansas.

The rationale for selecting California and Kansas is to compare a traditional migration gateway that borders Mexico and boasts a racially diverse population with a predominantly white state distant from the border. California's population is 39.4 percent non-Hispanic white, whereas Kansas' population is 85 percent non-Hispanic white, and the nation's population is 63 percent non-Hispanic white. The nation is comprised of 16.9 percent Hispanic persons (of any race), whereas California, at 38.2 percent Hispanic, is over double that figure and Kansas, at 11 percent Hispanic, is well below the national percentage (U.S. Census 2012). Regional comparisons can yield information concerning the importance of place, from the salience of immigration patterns to race relations (Jiménez 2010; Marrow 2011).

The (Re)Production of Endogamy

Analysis of the data yielded four main findings that collectively demonstrate the production of endogamous partnerships. First, I show how residential segregation limits dating options and shapes preferences by restricting the field of possibilities. Second, I show how Latinos discipline their preferences away from whites by internalizing punishment and interpreting whites as "incompatible" mates. Third, I examine how white parents discourage their children's interracial relationships with Latinos. Finally, I illustrate how Latinos deploy anti-black prejudice to safeguard their position in an intermediate position in the racial hierarchy. I argue that disciplined preference is the result of racialized and gendered treatment of Latinos that punishes interracial intimacy and encourages racial endogamy. Just as this preference is disciplined, so too is it disciplining: this acquired preference shapes the self while simultaneously marginalizing subordinated racial out-groups.

Segregation and Socioeconomic Status

Endogamy is associated with both segregation and socioeconomic status: underclass Mexican Americans who do not attend college—and do not experience expanded marriage pools—but continue to live in segregated ethnic enclaves are unlikely to intermarry (Landale et al. 2006). Due to spatial isolation, neighborhood public schools concentrate racially homogenous communities, delimiting dating options (Alba and Nee 2003; Lichter et al. 2007; Massey and Denton 1993; Rosenfeld 2009). Julia and Lisandro Quinonez, both Mexican American, agree that living in predominantly Latino East LA made endogamous romance seem inevitable. Julia remarked, "our high school was like 90 percent Latino. . . . [M]y [dating] options were pretty limited [laughing]. . . . Everybody was Mexican." Lisandro concurred, "Because everybody was Chicano or Latino in high school, it wasn't really a question." Residential segregation is not exclusively a California issue, as 46-year-old Cynthia Herrera-Redgrave from Kansas made clear: "When I was [in] high school I . . . [thought] I was gonna marry somebody who was Mexican. . . . That's what I mostly [saw] around me." Neighborhood segregation naturalizes endogamous partnerships, shaping fields of vision in both a practical and cognitive sense. As Cynthia stated, "You wouldn't even think about it."

Thirty-six-year-old Vincent Venegas, who arrived in the United States from Mexico at age seven, lived amongst poor Mexican Americans and African Americans in Los Angeles in his youth. Residential propinquity shaped Vincent's understanding of racial boundaries and attractiveness: "I had several crushes on African Americans and Latinas. . . . I didn't perceive the other races to find my race or myself attractive. . . . I dated Latina and African American. . . . We were close [in social] class. His gang affiliation limited his social circle and disciplined his preferences to include similarly lower-class non-white groups: "Since I was a gang member . . . the possibilities are even smaller. You encircle yourself in a little bubble of . . . gang life: the gang members and the gang girls. I built myself a smaller bubble and it contained me."

One of the poorer interviewees in his youth, who stopped his education at high school, Vincent's segregated adolescence was his "little bubble" that naturalized dating within his socioeconomic stratum. In a social environment that "contained" him, segregation supplanted the need for active discipline and shaped his notions of attractiveness and his marital outcome (he married a local Mexican American "party girl"). Residential segregation curtails dating options, this structural characteristic eradicating the need for meso-level discipline by making endogamous partnerships seem inevitable.

The least geographically mobile groups are endogamously married and, inversely, intermarriage is most common among the more educated classes (Alba et al. 2014; Kalmijn 1998, 2010; Spickard 1991; Telles and Ortiz 2008). Slightly more than half of my interviewees earned a college degree or higher, this higher educational and class status assuaging third parties' concerns around downward class mobility. College-educated individuals who dated interracially faced less discipline than their lower-educated counterparts. Not only did the college-educated experience expand dating pools, they were usually removed from their family's sphere of influence, this independence tempering criticism (Rosenfeld 2009). In contrast, interviewees without college education led more segregated lives with fewer opportunities for cross-racial dating. If the less educated crossed the color line, they faced harsher forms of discipline than their higher-educated peers because if dating "up," their low class status multiplied their disadvantage and unsuitability and if dating "down," they faced tighter social control by spatially proximate kin and peers.

Learned Incompatibility: Racialized Rebuffs, Failed Romance, and Familial Pressure

Outside of segregated spaces, which structurally limit choice, repeated racializing and disciplining encounters teach Latinos to curtail their romantic options. These racist social forces meant to preserve white privilege accumulate to a *learned incompatibility* with whites, which Latinos nonetheless reinterpret as a "choice" to preserve their agency.[3] Repeated rejection taught Latino men and women to discipline their preferences in socially acceptable ways, and interviewees used a language of defeat ("it'll never work out") to explain their dim prospects with whites.

Latinos' learned incompatibility with whites results from displeasing interracial dating experiences. Omar Zelaya, a 48-year-old U.S.-born son of immigrants, internalized repeated racial messages from women who declined to date him:

> I got along with white women fine. I had no problem with them. But, I used to shy away from them a little bit more. . . . We couldn't be as readily acceptable to each other. . . . Some of these white girls . . . didn't really pay attention to you . . . [they were] stuck up or arrogant. . . . Maybe my accent gave me away. . . . Some of them were . . . unfriendly [and] had the tendency to . . . you off.

Disregard from white women disciplined Omar to avoid situations that would likely incur rejection. Externally imposed discipline converted to internally imposed self-discipline when he withdrew from white potential dates to avoid shame. Mentioning his Spanish accent that may be misinterpreted to indicate foreign-born status (Jiménez 2010), Omar comprehended white women's insouciance as based on race or (incorrect) assumptions about his nativity. Since he "got along fine" with white women, he placed the onus on them for failed romance. When white women rejected him and status contamination in one move, Omar learned that they are not "readily acceptable to each other." After repeated interactions, Omar internalized the racial order, "shying away" from white women. He ultimately married a less educated Mexican national over whom *he* holds the power advantage.

Awareness of mainstream racism and sexism can inspire preference for intraracial romance (Nemoto 2009), and yet racialized rebuffs from whites function differently for men and women. Varying forms of gendered racialization play out in the dating realm: men are taught to view themselves as unattractive, menacing, and excluded, whereas women's dating encounters consign them to a sexualized, othered, and borderline-acceptable position (Vasquez 2010). Xochitl Velasco, a 39-year-old Mexican American from Kansas who is married to a Bolivian national, asserted that in-marriage avoids racialized and gendered stereotypes that she confronted in interracial romances with white men.[4] Xochitl desired to escape a problematic set of stereotypes white men held about Latinas, this learned incompatibility resulting from failed interracial romances. She found Latino men to be more suitable for her because they offer refuge from disconcerting stereotypes:

> I always . . . knew I wanted to be married to a Latino. I always was partial to Latinos, boyfriends and everything. . . . [In] college [I] started dating a white guy . . . [and saw] differences between him and I. . . . Some white men that are married to my Latina girlfriends . . . like the "Latina Spice." . . . They make fun of her accent. They think it's cute. . . . They like that exoticness. . . . I didn't ever like that. I don't want to be treated as an "other" in my relationship. I knew with Latinos there was never that "other" factor. . . . I was just Xochitl Borges and there was nothing particularly Latina about me—I [did not] have to put on this Latina-ness or take it off.

Experience with racialized and gendered stereotypes disciplined Xochitl to conclude that whites were a mismatch and to desire Latinos. She learned from personal experience and observation that white men's exoticization of her would be alienating, her conclusion of incompatibility an acquired perspective. With Latinos, she reasoned, she could avoid being "treated as an 'other'" in an intimate relationship.

Disciplined preference does not rob individuals of agency. Instead, disciplined preference (whites as incompatible and Latinos as preferable) is self-protective, stemming from the need to preserve racial dignity and avoid misapprehension. Rob Esposito, married to a Mexican American/Native American woman, stated:

> I knew I wasn't going to marry a white girl. I knew I was going to marry a Mexican or Indian girl. . . . You . . . dated white girls for one reason and then you had the [Mexican American and Native American] girls you were going to marry (Laugh).

Holding different standards for dating and marriage is notable; some interviewees were adventurous in dating yet restrictive relative to marital prospects (Blackwell and Lichter 2004). Oscar Cota, a 44-year-old Kansan, used similar imagery to explain his dating patterns:

> My [Mexican American] wife says, "you always wanted to go with the white girls because you knew they were easier". I . . . knew that I would marry a Mexican woman. Because when you think of family, being able to raise families, being good wives . . . and maybe [that is] stereotypical—good wives, good cooks—[but] . . . I always knew I would marry a Mexican woman.

"Heteronormative sexual stereotypes" such as these tap into ethnic cultures' "gender regimes" and are used to evaluate moral value (Nagel 2000:113). Stereotypes about white women as "easy" and Mexican women as "wifely" shape Latino men's marital preferences: these men pursue interracial sexual liaisons before engaging in a "winnowing" process (Blackwell and Lichter 2004) and selecting proper, endogamous marriage partners.

This dichotomous thinking about Mexican and white women is a sexualized way for Latino men to recuperate agency. Use of value-laden ascriptions of "family oriented" and "marriageable" valorize Latina women, denigrate white women who are off-limits, and rationalize the "choice" of endogamy. While dating and marriage are not entirely agent-centered processes, claiming the "choice" of endogamy rhetorically resists the confines of a socially constricted marriage market. Repeated encounters with whites coach Latinos to believe that they are only suitable for other Latinos, reproducing endogamy and maintaining the racial hierarchy.

Preserving White Privilege: Anti-Latino Surveillance and Violence

White parents discriminate against Latinos through violence, threats, and exclusionary tactics in order to preserve their family's white privilege. Racialized and gendered stereotypes mark Latino men as agents of racial taint and white parents attempt to protect their daughters from becoming "unwhitened" (Frankenberg 1993; Twine 2010), whereas they view relations with Latina women as more acceptable (Vasquez 2010, 2011). Accordingly, Latino men are punished more harshly than Latina women when dating whites. White parents' prejudicial (sometimes violent) messages about their children's Latino romantic interests encourage endogamy, this disciplining during adolescence having repercussions in adulthood.

For example, in high school, Nathan Lucero, a Mexican American from Lawrence, Kansas, who is now 51 years old, faced threats of bodily harm from his white girlfriend's father:

> [She] was a brunette with green eyes. . . . Her dad hated me. He didn't give me a chance 'cuz I was Mexican. . . . I only met [her dad] once. . . . She came out [when I arrived to pick her up] and said, "My dad wants to know if your car can outrun a bullet."

Such threats are an aggressive way to police the symbolic boundary between whites and Latinos. Nathan noted that he was driving a "decent car," preemptively asserting his financial stability and ruling out class status as the reason for the father's extreme measures. Coming from a similar class status, this interaction highlights the centrality of race, class status not serving as a protection against racism (Feagin and Sikes 1994). While younger cohorts are more racially tolerant than older cohorts (Taylor et al. 2006), white parents vigilantly police racial boundaries through surveillance and violence.

Historically, white women have been vigilantly guarded, their whiteness, reproductive capacity, and symbolic role as mothers of the nation at stake in intimate encounters (Collins 1991; Hodes 1997; Kennedy 2003; Root 2001; Yuval-Davis 1997). In keeping with this gendered rationale, among interviewees, most reported incidents of violence were directed against minority men, mainly by relatives of white women reacting violently to cross-racial intimacy. Fifty-two-year-old Mexican American Rob Esposito, also from Kansas, told a tale similar to Nathan's of white parents' prohibition against interracial dating. In this situation, both the girl and her brother who defended her were injured:

> We were going to go to prom together . . . [but] her dad wouldn't let us date. . . . She was pretty adamant about wanting to date me. . . . Her dad [threw] her down the stairs . . . when they were fighting about it. [Her brother] intervened and . . . his dad pushed his head through a glass book-case. All over me—because [her] dad was no way going to let [her] date a Mexican.

While the violence was not directed at a minority male, the action served to discipline romantic tastes and oversee white women's sexuality. Rob did not address whether this violence forced a breakup. In general, he stated, "[the girls] wanted to date me, their fathers were the problem." Given the categorical rejection coming from white girls' parents, he retrospectively called white girls "prohibited fruit."

White parents considered Rob a threat to their daughters—a source of hypermasculinity and status contamination—yet they lauded him as a star athlete. Collins (2004) argues that the same minority masculinity that is deemed physically and sexually menacing is cheered when displayed as athletic prowess. White girls' parents approved of Rob in sports:

> After a ball game . . . and scoring 25 points . . . I'd go into the local steakhouse . . . [and] parents . . . would order up a hamburger and fries and . . . paid for it. . . . Even the parents that didn't want me going out with their daughters were like, "Great game!" Yeah, but when it came down to dating their daughter, it was . . . "we're not going to let you touch our daughters."

Although praised for sports achievement, Rob encountered disapproval when dating white girls. These conflicting reactions—personal discouragement and public congratulations—show how white parents respond to Latino masculinity: they regulate it in the private domain that contains a white daughter's sexuality but applaud it in a public arena that requires sports skill. Especially in the Kansas context where whites drastically outnumber Latinos, border patrolling to prohibit whites from crossing the racial line is marked by threats and violence.

Region matters less for women than for men: while Latino men were victimized by physical, verbal, and symbolic violence in Kansas, women faced milder forms of rejection in California and Kansas. Latina women were subject to surveillance and racial slights by white parents of romantic interests. Forty-one-year-old Californian Corrina Nuñes's Hispanic identity cost her a boyfriend:

> A [white] young man [I was dating] came to school one day and completely avoided me. . . . His brother had gotten mad at him . . . told his father that he was dating a Hispanic girl and his dad beat him up.

Parents who police the color line when their children were open to romantic boundary crossing show how age, time period, and generation play a role in boundary maintenance (Taylor et al. 2006).

Region affects attitudes on interracial intimacy: whites resisted Latinos more vigorously in Kansas than in California. Group size impinges upon racial attitudes: families and communities judge whites' interracial dating practices in a largely white context to be a more glaring and punishable offense than in a locale with a limited white dating pool. Racial heterogeneity both increases the chances for interracial romance and decreases the likelihood of sanctions (Kreager 2008). In diverse California, cross-racial dating was perceived as less unlikely and therefore less transgressive.

Two caveats concerning region and generation in the United States deserve mention. First, while Latino families in both sites encouraged endogamy, exogamy with whites was perceived as a reasonable option in Kansas. Because of the small number of Hispanics in the area and because of the value of whiteness, Latinos condoned cross-racial intimacy with whites. Twenty-eight-year-old Liz Downing explained the impact of living in a majority-white town: "It'd kind of be a joke that I couldn't date any people that were Mexican in Lawrence, because we were related to most of the Mexican people in Lawrence [laughs]!" Orlando Puente, from Topeka, explained that he dated white women "mainly because there wasn't [sic] very many Mexican girls to date. . . ." Because of supply-side demographics, Latino and white intermarriage was understood as a probable outcome in Kansas.

Second, generational status is influential: immigrants favor endogamy, whereas the U.S. born are more open to exogamy. These attitudes follow the noted trend of immigrants marrying co-nationals and later-generation Latinos more likely to marry outside of their racial group (Alba et al. 2014; Chavez 2008; Landale and Oropesa 2007; Murguia 1982; Telles and Ortiz 2008). One woman's immigrant father was "shocked and appalled" when a white boy came to the house: "What was I doing having a [white] boy come to the door and ask for me? [My father thought] . . . must be doing something [sexually] loose." By depicting minority women as morally superior to dominant culture, immigrant parents reaffirm minority self-worth within a context of subordination (Espiritu 2000; Nagel 2000) and encourage endogamy on cultural grounds.

While both Latino men and women underwent racialized processes of learned incompatibility relative to whites, their experiences varied by gender. Men cited cultural mismatch as the chief reason why white women disregarded them. They disciplined their preferences away from white women and used a cultural explanation of Latina women as suitable and family oriented to legitimate their same-race relations. Women engaged in self-discipline by circumventing objectifying stereotypes white men may have by withdrawing from them. These same women, however, in their turn to Latino men, faced different racialized and gendered preconceptions. The critical difference, however, is that imagery Latino men have of Latina women resonated more with these in-married women's beliefs about themselves. Unlike their intermarried counterparts, in-married Latina women did not complain of domineering fathers or submissive mothers. Instead, endogamously married Latinas had pleasing home lives in their youth and were comfortable with their parents' displays of femininity, masculinity, and culture.

Preserving Relative Group Privilege: Anti-Black Prejudice and Staying in the Racial Middle

Non-dominant classes can also protect their relative privilege. Racial discourses influence romantic preferences (Shiao and Tuan 2008), contributing to Latinos' preference to date Latinos or whites more so than blacks

(Feliciano, Lee, and Robnett 2011). The aim of anti-black prejudice is to avoid slipping down the racial ladder. Anti-black prejudice among Latinos is expressed in axioms such as, "chickens go with chickens," "stick to your own," or direction not to "marry down." As an exertion of power, anti-black prejudice calcifies the boundary between Latinos and blacks and preserves Latinos' relative group privilege.

Less than a quarter of the Latino interviewees dated blacks (two were currently married to biracial blacks) and, of those, women reported more surveillance by family and peer groups than men. The majority of those who dated blacks were darker skinned (skin color code #3 or above), no light-skinned individuals (skin color code #l) reported interracial intimacy with blacks. While black/non-black relationships elicit strong negative reactions generally (Kreager 2008), nearly all of the interviewees who reported surveillance or punishment regarding romance with blacks were Latinas from Kansas. Region and gender intersect such that families in Kansas guarded Latinas against "downward" racial mixing; cross-racial dating with blacks was viewed as an avoidable norm violation in a locale with a large non-black population.

Latinas in Kansas who dated black men did so against family counsel. Adriana Guthrie, age 41, recalled lateral surveillance by her cousins: "I did date a black guy. . . . My cousins kept saying, 'You're brown and you should be with brown people.'" Forty-three-year-old Lorena Cota dated a black man covertly: "I [wasn't] able to tell my family that I was dating an African American. . . . My dad . . . wouldn't have approved. . . . Social pressures [were] to date Caucasian and Hispanic . . . only."

Such "social pressures" include peer surveillance from African American women who treated her as if she was "trying to take away their men." These slights by black women are likely based on black women's expectation of their own endogamy and the lack of "marriageable" black men due to the disappearance of well-paid jobs for black men (Cherlin 2009; Collins 2008) and high rates of incarceration (Pettit 2012; Western 2006). Cassie Hoffman, age 46, who was previously married to a black man, was "a little nervous" to inform her parents of her engagement because, she confessed, "he was black and I didn't know . . . if they would approve or not."

Immigrant parents' expectations of endogamy and anti-black bias compelled 34-year-old Mario Bermudez to conceal his cross-racial romances. Mario, who eventually married a woman with Mexican American and white heritage, likened interracial intimacy to homosexuality to underscore the transgressive quality of such a pairing. Growing up in an ethnic enclave where "everything was Mexican," Mario explained his self-surveillance when dating non-Mexicans:

> When I used to bring home a . . . black girl . . . I would never bring her around . . . my whole family. . . . Just, say a few *tías*

[aunts] who I thought were cool, you know? It's almost like you're gay, kinda. Like . . . you're "coming out." . . . The same thing happened with Ana [his half Mexican American, half white wife]: I would only bring her around my three cool *tías* [aunts]. That's not the way it's supposed to be.

For his Mexican immigrant relatives, it was "a big deal" for Mario to date non-Mexicans and he believed that a black woman would never have gained acceptance. While dating a black woman was taboo, marrying a woman with Mexican American descent ensured his "racial authenticity" (Vasguez and Wetzel 2009) within his immigrant family.

Even in non-immigrant families, Latinos in the "racial middle" (O'Brien 2008) of a three-tiered hierarchy execute anti-black prejudice to safeguard relative privilege and attempt to achieve "honorary white" status (Bonilla-Silva 2003; Haney López 1996). According to Eduardo Bonilla-Silva (2004), "honorary whites may be . . . believing they are better than the 'collective black,'" which would require the development of "white-like racial attitudes befitting their new social, position and differentiating (distancing) themselves from the 'collective black'" (p. 937).

Skin color is an important dimension to endogamy, as intensity of disciplined preferences varies by skin tone. The darker skinned are more committed to endogamy than the lighter skinned, this stance providing those who are least likely to intermarry with whites (taking a cue from low black/white intermarriage rates [Lee and Bean 2010; Qian 2002; Qian and Lichter 2011]) with a strategy to preserve relative privilege. Darker-skinned parents advocated endogamy for their children, despite their recognition of the social value of whiteness. Oscar Cota, bearing medium-tan skin, counseled his three pre-teen children on intragroup relations: "Would race play a role? Unfortunately, it would. . . . I would [prefer] to have my kids marry a Hispanic, a Latina, or a Mexican. . . . I would push to keep . . . a pure bloodline. . . . That's . . . a prejudice." Experiencing "daily racisms," Oscar may have viewed endogamy as a protective device that would shield his children from more integrated social spaces that would make them vulnerable to racial discrimination (Ortiz and Telles 2012). Looking both "up" and "down" from the racial middle, by favoring endogamy, Oscar also guarded against status loss that threatens to accompany interracial intimacy with blacks.

Marriage advice encouraging racial endogamy among darker-skinned Latinos is not gender specific. Noelle Puente, who has medium-tan skin, remarked: "Would I like to have a minority walk through my household? Sure, I would. I can't help that. I do want [my children] to bring somebody home that's Mexican. . . . Honestly, I think it's [about] family." This logic hints at not only a racial and color mismatch but also a cultural one, positioning Mexican culture as more family oriented than other racial groups. Similarly, 53-year-old Mexican immigrant Rosalinda Ornales, who also has medium-tan skin and lives in California, remarked: "I would like to see [my children] with somebody Latino. That's my opinion. . . . My dad used to say: *'Gallinas se juntan con gallinas.'* Chickens go with chickens. . . . You look for your own kind." Coming from darker-skinned Latinos who intramarried, this marital advice suggests prior racializing experiences that disciplined them into abiding by the color line and shaped the disciplining counsel they give to the next generation. Emphasis here is on racial, color, and cultural commensurability. This racialized advice that stresses parity attempts to balance positions of power, disciplinary moves that illuminate how most marriages come to involve partners of relatively equal status (Kalmijn 1998; Rosenfeld 2005; Spickard 1991).

Complementing the finding that darker-skinned Latinos were more committed to endogamy, families pushed lighter-skinned Latinos toward exogamy in order to "whiten" the race. While Xochitl Velasco, discussed above, ultimately married a Bolivian for cultural compatibility and racial/gender comfort reasons, her family communicated that she, as a light-tan-skinned woman, could improve her racial standing through intermarriage with a white person. A perceptible grade lighter than the aforementioned interviewees who practiced and advocated endogamy, Xochitl's family telegraphed a clear message about the racial hierarchy and the potential achievement of higher racial status through intimacy:

> When [my cousins] brought white boyfriends home it was kind of . . . like, "Congratulations!" . . . The white men were considered . . . moving up, successful. . . . [It] would never be appreciated to bring an African American man . . . [or] woman home as a boyfriend/girlfriend. . . . And the Mexican men were looked . . . on as . . . status quo and not doing anything really great.

Like commitment to endogamy, familial pressure varies by skin color: darker-skinned Latinos were steered toward endogamy, whereas lighter-skinned Latinos were directed toward exogamy with whites. These intra-family, intergenerational messages are laced with implications about who is consigned to racialization versus who is best positioned to escape it. Skin color is an important factor in the construction of disciplined preferences, family counsel pivoting the lighter skinned toward whites, the darker skinned toward Latinos, and all away from blacks.

Intergenerational family advice about the acceptability of other racial groups, a form of surveillance and discipline, extends our understanding of endogamy. "What about the kids" rhetoric is a powerful tool of intrafamilial discipline aimed to contain sexual desire within acceptable, endogamous limits. Pressure not to "marry down" is intended to entrench symbolic boundaries and preserve relative group privilege. Anti-black prejudice is the means by which Latinos, protect their racial status that, while subordinate to whites, is superior to blacks, an even less privileged group.

Conclusion: Racial Border Patrolling and Disciplined Preferences Enforce Endogamy

Even as rates of intermarriage modestly increase—approximately 13 percent of American marriages involve persons of different races (Bean and Stevens 2003; Lee and Bean 2004:228)—interracial intimacy remains rare. Studying endogamy brings to light enduring social dynamics that undergird this pattern. Racial endogamy results from macro-structural, family, and community pressures that discipline individuals to prefer specific mates. This article makes three interventions. First, it identifies the practices through which third parties regulate interracial sexuality, biased interactions that demographic studies simply assume are operant. Second, it utilizes intersectionality to reveal how pressures toward endogamy vary by gender, skin color, and region. Third, it moves beyond the literature's focus on black/white couples and examines Latino experiences. This study reveals that what we customarily think of as "personal preferences" are, in fact, socially constructed. Family- and peer-disciplining processes consolidate group position and maintain symbolic boundaries. Surveillance, physical and symbolic violence, and notions of cultural (in)compatibility are all mechanisms of power that support endogamy.

Answering Kalmijn's (1998) question about what "third parties" are actually *doing* to entrench racial homogamy, I find that surveillance and punishment (violence, threats, censure, and advice) imposed from inside and outside of one's racial community that transform into self-discipline are the chief mechanisms enforcing same-race romance. Endogamous pairings do not occur by accident; they are constructed by a racialized social structure whose members police racial boundaries and punish transgressors. Surveillance, punishment, and self-discipline are the regulatory techniques that define acceptability, discipline preferences, and perpetuate endogamy.

APPENDIX

Table A1 Characteristics of Interviewees

Characteristic	Percent (*n*)
Ethnic origin	
Mexican American—monoethnic	70 (49)
Mexican American—multiethnic with white	14 (10)
Mexican American—multiethnic with Native American	4 (3)
Other Latin American	11 (8)
Gender	
Men	41 (29)
Women	59 (41)
Age	
20s	11 (8)
30s	20 (14)
40s	34 (24)
50s	14 (10)
60s	14 (10)
70s	6 (4)
Region	
California	51 (36)
Kansas	49 (34)
Skin color	
1 (racially white appearance)	33 (13)
2 (light-tan)	27 (19)
3 (medium-tan)	37 (26)
4 (dark-tan)	17 (12)

(Continued)

Table A1 (Continued)

Characteristic	Percent (*n*)
5 (racially black appearance)	0
Interracial or intraracial marriage[a]	
Intraracial: Latino/Latino	68 (47)
Interracial: Latino/white	23 (16)
Interracial: Latino/non-Latino minority	9 (6)
Education	
Less than high school	3 (2)
High school degree/GED	16 (11)
Some college	29 (20)
College degree	23 (16)
Master's/professional degree	24 (17)
Doctoral degree	6 (4)
Individual income	
Under $30,000	20 (14)
$30,001–$50,000	31 (22)
$50,001–$70,000	20 (14)
$70,001–$150,000+	26 (18)
Not reported	3 (2)

Note: $n = 70$.

[a]These counts include current and dissolved marriages (four interviewees are divorced). One single/never married adult is excluded.

DISCUSSION QUESTIONS

1. What is learned incompatibility? What is disciplined preference? How did this play out in the lives of those interviewed?
2. Endogamy was enforced at several different levels. What specific individuals influenced choice of dating partners? How did larger social stereotypes influence these decisions?

3. What role did location play in how likely endogamy was? What about immigrant status? Why do you think these differences existed?
4. Do you feel completely free to marry anyone of any age, gender, race, or religion? How are your dating choices subtly supported, or discouraged, by your culture?

REFERENCES

Alba, Richard, Tomás R. Jiménez, and Helen B. Marrow. 2014. "Mexican Americans as a Paradigm for Contemporary Intra-Group Heterogeneity." *Ethnic and Racial Studies* 37(3):446–66.

Alba, Richard D. and Victor Nee. 2003. *Remaking the American Mainstream: Assimilation and Contemporary Immigration*. Cambridge, MA: Harvard University Press.

Bean, Frank D. and Gillian Stevens. 2003. *America's Newcomers and the Dynamics of Diversity*. New York: Russell Sage Foundation.

Blackwell, Debra L. and Daniel T. Lichter. 2004. "Homogamy Among Dating, Cohabiting, and Married Couples." *The Sociological Quarterly* 45(4):719–37.

Bonilla-Silva, Eduardo. 2003. *Racism Without Racists: Color-Blind Racism and the Persistence of Racial Inequality in the United States*. Lanham, MD: Rowman & Littlefield.

Bonilla-Silva, Eduardo. 2004. "From Bi-Racial to Tri-Racial: Towards a New System of Racial Stratification in the USA." *Ethnic and Racial Studies* 27(6):931–50.

Chavez, Leo R. 2008. *The Latino Threat: Constructing Immigrants, Citizens, and the Nation*. Stanford, CA: Stanford University Press.

Cherlin, Andrew J. 2009. *The Marriage-Go-Round: The State of Marriage and the Family in America Today*. New York: Vintage.

Childs, Erica C. 2009. *Fade to Black and White: Interracial Images in Popular Culture*. Lanham, MD: Rowman & Littlefield.

Collins, Patricia Hill. 1991. *Black Feminist Thought*. New York: Routledge.

Collins, Patricia Hill. 2004. *Black Sexual Politics: African Americans, Gender, and the New Racism*. New York: Routledge.

Collins, Patricia Hill. 2008. *Black Feminist Thought: Knowledge, Consciousness, and the Politics of Empowerment*. New York: Routledge.

Dalmage, Heather M. 2000. *Tripping on the Color Line: Black-White Multiracial Families in a Racially Divided World*. New Brunswick, NJ: Rutgers University Press.

Deaux, Kay. 2006. *To Be an Immigrant*. New York: Russell Sage Foundation.

Espiritu, Yen Le. 2000. "We Don't Sleep Around Like White Girls Do." *Signs* 26(2):415–40.

Feagin, Joe R. and Melvin P. Sikes. 1994. *Living with Racism: The Black Middle-Class Experience*. Boston: Beacon Press.

Feliciano, Cynthia, Rennie Lee, and Belinda Robnett. 2011. "Racial Boundaries Among Latinos: Evidence from Internet Daters' Racial Preferences." *Social Problems 58*(2):189–212.

Frankenberg, Ruth. 1993. *White Women, Race Matters: The Social Construction of Whiteness*. Minneapolis: University of Minnesota Press.

Haney López, Ian. 1996. *White by Law: The Legal Construction of Race*. New York: New York University Press.

Hodes, Martha Elizabeth. 1997. *White Women, Black Men: Illicit Sex in the Nineteenth-Century South*. New Haven, CT: Yale University Press.

Jiménez, Tomás R. 2010. *Replenished Ethnicity: Mexican Americans, Immigration, and Identity*. Berkeley: University of California Press.

Kalmijn, Matthijs. 1998. "Intermarriage and Homogamy: Causes, Patterns, Trends." *Annual Review of Sociology* 24:395–421.

———. 2010. "Consequences of Racial Intermarriage for Children's Social Integration." *Sociological Perspectives* 53(2):271–86.

Kennedy, Randall. 2003. *Interracial Intimacies: Sex, Marriage, Identity, and Adoption*. New York: Pantheon.

Kreager, Derek A. 2008. "Guarded Borders: Adolescent Interracial Romance and Peer Trouble at School." *Social Forces* 87(2):887–910.

Lamont, Michele and Virag Molnar. 2002. "The Study of Boundaries in the Social Sciences." *Annual Review of Sociology* (28):167–95.

Landale, Nancy S. and R. Salvador Oropesa. 2007. "Hispanic Families: Stability and Change." *Annual Review of Sociology* 33:381–405.

Landale, Nancy S., R. Salvador Oropesa, and Cristina Bradatan. 2006. "Hispanic Families in the United States: Family Structure and Process in an Era of Family Change." In: *Hispanics and the Future of America*, edited by M. Tienda and F. Mitchell. Washington, DC: National Academies Press, pp. 138–78.

Lee, Jennifer and Frank P. Bean. 2004. "America's Changing Color Lines: Immigration, Race/ Ethnicity, and Multiracial Identification." *Annual Review of Sociology* 30:221–42.

Lee, Jennifer and Frank P. Bean. 2010. *The Diversity Paradox: Immigration and the Color Line in Twenty-First Century America*. New York: Russell Sage Foundation.

Lichter, Daniel, J. Brian Brown, Qian Zhenchao, and Julie Carmalt. 2007. "Marital Assimilation Among Hispanics: Evidence of Declining Cultural and Economic Incorporation?" *Social Science Quarterly* 88(3):745–65.

Marrow, Helen B. 2011. *New Destination Dreaming: Immigration, Race, and Legal Status in the Rural American South*. Stanford, CA: Stanford University Press.

Massey, Douglas S. and Nancy A. Denton. 1993. *American Apartheid: Segregation and the Making of the Underclass*. Cambridge, MA: Harvard University Press.

Merton, Robert K. [1941] 2000. "Intermarriage and the Social Structure: Fact and Theory." *Interracialism: Black-White Intermarriage in American History, Literature, and Law*, edited by Werner Sollors. New York: Oxford University Press, pp. 473–92.

Moran, Rachel F. 2001. *Interracial Intimacy: The Regulation of Race & Romance*. Chicago: University of Chicago Press.

Murguia, Edward. 1982. *Chicano Intermarriage: A Theoretical and Empirical Study*. San Antonio, TX: Trinity University Press.

Nagel, Joane. 2000. "Ethnicity and Sexuality." *Annual Review of Sociology* 26:107–33.

Nemoto, Kumiko. 2009. *Racing Romance: Love, Power, and Desire Among Asian American/White Couples*. New Brunswick, NJ: Rutgers University Press.

O'Brien, Eileen. 2008. *The Racial Middle: Latinos and Asian Americans Living Beyond the Racial Divide*. New York: New York University Press.

Ortiz, Vilma and Edward Telles. 2012. "Racial Identity and Racial Treatment of Mexican Americans." *Race and Social Problems* 4(1):41–56.

Pettit, Becky. 2012. *Invisible Men: Mass Incarceration and the Myth of Black Progress*. New York: Russell Sage Foundation.

Qian, Zhenchao. 2002. "Race and Social Distance: Intermarriage with Non-Latino Whites." *Race & Society* 5(1):33–47.

Qian, Zhenchao and Daniel T. Lichter. 2007. "Social Boundaries and Marital Assimilation: Interpreting Trends in Racial and Ethnic Intermarriage." *American Sociological Review* 72(1):68–94.

Root, Maria P. P. 2001. *Love's Revolution: Interracial Marriage*. Philadelphia, PA: Temple University Press.

Rosenfeld, Michael J. 2002. "Measures of Assimilation in the Marriage Market: Mexican Americans 1970–1990." *Journal of Marriage and the Family* 64(1):152–62.

Rosenfeld, Michael J. 2008. "Racial, Educational, and Religious Endogamy in the United States: A Comparative Historical Perspective." *Social Forces* 87(1): 1–31.

Rosenfeld, Michael J. 2009. *The Age of Independence: Interracial Unions, Same-Sex Unions, and the Changing American Family*. Cambridge, MA: Harvard University Press.

Roth, Wendy D. 2012. *Race Migrations: Latinos and the Cultural Transformation of Race*. Stanford, CA: Stanford University Press.

Sherman, Jennifer. 2009. *Those Who Work, Those Who Don't: Poverty, Morality, and Family in Rural America*. Minneapolis, MN: University of Minnesota Press.

Shiao, Jiannbin Lee and Mia H. Tuan. 2008. "'Some Asian Men Are Attractive to Me, but for a Husband . . .': Korean Adoptees and the Salience of Race in Romance." *Du Bois Review* 5(2):259–85.

Spickard, Paul R. 1991. *Mixed Blood: Intermarriage and Ethnic Identity in Twentieth-Century America*. Madison: University of Wisconsin Press.

Stevens, Gillian and Gray Swicegood. 1987. "The Linguistic Context of Ethnic Endogamy." *American Sociological Review* 52(1):73–82.

Swidler, Ann. 2001. *Talk of Love: How Culture Matters*. Chicago: University of Chicago Press.

Taylor, Paul, Cary Funk, and Peyton Craighill. 2006. "Guess Who's Coming to Dinner: 22% of Americans Have a Relative in a Mixed-Race Marriage." Pew Research Center, Washington, DC.

Telles, Edward and Vilma Ortiz. 2008. *Generations of Exclusion: Mexican Americans, Assimilation, and Race*. New York: Russell Sage Foundation.

Twine, France W. 2010. *A White Side of Black Britain: Interracial Intimacy and Racial Literacy*. Durham, NC: Duke University Press.

U.S. Census Bureau. 2012. "2012 Population Estimate." Retrieved July 21, 2014 (http://factfinder.census.gov/faces/nav/jsf/pages/index.xhtml).

Vasquez, Jessica M. 2010. "Blurred Borders for Some but Not 'Others': Racialization, 'Flexible Ethnicity,' Gender, and Third-Generation Mexican American Identity." *Sociological Perspectives* 53(1):45–71.

Vasquez, Jessica M. 2011. *Mexican Americans Across Generations: Immigrant Families, Racial Realities*. New York: New York University Press.

Vasquez, Jessica M. and Christopher Wetzel. 2009. "Tradition and the Invention of Racial Selves: Symbolic Boundaries, Collective Authenticity, and Contemporary Struggles for Racial Equality." *Ethnic and Racial Studies* 32(9):1557–75.

Western, Bruce. 2006. *Punishment and Inequality in America*. New York: Russell Sage.

Yuval-Davis, Nira. 1997. *Gender & Nation*. Thousand Oaks, CA: Sage Publications.

NOTES

1. While this article concerns heterosexual couples, it is worth noting that heterosexuality itself is highly regulated and rewarded (Schilt and Westbrook 2009) and nonconformity is punished (Pascoe 2007). A study that compares interracial heterosexual and same-sex partnerships suggests that institutional protections benefit interracial straight couples, whereas a double minority status (being queer and interracial) can aid connection among cross-racial gay couples (Steinbugler 2012:125, 128).
2. I use Foucault's (1995) concepts of surveillance and discipline as a starting point, though our definitions of discipline vary significantly. Whereas Foucault theorizes that subjectivity is produced through disciplinary power, I maintain that subjects understand external disciplinary actions and restrictions as social facts and largely conform accordingly. In my usage, subjects do not necessarily *believe* in their circumscribed social power, their subjectivity more removed from the disciplinary process than Foucault theorized.
3. In discussion of spouse selection, most interviewees used the language of "choice." Although this terminology sounds like a rational choice—as if people weigh potential costs and benefits of romantic partnerships—many said they "just fell in love."
4. By contrast, Asian American women view intermarriage with white men as a way to repudiate negative stereotypes from their own racial community (Nemoto 2009).

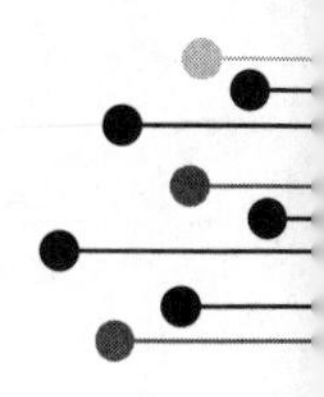

Rethinking Colorblindness

How Role Conflict Shapes Administrators' Responses to Racial Inequality at a Predominantly White University

Cedrick-Michael Simmons

Many colleges now have offices and administrators whose mission is described as improving the representation and experiences of minorities on campus. They often have names like the "Office of Diversity" or "Division of Community and Belonging" and employ specialized staff whose job it is to address concerns and help solve problems related to diversity and inclusion on campus. While many such offices address issues related to social class, gender, sexual orientation, religion, and physical disabilities, diversity efforts related to racial and ethnic identity tend to be central to the work of these offices and their staff. Yet, despite a significant increase in the number of offices and associated employees on many campuses, relatively little has actually changed in terms of diversity among faculty and administrators and the experiences of people of color in their day-to-day interaction on campus.

In this reading, Cedrick-Michael Simmons shares the results of his interviews with what he calls student-centered administrators (SCAs)—administrators in roles that bring them into daily contact with students and who are tasked with improving the representation and experiences of racial and ethnic minorities on campus. He differentiates these administrators from what he calls executive-level administrators (ELAs), who are administrators like the president of the college—those who determine the overarching policies, funding, and direction of the university and don't interact with students on a daily basis. His research addresses some of the structural forces that hinder colleges from making meaningful changes around diversity and inclusion on college campuses. As is often

---

Excerpt from "Rethinking Colorblindness: How Role Conflict Shapes Administrators' Responses to Racial Inequality at a Predominantly White University" by Cedrick-Michael Simmons. Presented at the 2019 New York State Sociological Association annual meeting November 15–16. Nazareth College, Rochester NY.

the case, how power is distributed plays an important role in the actions available to those in different roles.

Simmons finds that SCAs engaged in diversity work often experience role conflict—a term sociologists use to describe instances when the obligations and expectations of two different roles are incompatible. You may have experienced this if you have ever been scheduled to work on the night before an exam. The expectation for your role as an employee is that you show up to work when scheduled. This conflicts with the expectations of your student role—that you study for exams. Simmons found that SCAs regularly felt caught between supporting the students of color that they are there to serve and assist, and the expectations of ELAs that they not do or support anything that would damage the reputation or financial prospects of the school. This conflict was particularly notable when students and faculty staged protests against the wishes of the ELAs. The SCAs he interviewed noted that as employees of the university, their job obligated them to support the college's policies around student conduct, yet as diversity workers tasked with improving conditions for people of color on campus, they also wanted to support student protests and thought that it would make a difference. These types of situations brought them into role conflict. They articulated that this conflict was a significant source of frustration for them, and that their relative lack of power relative to the ELAs who actually controlled campus-wide budget and policy decisions significantly hampered their efforts to advocate for meaningful improvements in the climate around race on campus.

The concept of role conflict is also applicable in a wide range of social situations. As you read, think about other examples of role conflicts in your life and the role that power plays in how you try to resolve those conflicts.

Though the current literature on structural racism have documented *what* disparities persist in life chances among "racial" groups and *why* both racial attitudes and scholarship that suggest race has declined in significance are reflective of ideology rather than social reality, there are few sociological frameworks to account for *how* social contexts compel POC and Whites to aid in the reproduction of racial inequality. I contribute to the research by underscoring and specifying the need to examine the reproduction of racial inequality within a context of political and economic forces. To accomplish these tasks, I evaluated the context in which administrators determine how to respond to students seeking advice and institutional resources to address racial inequality at their historically-white university. Specifically, I asked: *Under what conditions do administrators experience role conflict when discussing and working to address racism on campus? What strategies do they use to resolve this role conflict? Lastly, what are the identifiable consequences of these strategies for maintaining or disrupting racial inequality?*

Using interviews with 13 key informants (Tremblay 1957) about their role as gatekeepers (Devers and Frankel 2000), I demonstrate how focusing on the typologies of their colorblind or color-conscious attitudes renders the political and economic incentives for social actors to reproduce inequality invisible. In these interviews, the informants explained how they are employed and promoted based on the evaluation of their employers who prioritize the accumulation of revenue and the university's prestige over current students' costly concerns about racism. In fact, I show how regardless of the varying frameworks espoused by these gatekeepers to account for the significance of racism, administrators were structurally positioned to engage in similar practices. This is important because a critical examination of the consequences of these practices reveals a problematic displacement of labor to combat racial inequality from employees *paid* by the university to students *paying* to attend the university.

One analytical tool sociologists have used to account for the role of these social contexts in shaping practices is the study of role conflict (Kahn, Wolfe, Quinn, Snoek, and Rosenthal 1964; Rizzo, House and Lirtzman 1970). To briefly summarize, a social actors' role refers to the combination of expectations, rights, and responsibilities that come with their status or position (Gullahorn 1956). Role conflict arises in "situations in which incompatible demands are placed upon an actor (either an individual or a group) because of [their] role relationships with two or more groups" (p. 299). For example, an early study on role conflict showed that emergency respondents to crises, such as tornadoes, have to simultaneously help with assisting the larger community and yet have an obligation to ensuring their family's safety and security. The type of role conflict they experienced was shaped by whether they were with their families or near the site of crises, and how their different contexts determined which obligations they decided to address when they had to choose one option. Furthermore, these studies have indicated the importance of analyzing the strategies they used to ensure their other obligations were met by others (Gullahorn and Gullahorn 1963; Floyd and Lane 2000; Kras, Rudes, and Taxman 2015). These strategies of displacement further illustrate how role conflict problematizes the notion that their practices as gatekeepers and employees can be explained solely by their attitudes about the constituents they were serving. In short, scholars can examine role conflict to help identify the social, political, and economic constraints that inform our studies of how people make decisions to address sensitive issues and moments of crises.

Focusing on the strategies gatekeepers use to resolve their role conflict, this study aims to inform our understanding of how the exploitation of labor arises within higher education. Research on the experiences of students shows that POC experience role conflict in higher education when they are expected to educate their white counterparts about racism without exhibiting any physical or emotional reactions to the ambivalence and blindness to racial trauma on campus (Wilkins 2012; Gutierrez y Muhs, Niemann, Gonzalez, and Harris 2012). Scholarship on faculty roles in the academy show that POC are expected to simultaneously offer counseling to students who experience racism on campus, sit on a disproportionate amount of committees about diversity that are rarely provided with resources to actualize their recommendations, and fulfill their research and teaching obligations to achieve tenure (Gutierrez et al. 2012; Thomas and Hollenshead 2001). Due to time constraints, they experience role conflict when they have to choose between helping students cope, educating their white peers, crafting policy recommendations on committees, and achieving their professional goals despite the prevalence of racism in departments and teaching evaluations (Thomas and Hollenshead 2001). Similarly, managers hired to address problems related to racism and other "diversity" issues have the responsibility to help improve campus climates among students and employees in contexts where resources are more often distributed to career services, fundraising, and marketing their university already as an "inclusive" space for POC (Ahmed 2012). In sum, the RSS perspective combined with the study of role conflict helps provide a more nuanced account for the conditions in which people are structurally positioned to manage the competing obligations of creating diverse organizations by participating in a market that historically relies on the exploitation of labor, especially from POC.

Methods

Study Participants

I conducted in-depth interviews with 13 college administrators at one historically-white university in the northeast of the United States. The selection of participants and interview questions derive from the key informant technique. The key informant technique is an effective approach when gathering qualitative data that is difficult to unearth, especially when dealing with sensitive information (Temblay 1957). Key informants are participants in "privileged" positions that can provide specialized information on local and/or organizational contexts and informal protocols that aren't typically documented and publicly available. By purposely selecting key informants that have access to valuable and sensitive information, this technique has proven to elicit insights into: the ways in which those in power organize, manage, and justify their encounters with those who have more and less power (Elwyn, Edwards, Kinnersely, and Grol 2000); organizational processes (Pauwels and Hardyns 2009); and assessing organizational characteristics more generally (Frenk, Anderson, Chaves, and Martin 2011). This is important because the work on RSS suggests that institutional practices that reproduce racial inequality are increasingly overt in the post-Civil Rights Era.

The data collected from the interviews included information about practices and procedures about the sensitive topic of racism on campus. Hence, a note about my positionality as the interviewer and researcher is warranted. As a black male conducting the interviews, I recognize that many of the white informants most likely provided a conservative amount of examples regarding practices that may appear "racist," especially if they described their personal decisions. While this limitation is important, I argue that it was actually more relevant for this study to understand how administrators interact with POC who are waging complaints and demands. Furthermore, the goal of this study wasn't to produce generalizable data about all administrators but to investigate practices that may be logically generalizable as potential barriers for racial justice in higher education. Finally, the informants talked about decisions that were the "commonsense" among fellow administrators that nonetheless led to discussions about socially undesirable practices many of the informants were willing to share because there were few opportunities to reference their concerns in ways that would be documented on campus. At the conclusion of the interviews, most of the informants emphasized their willingness to participate due to the potential to inform their peers when these examples are typically undocumented, and have the insurances that the researcher providing the analysis and recommendations for their profession would not violate their confidentiality and anonymity.

Findings

Chain of Command: The Mechanism for Channeling Student Issues Into Institutional Policy

The informants stressed that the context in which administrators decide on what should be done about racism on campus has to take into account the distinction between administrators. I reference the informants who primarily work with students as student-centered administrators (SCAs). Also, I refer to their bosses who have the authority to determine how which policies, statements, and investments of resources are made on behalf of the university as executive-level administrators (ELAs).

The institutional mechanism for fulfilling their roles as gatekeepers to help distribute resources and crafting campus-wide policies includes: students presenting their problems or proposals for funding to the SCAs, who then present these proposals or their amended recommendations to the ELAs seeking final approval. This "chain of command" is where expectations, values, and decisions are mediated by SCAs between students and

ELAs. For example, Carl summarized this role as: "It could be brainstorming how to get things done. It could be advising them on how to get things done." To give additional clarity, he said:

> Well, it usually looks like me trying to get a feel from the students of what it is they want to do. . . . [T]hen it's trying to do as much groundwork with them to get as much information to file up the "chain" as it were. [For example,] we ask students to create some kind of proposal about who [a speaker or artist] is, why they want to bring them, what's their purpose, what is the purpose of the program and how much it will cost. . . . That sort of groundwork. And then I'll take that up the chain [of command] and say, "The students want to do this" and I'll work with [ELAs] on that. . . . "The students want to do this, let me know what you think."

As Carl points out, SCAs have two constituencies they are answerable to within this chain of command: students (and their representatives) and ELAs. Most of the informants referenced recommendations that reduce class sizes, improve quality of students and faculty, enhance application numbers and acceptance rates, increase fundraising and other initiatives that affect the university's revenue and rankings as "meaningful accomplishments" by the ELAs. For the SCAs, the important point is that these accomplishments are also helpful for students on campus while the ELAs value decisions that yield long-term financial and reputational gains for the university. For example, Franklin builds on this provided a snapshot of how his colleagues perceive the interests of ELAs:

> What's the return on this investment—it may not be financial return but it could be we'll get better students, or the students will have better prospects in the job market or we'll attract better faculty. [For example,] there are all kinds of reasons to build a building that don't necessarily have a financial payout, but a school that doesn't have high quality facilities tends to start losing high quality students and faculty. . . . There are certain things that SCA units have total control over, so you can make those decisions. But there are other decisions where the funding comes from, where the authority comes from, the [ELAs'] offices, so you have to go through the chain [of command] and get people to buy-in at every level.

Similar to Franklin, the informants reiterated how SCAs may have autonomy over decisions within the realm of their offices but ELAs have control over funding decisions that impact the campus as a whole.

To the SCAs, these decisions are comparable to a business transaction: resources are likely to be provided by ELAs if there are foreseeable returns on these investments. Therefore, the chain of command relies on SCAs achieving "buy-in" from ELAs by understanding how resources are allocated to proposals similar to businesses where managers seek investments from stakeholders.

While these considerations focus on macro-level decisions for the university, Jolene shared how the role of SCAs can best be understood as bridging the gap between micro-level issues shared by students with the macro-level decisions about policies and distributing resources prioritized by ELAs. Jolene said "if we want to provide conference funding for our students to attend conferences . . . [it] will increase name recognition for the school and visibility of our students and all of the great things that they are doing." As she points out, the convergence of interests between students wanting to attend conferences or having improved facilities with ELAs hoping for increasing the name-recognition and profitability of the university's brand are useful connections to make for SCAs hoping their investments will be approved. As Carl, Franklin, and Jolene's comments illustrate, the chain of command is the mechanism by which SCAs can channel day-to-day concerns from students into recommendations for institutional policies and investments.

Pamela frequently described how a main aspect of being the middle-person between students and ELAs is ensuring that the concerns of students of color are considered important despite the fact that they are in the numerical minority of students, employees, and donors on their historically-white university campus. When describing the work of her and colleagues that specifically help students of color she said:

> We support students of color on this campus, help them navigate their journey. . . . We also do advocacy on behalf of the students in different ways either for individual students or by sitting in committees across the university to make sure that they are recognized for their efforts and what they do, and that people are taking into account their experiences. That they . . . think about them and about the issues that they have, and to make sure that the [ELAs], if they need to take corrective measures, take corrective measures, [and] they take them into consideration with their decision-making.

Even Pamela, who works specifically as an advocate for POC students, noted how the role of SCAs is to ensure that students' concerns are taken into account by ELAs when determining policy and how to allocate resources. To summarize, the SCAs simultaneously advise students about ways to access resources on campus that address their individual needs (such as housing or fear to speak with administrators about racism they've encountered) or organizational needs (like funds for having a speaker come on campus), and provide recommendations to ELAs about potential investments to help students. These recommendations have to take into account the interests of the ELAs whose priorities center on helping improve the rankings and revenue-accumulation for the university. While this section focused on the clearly defined roles for administrators and the use of the chain of command as the mechanism available for SCAs to translate student concerns into investments from the university, the next section focuses on the conditions in which SCAs experience role conflict when addressing racial inequality as a student concern.

Role Conflict for Administrators Addressing Racial Inequality

Maintaining Trust with Students and Favor from ELAs

All of the informants agreed that institutional support is available for SCAs to at least *talk* about racism as a broad societal issue. This point was celebrated most often by the white SCAs who felt the willingness to talk about racism as a social problem is important for creating an increasingly diverse and inclusive campus. For example, Elizabeth described a popular event she helped create on campus that has the mission of facilitating difficult dialogues about race on campus. She described the mission as the following:

> We don't come to an agreement but we walk away and say thank goodness we can talk about it. Thank goodness we're talking about it in the context of values. Thank goodness we're learning that we can do this and that we need to be accountable to a bigger picture too and a deeper picture not just my own way. Hopefully we understand another point of view a little bit more deeply and sensitively. . . . For example, race—I think there's a real attention and effort to saying that's a problem in our society and we've got to do something about it.

Pamela also stated that during the winter months, with celebrations for Black History Month and Martin Luther King Jr. day, the programs to award POC students for their hard work on campus are well-attended because "people want to make a statement, 'I'm not a racist. So I come to these things and I'm learning.'" Caroline also stressed how she "purposely ask[s] very strong students of color to facilitate seminars even though they are predominantly white, because I think that their status needs to be elevated and these [white] kids need to realize that if they're racist or classist, it's time to challenge those beliefs." The supported discussions about racism focus on racism as an individual or macro-level social problem where POC students are the educators by which white students and employees can access distance from being seen as racist or engaging in potentially racist discourse.

Despite the use of scripts that "they're on the right track," as Jolene stated, or "we're making strides" as most of the other white informants claimed, all of the informants described how the racial diversity among faculty and administrators would plausibly lead students to conclude that Whites are more likely to be hired and retained as employees on campus. Elizabeth openly stated, "We have a very white faculty and we have a very male faculty" and Jasmine characterized the relationship between political power on campus and race as the following:

> For administrative staff heavily female. For leadership positions heavy white male. Few white females. Smaller amount of people of color. . . . For the custodial and kitchen staff that's primarily Hispanic and Latino. . . . The higher you go the whiter it gets. The lower you go the more people of color you see and then that's structural. I don't see that changing very much.

Jolene described how in her specific school at the university "there are no black faculty" and Samantha mentioned how her white female colleagues joke about how the ELAs who have the most formal and informal control over policies on campus are the "five white guys meeting." Carl and Justin reiterated this point by stressing how even as white men they can see how ELAs are "[a] lot of old white guys who are usually in positions of authority. I mean if you look at the administration of this institution it is exclusively white men, old white men," as Justin summarizes. Surprisingly, all of the informants talked about racial inequality as a problem evidenced by the rare instances of POC being hired and retained in positions of authority on campus. In other words, none of the informants claimed to "not see race" or advise students to stop "playing the race card" if they express critiques about the lack of racial diversity on campus.

However, informants also agreed that administrators experience role conflict when they are asked by students to condemn racial inequality as a problem specifically at their university, and to identify how they are working to hold their colleagues and the ELAs accountable for how they participate in the reproduction of racism on campus. Although Jasmine's responsibilities aren't specifically geared towards helping students of color on campus like Pamela, she expressed similar sentiments about her role as an administrator and POC herself to help POC students "navigate their journey" on a historically-white campus. However, a major roadblock she identified is the lack of racial diversity among faculty to educate students and work with fellow faculty and SCAs. This roadblock is especially clear when her colleagues usually use the following script when asked to discuss racial diversity to potential and current students and employees:

> They'll say we're "the leading edge of diversity." We have a [diversity and inclusion] leadership program. It's a grant that supports low-income, underresourced students so either you're a student of color or you're from a low-income background. . . . Then you can get support that way. . . . I think they base it all on that, which is a great program. But it doesn't change the culture around, and not every student is in that program.

A consequence is that when white SCAs are confronted by students seeking examples of the steps administrators have taken to address racial inequality on campus, their attempts to even interact with students of color are shaped by a rational skepticism that the problem will even be validated and addressed by them if they are also white administrators. For example, Caroline stated, "the kids who need help the most are the kids who are least likely to ask. The kids of color will not ask, because they feel 'oh I'm here, I don't deserve it' well that's bull; they deserve it just as much as anyone else." Carl described how he, as a white male, has to confront the reality that students of color may plausibly critique the lack of role models among administrators on campus and conclude that combating racial inequality fails to be an institutional priority when he said:

> Well I know our students are concerned with the number of minority students and faculty on campus. And in the [ELAs] of the institution. . . . Like 95% white male. And I'm a white male. I want to be in one of those [ELA] pictures someday but I don't want to be there in that sort of pigeonhole either. That's the professional challenge for me.

Therefore, the professional challenge for the white SCAs included the reality that as they attempt to advance their position up the chain of command to potentially become ELAs, the critiques from students of color about racial inequality failing to be priority from ELAs seems valid in their own observations as well. As white SCAs, role conflict arises when attempting to build trust with students of color because of a clear contradiction: their professional advancement partly hinges on addressing these critiques that are, ironically, evidenced by the fact that they occupy their positions and are more likely (as Whites) to become ELAs in the first place.

While the issues for white SCAs focused on building trust with students, both white and POC informants unanimously expressed disappointment with ELAs failing to translate recognition of inequality into investments to address racial inequality. Roger, Pamela, Jasmine, and Franklin all described a "normal" yet disappointing prioritization of market-based logics in discourse about campus-wide problems over attempts to change institutional practices by the ELAs. For example, Jasmine stated:

> I know that I've been involved in certain conversations with certain VPs who just don't want to talk about it. They understand it's an issue. But it's what brings money, what makes [the university's] higher ranking—those are their priorities and not necessarily are we inclusive, are we giving support to the students and faculty and staff that are of color.

As Jasmine's analysis of the opportunity structure at the university shows, even when students and SCAs felt supported in their efforts to talk amongst each other about racism as a societal issue, discussions with ELAs about campus-wide policies to address racial inequality are either unlikely or typically fruitless discourse. The POC informants also talked about POC students having similar disappointments about discussions with their white peers and SCAs. The supported programs to talk about racism are much more abstract than any consideration of how social problems affect their lives on campus. For example, Franklin reflected on panel discussions and town-hall events he attended in response to the protests from Black Lives Matter receiving national attention:

> I do sense that students of color, especially in the last year with things happening nationally, may feel that their voices are not being fully heard, and that the community needs to be a little bit more thoughtful about how what is going on around the country in terms of interactions with the police . . . and how some of those issues translate into life on the campus.

Samantha described this issue with a focus on campus policies when explaining how campus climate surveys were considered by SCAs and ELAs at the time of the interviews. She said that ELAs and SCAs engaging in practices that lead to the documentation or naming of racism as an institutional problem are hard because their employment and promotional prospects are dictated by ELAs. As previously discussed, these ELAs prioritize and assign value to "meaningful accomplishments" from SCAs that positively impact on the revenue and reputation of the university. When working on the campus climate survey, Samantha had an up-close view of how even ELAs are incentivized to avoid or minimize documentation of racism that will likely have a negative impact on these goals. Samantha reiterated the point about this conflict in detail when she said:

> We did sort of have a lot of discussion. So a [ELA], a new white guy who is very nice, was in all of these meetings because he was overseeing the staff questions. . . . He's like "I am hesitant" and he says this, "I am really scared to ask questions that we don't want to know the answer to" . . . I mean, he gets persuaded. He's definitely a good guy who is interested in this stuff and really deep down cares about all humans. It was more than I thought. . . . So we're not open to begin with so I think that's [from] what [ELAs] have been told. So this poor guy is new in the position. I know he wants to help people but he's like I don't know if we can say that. I think that's the pressure being put on him.

Similarly, when I asked Justin about the impact of having to answer to an almost all-white group of ELAs on the SCAs' ability to fulfill their role as advocates for students, he said discussions with ELAs about documenting the racialized experiences of students are difficult in part because ELAs are not also answerable to students. For example, when talking about his support for an online portal for students to document their complaints about bias after anti-racist protests erupted on campus, he reflected on the ELA's aversion to this idea when he said:

> I am like this is not fucking difficult and I think [a bias response team] is a template for how you do it because it is not rocket science. You meet with people and listen to them. For administrators here at high level positions to not be able to meet with the students . . . and really manage a conversation is frightening to me. It just blows my mind [that] I can't even go more than that.

As both Justin and Samantha share, SCAs are in a position of role conflict when they witness ELAs either unwilling or unable to engage in discourse with students about the problems they face on campus. If the chain of command hinges on ELAs listening to concerns from students and recommendations provided by SCAs, conflict arises when attempts to fulfill their roles rely on unreceptive constituents. This lack of receptivity also negatively impacts their ability to solicit trust from POC students, especially for white SCAs, if there's a plausible understanding that their calls for institutional change will yield little results.

Condemning Student Protests as a Method When the Chain Is Broken

Building on our discussions about the pressure and tension that comes for SCAs and even ELAs to avoid "ask[ing] questions that we don't want to know the answer to," the most commonly referenced example of the conditions in which this tension arises was when students and faculty organized a die-in protest in solidarity with Black Lives Matter and other anti-racist protests on college campuses. The informants unanimously agreed that the protests put them into a position of role conflict because they were simultaneously expected to help condemn and punish students for organizing a demonstration without receiving a permit approved by ELAs. However, by helping punish students for organizing anti-racist protests they would be violating the trust they attempt to develop with students of color that they are committed to validating and addressing their complaints about racial inequality on campus. As Carl illustrates:

> One of the buildings that were just recently renovated was just opening. It wasn't officially opened yet but they were fundraising through the [renovations], some high-profile event for the University. And the students and the faculty members decided that that was the time and place that they wanted to do the die-in. . . . The police wanted to identify who the students were and came to [other SCAs to] look at the tapes to identify the people. . . . It goes against everything that I stood for. I did recognize a couple of people and I didn't say anything. Is that ethically challenged of me? Maybe. But I think I was holding myself to my own moral compass on the issue. But to me, it sort of speaks to the mentality of the leadership. . . . I said I don't agree with this and the response was, "Well you get paid by [the university], you need to do this!" I said "ok, I'll go down there [and said] I don't recognize anybody."

While Carl was the only person who explicitly talked about being asked to identify students for police officers on campus, all of the informants described how SCAs are put into a position of role conflict when students can be punished for condemning racism through protests. On one hand, they are paid by the university and expected to help actualize the decisions provided by the ELAs about enforcing policies for student conduct. On the other hand, helping aid the punishment of students negatively impacts the trust that SCAs are supposed to help combat similar issues that were being protested in the first place. In response to the same protest on campus, Samantha provided details from a meeting she attended between ELAs about possible sanctions. She described how ELAs were also in a position of role conflict as punishing anti-racist students may negatively impact the reputation and revenue of the university rather than the impact on students. At one point an ELA stressed the need to expel the students for failing to receive a permit for the protest that the SCAs agreed would have been denied in the first place; "thankfully" another ELA had to threaten to resign in order to protect students from expulsion. While the threat was important, Samantha felt another explanation was plausible for the decision not to expel the students:

> Would those kids have gotten expelled? I don't know. I bet enough people would have backed, [well] I think at one point too, which is totally the wrong reason, it was about the fear of publicity, right? If it got out that [the university] expelled students for standing up for this, maybe that's what helped. That's probably the only thing that the [other ELA] gave a shit about and that may have been the only thing that convinced [the ELAs]. I don't know.

When I asked Pamela about how the rush to criminalize rather than consider why people protested on campus impacted her relationship with students of color on campus, she pointed out the distinction between how ELAs and SCAs were impacted. For ELAs, she said:

> It's like let's control them, let's figure this out so they won't mess up our reputation. But they don't work with students. They leave at 5 PM and they don't have interactions with students where the students are going to come back to them. Students come to me and they're like, "What are you doing about it?" I was doing stuff! It's just they weren't things that I could discuss with them because they were administration things, talking to my colleagues creating awareness and trying to code some of the decisions they were making but those are not discussions I'm at liberty to have with the students. . . . It's hard because yeah, many of the things I have to do as a[n SCA] are not visible to the students. But it's something I do because of my job. I feel it's part of my job to bring this awareness to my colleagues. But at the end of the day, the [ELAs] make their own decisions and I'm an employee. I need to uphold whatever decisions they end up doing as an employee of the institution. It's hard. Personally it is hard.

The informants frequently stated that even if they personally feel protests are a rational approach to publically and financially pressure ELAs into investing resources to address racial inequality on campus, they are professionally obligated to condemn this method. However, helping with the punishment and criminalization of students simply trying to elicit a substantial response from ELAs negatively impacts their efforts to build trust with students working to help improve conditions for POC on campus.

Naming the Problem Yields Less Power to Address Racial Inequality

After talking about the rush to condemn protestors despite students receiving encouragement that the university is a site where they learn how to understand and address inequality, Roger shared how he learned to also manage his discourse to maintain his status as an SCA:

> I am very careful around what I say in certain circles. If we are having lunch, if we were doing this interview I signed that consent agreement, so I won't be identified so it is one of those [situations] where if we are having lunch and we are having this conversation or whatever it is I let it rip. It is freedom of my office, freedom of my home almost and away we go and say anything. This is just smart. [But] if we are at a meeting and the [ELAs are] there why would I, on any planet get up, and start railing against the institution? And in fact I have changed my entire narrative. If you talk to anyone about their conversations with me, especially faculty, I am pro-university! I will make every excuse under the sun to appear as though I support the university.

Though SCAs are hired to identify and address student concerns, Roger's comments ironically equivocate voicing critiques about the university with "railing against the institution" and stressed how only in private moments will he "let it rip" because "this is just smart." As Jasmine similarly argued, though there are administrators whose job description suggests protections to publicly acknowledge and address racial inequality as an institutional problem, these are "powerless positions." Therefore, she stated students cannot assume that ELAs are simply colorblind or ignorant, as the problem has more to do with the structure of power to actualize anti-racist policies rather than a lack of understanding when she said:

> It's more of a business mentality of let's keep the show running and do things that we do well and promote that. . . . All the times they give me these reports and they're like "It's hidden, don't tell anyone about it." It's like really? You don't want it public? You know what's going on, but you just don't want people to know

> about it. How many of these reports I've seen. . . . So, I think [ELAs] know about it. I think they're having discussions about it but they keep it top secret. They don't want anybody to get that information either and they're just trying to run a business.

As the informants share in this section, this "business mentality" appeared to be normal for the SCAs as most of the informants talked about the conflict they experience when dealing with silence and rejection from ELAs if recommendations to address racism will be considered costly as the nature of their work. Therefore, the SCAs are in a position of role conflict once their colleagues also choose to focus attention on "meaningful accomplishments" like the rankings and revenue of the university rather than the experiences of marginalized students on campus. As Carl later states, "As it deals with vision, we haven't really embraced this is everybody's responsibility to some extent and how can we work with our majority of students to better understand these issues." When I asked why, he said, "Because there is not a commitment to it on the highest level. Plain and simple. If there was a commitment to it, it would look different" with a clearly "matter of fact" tone. For the informants, conflict arises when the students and employees willing to acknowledge racial inequality aren't in a position of power to change institutional policies and practices.

All of the informants agreed that racial inequality is a problem on campus but also described how the structure of power and market-based incentives explain why inequality persists. Even though the informants who are POC more frequently described in rich detail how they experience role conflict as SCAs, all of the informants acknowledged how the "business mentality" from ELAs negatively impacts their ability to help students' efforts to acknowledge racism. Therefore, adopting this business-mentality or assimilating to the culture of silence is profitable for their individual prospects as SCAs.

DISCUSSION QUESTIONS

1. How do student-centered administrators (SCAs) act as gatekeepers between students and executive-level administrators (ELAs)?
2. The white SCAs that he interviewed faced an additional conflict between the work they are tasked with doing and their own professional ambitions. What was this conflict? How do you think they should resolve it?

3. One SCA described an ELA saying: "we don't want to ask questions that we don't want the answer to." What did they mean by this, and why is that problematic?
4. What type of diversity and inclusion work happens on your campus? Who does your school employ with this type of work as part of their job description? How effective are your school's efforts in improving the representation and experience of racial and ethnic minorities on campus?
5. There are many reasons why schools do not admit more students of color. One is that admissions officers can be biased against minority students who express a clear interest in racial justice and equality. Learn more by reading the article "Do Universities Want Black Students?" from *Context* magazine, available at https://contexts.org/articles/do-universities-want-black-students/

READING 9

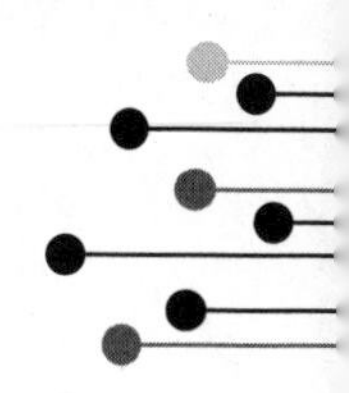

Neither Clear Nor Present

The Social Construction of Safety and Danger

Ruth Simpson

Originally published in 1996, this reading by Ruth Simpson on the social construction of danger is an excellent example of how sociological concepts and thinking can help us understand our current circumstances, even if the original ideas were written about many years ago. Her topic is how safety and danger are intersubjective—products of social construction, collective agreement, and socialization—rather than simply being objective conditions in our environment for us to seek out (safety) or avoid (danger). She doesn't argue that there is no such thing as observable danger (e.g., fire), but rather that there are many things that are dangerous that we can't observe (e.g., carbon monoxide poisoning). She posits that how we think about the source of danger in our environment reflects social convention rather than inherent features of the environment.

She describes three cognitive frameworks that we employ when we try to determine what is dangerous and what is safe. In the Cautious framework, *everything is considered dangerous unless it is marked*[1] *otherwise. When we say someone is being "paranoid," we are essentially saying that they are using the Cautious framework when it isn't merited according to social convention. Conversely, in the* Confident framework, *the assumption is that we are safe unless something is marked as dangerous. Children often exhibit the Confident framework, leaping from dressers to see if they can fly, running into traffic, and touching hot stoves, much to the chagrin of parents who work diligently to teach them the socially acceptable contours of safety and danger. Generally, exclusive use of either of these frameworks is considered socially unacceptable and it is relatively rare. Instead, we usually rely on what Simpson calls the* Neutral framework. *Here, the background (our general environment) is considered neutral—neither dangerous nor safe—and only specific aspects of the environment are marked as safe or dangerous. Most of our social and environmental spaces are perceived this way. Think of going for a hike at a park. Some areas may be marked as especially dangerous (Warning: Steep trail ahead) and*

Excerpt from "Neither Clear nor Present: The Social Construction of Safety and Danger" by Simpson, R. *Sociological Forum* (1996), 11, pp. 549–562. Reprinted with permission.

others as safe (Scenic overview ahead), but the park itself is assumed to be neutral, as it is unmarked.

Day-to-day public life in the United States was characterized by the Neutral frame until the COVID-19 virus swept the nation. Public health officials essentially urged the adoption of the Cautious frame—to assume that previously routine, normal, unremarkable interactions and tasks like going to the grocery store or having dinner with a friend were now dangerous (unless masks and six-foot distancing marked those activities as safe). Those who refuse to wear masks for nonmedical reasons are adopting the Confident frame; they are assuming (and insisting) that interactions are safe even in the face of observable evidence (the drastically increasing infection rate and death toll in places where masks are not worn). So the tug of war over whether or not mask-wearing is necessary can be partially understood as a contest between the Confident and Cautious frame. This is just one example of how sociological concepts are applicable across many different circumstances and at different points in time.

Introduction

In a famous scene from *Jaws,* a great white shark rushes toward an unsuspecting swimmer. Even before the attack, the audience is tense, aware that the swimmer is in danger. The scene is gory and brutal. The audience screams.

In *Monty Python and the Holy Grail,* a small white rabbit viciously attacks the Knights of the Round Table. In a chaotic and bloody scene, the rabbit springs from knight to knight sinking its teeth into their flesh. The audience laughs.

These two scenes, quite similar in many ways, elicit very different responses. A vicious attack on a human by an animal qualifies in one case as horror and in the other as comedy. The different reactions stem in part from the belief that danger and safety are *objective* qualities of animals. Sharks, especially large ones, are dangerous. Rabbits of any size are not.

The sense that danger and safety are objective qualities extends beyond perceptions of animals. Warning labels, safety equipment, and other precautions assume danger exists as part of an objective environment to which we must adapt our behavior. Biological arguments that humans instinctively fear snakes and other dangers make a similar assumption—by the logic of evolution, those lacking the appropriate instincts long ago fell prey to very objective threats (Goodwin, 1983). Similarly, psychologists and psychiatrists in studying, and especially in treating phobias, express that danger is real, there to be perceived or, as with phobics, misperceived. Together, these examples suggest a world where safety and danger exist independently of our own cognition.

Here I argue that perceptions of safety and danger are "intersubjective"—products of social construction, collective agreement, and socialization (Zerubavel, 1991). I do not dispute that objective danger exists. Rather, I argue the objective environment provides only inconsistent and ambiguous clues about danger, leaving wide latitude for inference and interpretation. Given this ambiguity, beliefs about danger, and particularly safety, can arise with little or no reference to the objective world they describe.

Against this uncertain background, we perceive safety and danger through three cognitive frameworks: the Cautious, Confident, and Neutral frameworks, which I describe in the second section. Each framework classifies safety and danger by splitting the world into marked and unmarked categories. The unmarked category reflects a default assumption about the world, while the marked category identifies exceptions to this default assumption. Thus, the Cautious framework assumes a dangerous background and marks certain items as specifically safe. The Confident framework assumes a safe background and marks certain items as dangerous. And the Neutral framework assumes a neutral background and marks items as either safe or dangerous. Collective agreement designates the appropriate framework for a specific situation.

Objective and Intersubjective Danger

There is something strikingly real about danger. Harm manifests itself in obvious ways, whether through personal injury or the destruction of property. Even reactions to danger are physical and observable: when frightened, humans shake, perspire, and feel their skin "crawl."

The physical reality of harm and fear makes the view that danger is objective compelling. By this argument, belief follows from observation and experience—we do not construct distinctions between safety and danger but observe them already present in the environment. Thus, poison is dangerous because it makes us sick, tornadoes are dangerous because they destroy property, and tigers are dangerous because they eat people.

But objective dangers often occur without observable symptoms. While "danger signs" can warn of approaching harm, danger often occurs without any warning at all. Danger can enter with bombs, fire, or high winds, but it can also enter insidiously and silently, as radon and radiation do. The absence of observable danger, then, does not indicate the absence of danger itself.

Because danger is often unobservable, it is impossible to determine for certain when we are safe. As the absence of danger, safety is the absence of something that is often unobservable in the first place. While it is sometimes possible to tell when danger is present, it is impossible to tell for certain that it is completely absent. Since there are numerous ways for any item or situation to be dangerous, designating something as safe requires ignoring all possible ways it might be dangerous.

In addition, safety does not manifest itself in any observable way. There are no "safety signs" to establish unequivocally when we are safe, as danger signs warn about harm. Safety, ironically, may be a more uncertain and unstable state than danger: in safety there is always the possibility that danger lurks unseen.

Safety zones, therefore, are human constructions—areas we define as free of danger, even though it is impossible to establish this for certain. Perceiving any object as safe requires ignoring the potential for harm. While perceiving danger can sometimes be a simple matter of observation, perceiving safety necessarily involves rationalization.

But even when danger is clear and present, observation does not definitively determine beliefs about danger. Even in the presence of observable harm, there is room for inference and interpretation. For any harmful event, there are many possible sources to blame and the objective environment will not necessarily privilege one explanation over others. For example, the distinction between snakes as dangerous animals and turtles as safe ones rests entirely on where we identify the source of danger. Snakes can cause illness and death by transmitting venom. Turtles can cause illness and death by transmitting the bacteria that cause salmonella. In each case, the process is the same: physical contact with fluid from an animal causes illness and possibly death. But despite the similar process, we treat snakes as agents of danger while turtles are merely benign carriers of a dangerous disease. We could, just as logically, view snakes as benign carriers of poison.

Disputes over danger often involve conflict over the source of harm. For example, some classify the disease AIDS as dangerous, while others blame the carriers and advocate banning them from the workplace, schools, and the country (i.e., the detention of HIV positive Haitian refugees). The same logic underlies the anti-gun control slogan: "Guns don't kill people. People kill people." The slogan casts people as dangerous carriers of a neutral tool, locating the source of harm in the carrier rather than the weapon itself (Garry Trudeau's satirical version of the same slogan, "Guns don't kill kids. Kids kill kids," strikes a chord because it relocates the danger from the gun to children.) Similarly, Gusfield (1981) demonstrates that the lack of public transportation and the remote location of bars cause alcohol-related accidents as much as the "killer drunk" does.

Finally, forming beliefs about danger often does not require observation of the empirical world at all. Through socialization and communication we share our fears. Residents of the East coast recognize earthquakes as dangerous even though many have never experienced one. Children learn to identify danger from adults who tell them they should not talk to strangers, cross the street alone, or play with matches. Indeed, in issuing these warnings, parents specifically hope children will avoid experiencing and observing these activities themselves. We can even socialize children to believe in dangers that do not exist—dangers that are, therefore, impossible to observe.

Cognitive Frameworks for Danger

Perceiving danger is not simply a process of classifying items as dangerous or safe. Rather, we perceive danger within one of three larger frameworks: the Cautious, Confident, and Neutral frameworks. Each framework makes a different default assumption about the unclassified world—that it is either safe, dangerous, or neutral. We perceive safety and danger in relation to this default assumption. In each framework we highlight or "mark" those entities that defy the framework's default assumption.

The Cautious Framework

The "cautious" framework assumes things are dangerous until proven safe. Using this framework, we identify safe areas, leaving dangerous areas unmarked. Paranoia exemplifies this framework. The paranoiac organizes the entire world through a cautious framework, viewing everything with suspicion. That we consider paranoia a mental disorder suggests the cautious framework is socially unacceptable as a general framework through which to view the world.

However, in specific situations, a cautious framework is expected. In New York City, for example, residents and visitors are cautious when walking through public areas; they assume the worst about the strangers surrounding them. Similarly, many women adopt a cautious framework when they walk alone at night and, in fact, may face criticism for not being sufficiently cautious.

Some adopt the cautious framework when focusing on specific groups or things. Prejudicial fear applies a cautious framework to a specific group, classifying all members of the group as dangerous and marking as exceptions any who threaten the stereotype.

Various symbols distinguish safe items from a generally dangerous environment. For example, in wartime, white flags and written agreements mark cease-fires as temporal and spatial safety zones. Governor Florio, after vetoing the New Jersey state legislature's ban on serving partially cooked eggs, invited a group of reporters to watch him eat eggs at a diner. Doing so, he marked the change in their status from dangerous to safe food. In a separate incident, the governor of Colorado publicly ate a cantaloupe to demonstrate that, despite fears of salmonella-infected cantaloupe, the fruit was safe for consumption.

The Confident Framework

In contrast, the "confident" framework assumes everything is safe until proven dangerous. With safety as the default environment, this framework marks dangerous areas and leaves safe areas unmarked. As with the cautious framework, those who rely exclusively on a confident framework are extraordinary. For example, in some cases, confidence denotes insanity. David Koresh, the leader of the Branch Davidian cult in Waco, Texas, was considered pathologically overconfident by federal agents who cited his sense of invincibility as evidence of insanity. Similarly, in *Catch-22*, Joseph Heller associates confidence with insanity in the famous sentence, "Anyone who wants to get out of combat duty isn't really crazy."

In certain contexts, however, we exalt confidence as an example of courage or faith. During wars, the military awards medals for behavior that, in another context, would be insane or naive. One recipient of the Bronze Star and Croix de Guerre later described his actions as "foolish, crazy, and stupid" rather than courageous (personal communication, 1993). Similarly, many religions advocate the confident framework as the ultimate example of faith. Consider the following passages from the Old and New Testaments:

> Yea, though I walk through the valley of the shadow of death, I will fear no evil: for thou art with me; thy rod and thy staff they comfort me. (Psalms 23)
>
> And when Peter was come down out of the ship, he walked on the water, to go to Jesus. But when he saw the wind boisterous, he was afraid; and beginning to sink, he cried, saying, Lord save me. And immediately Jesus stretched forth his hand, and caught him, and said unto him, "O ye of little faith, why did you doubt?" (Matthew 29–31)

Both passages urge adopting a confident framework. The example of Peter walking on the water is an interesting parallel to reports of people under the influence of LSD "trying to walk on the sea." Depending upon the inspiration then, LSD or God, using the confident framework is either irrational behavior or a religious example.

Other times confidence represents innocence. Very young children exhibit a fearless curiosity about the world (later in childhood they may develop "irrational" fears such as a fear of the dark). Gradually, through adults and their own experiences, children learn to mark certain objects and activities as dangerous.

The Neutral Framework

As general ways to understand the world, the cautious and confident frameworks are socially unacceptable. The exclusive use of either framework is either pathological (e.g., overconfidence, paranoia) or exceptional (perfect faith, bravery, or childhood innocence). The third framework is an alternative to default assumptions of danger or safety. The neutral framework begins with the assumption that the environment is neutral and marks as exceptional entities considered explicitly safe or dangerous. The neutral framework dominates everyday life:

> Drowsy habitude and the ordinariness of the daily round rather than fright and despair are the common human lot. Even when a society seems hedged in by superstitious fears, we cannot assume that the people, individually, live in dread most of the time. . . . Even where the objective situation is truly horrible and threatening, people learn in time to adapt and ignore. (Tuan, 1979:9) .

Except in specific situations, like those discussed above, we view the world through this framework. It is in relation to this framework that the cautious and confident frameworks are at times either deviant or exceptional.

Examples of neutral "zones" abound. For example, in winter when lakes begin to freeze (but have not completely frozen), some townships post a red flag by lakes to indicate that the ice is still too dangerous for skating. When the ice is thicker, they mark it as safe with a green flag. In the summer, however, they use no flag at all, indicating the lake is once again a neutral zone (even though attempting to skate on water is at least as dangerous as skating on a partially frozen lake). Some towns concerned about lawsuits adopt the cautious framework and keep the red flag up all summer.

The neutral framework marks people as dangerous or explicitly safe, but assumes nothing about the unmarked. Prisons, mental institutions, and quarantines mark people we consider dangerous. Conversely, credentials—licensing doctors, nurses, and pharmacists, admitting lawyers to the Bar, and ordaining priests—confer a safe, trustworthy status upon an otherwise neutral entity. Indeed, a neutral or safe status is a requirement for entry into many occupations. Medical and law schools can deny entry to people previously marked as dangerous, such as convicted felons. "Block parent" programs are another example of the neutral framework. Many communities designate block parents—houses where someone is home during the day and can aid children if they have problems after school. Yellow signs mark specific houses as safe havens for children in trouble but do not imply the remaining unmarked houses in the neighborhood are dangerous. Outside prisons, professions, and other symbols of safety and danger, people are neutral—neither explicitly safe nor dangerous.

Violating Frameworks

The cautious, confident, and neutral frameworks affect more than our perceptions of safety and danger. In defining our expectations, they create opportunities for surprise, uncertainty, and deviance. Violations and contradictions of frameworks generate the surprise that leads to humor and horror. Uncertainty about which framework to use in a specific situation produces excitement and panic. And deviance from the appropriate framework forms the basis for some mental illnesses, such as phobias.

Horror, Humor, and Excitement

We are horrified when safe or neutral items become dangerous. The use of mundane items such as ice picks *(Basic Instinct)*, a shoe *(Single White Female)*, and scissors *(Dead Again, Dial "M" for Murder)* as murder weapons is more chilling than the use of a gun or other "dangerous" item. Alfred Hitchcock's *The Birds* is frightening because a neutral animal is suddenly dangerous. Stories of poisoned Halloween candy or poisoned aspirin unsettle us because they suggest we are using the wrong framework. Incest horrifies in part because it violates the safety zone of the family. Finally, Schepple and Bart (1983) report women who were raped in areas they defined as safe (i.e., their homes or workplaces) were more fearful afterward than women who were raped in areas they defined as dangerous (i.e., a deserted street at night). For women raped in "safe" areas, the experience of rape fundamentally disrupted and contradicted the framework they believed was appropriate.

Salmonella outbreaks are frightening in part because they represent the sudden threat of a safe entity. A range of safe and neutral items have been identified as carriers of salmonella. In various epidemics, eggs, cantaloupe, turtles, baby kangaroos, ducklings, oysters, and other previously innocuous animals and foods suddenly posed a threat *(Washington Post*, August 16, 1991; Svitlik, 1992; *The New York Times*, December 27, 1990; *Atlanta Constitution*, August 8, 1990; *Lancet*, 1988; *FDA Consumer*, December 1987). The titles of newspaper and magazine articles about salmonella sometimes recognize the changing status of these items. One title, "Food That Bites Back" *(Boy's Life*, July 1993), suggests innocuous food items have suddenly become dangerous enemies. Another title, "Trojan Eggs" *(The New York Times Magazine*, July 30, 1989), implies danger lurks within an apparently harmless exterior.

The same process that creates horror and fear also results in humor. A safe item that turns out to be dangerous inverts the expected framework. The "killer rabbit" in *Monty Python and The Holy Grail* is funny only because knights are not supposed to approach rabbits with caution (using a tiger in the place of the rabbit would have greatly undermined the humor of the scene). In another comedy, Woody Allen's *Sleeper,* 23rd-century scientists determine that candy is healthy while health food is harmful, inverting 20th-century frameworks. *All Things Considered* and other news programs produced tongue-in-cheek reports about an aggressive wild turkey that chased several residents of Wisconsin through the woods. Similarly, a story about a dishwasher falling on two University of Chicago undergraduates appears in Dave Barry's humor column.

Uncertainty about which framework to use leads to a sense of excitement. Thrill activities, such as rollercoasters or bungee jumping, are examples of such uncertainty. They have elements of risk: traveling at high speeds and falling from a great height. Also, they have elements of safety: the protective bars on a rollercoaster car and the bungee cord that will prevent us from actually hitting the ground. As Apter (1992) argues, they derive their appeal from their ambiguous nature:

> Think of looking at a tiger in a cage. Both the tiger and the cage are needed in order for one to experience excitement: The tiger without the cage would be frightening. The cage without the tiger would be boring. (Apter, 1992:27)

The safety regulations surrounding these activities suggest some discomfort with them. Following safety rules and creating safety equipment marks these thrill activities as safe, despite all appearances.

From a sociological perspective, beliefs about danger and safety do not directly reflect objective conditions but are instead intersubjective concepts. Ironically, it is an objective quality of danger—that danger is often unobservable—that permits and encourages intersubjective perceptions of safety and danger.

DISCUSSION QUESTIONS

1. Describe the three cognitive frameworks and give your own examples of each.
2. What are some other examples of danger that are not observable?
3. What does she say happens when there is uncertainty about which framework we should use? Think especially about how the COVID-19

pandemic and the need to wear masks and socially distance have violated previously held frameworks about safety and danger.

4. Our misperceptions of safety and danger can have significant consequences at both an individual and national level. Watch the talk titled "Unmarked Risk and the Mundanity of Danger" by Wayne Brekhus at the Center for Global Security Research, available at https://cgsr.llnl.gov/event-calendar/2018/2018-08-02, to learn how the way we interpret marked (and unmarked) activities have implications for national security.

NOTE

1. The term *marked* is borrowed from linguistics. When we mark something, we somehow indicate that it is out of the ordinary, not normal, or special in some way. Things that are unmarked are those that we take for granted and assume are normal, routine, and unremarkable. "First-generation college student" is a marked term; it denotes something different from a "normal" college student (who is presumed to have at least one parent who went to college). In this reading, Simpson applies the concepts of marked and unmarked to how we *think* about danger and safety.

PART

III

Constructing Deviance and Normality

READING 10

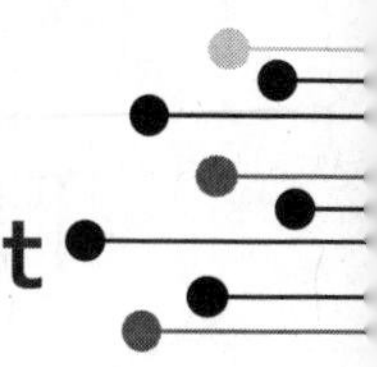

Situational Ethics and College Student Cheating

Emily E. LaBeff, Robert E. Clark, Valerie J. Haines, and George M. Diekhoff

Have you ever cheated on an exam or some other type of schoolwork? If so, you're not alone. The Internet is rife with websites where students can buy term papers, and new digital technologies make it easier than ever to share tests or other work. Some schools even outsource their anticheating efforts by using websites such as Turnitin.com to check student work against that submitted by others. Even an old-fashioned glance at a classmate's test or copying homework before class still happens with impressive frequency. Adults aren't exempt from this either. A recent spate of news stories has revealed that academics, politicians, journalists, and all sorts of other authors plagiarized writing and presenting it as their own. Yet, as widespread as cheating in various forms may be, it's something that is viewed by the wider society as deviant. If you've ever cheated, you probably didn't drop into your teacher's office or call your parents to brag about how proud you were of how you cheated. People know that cheating is wrong. While people may claim that they didn't realize a behavior counted as cheating, few would argue that they had no idea that cheating itself is wrong.

So how can we explain why cheating is so widespread when it is a form of behavior that is almost universally acknowledged as wrong (i.e., deviant)? In this reading, LaBeff et al. provide us with one set of answers. They argue that students who cheat use what they call techniques of neutralization to justify their actions. These rationalizations allow students to reconcile the wider cultural value that cheating is wrong, while simultaneously redefining their actions in such a way that does not feel that they have committed a deviant act.

While this is an article about college students and cheating, the ideas in it can be used to explain how people justify a myriad of other types of deviant behavior. As you read, think about whether you or those you know have ever used these techniques of neutralization (in any context) and how they might be applied to behaviors considered deviant other than cheating.

Excerpt from "Situational Ethics and College Student Cheating," by Emily E. LaBeff, Robert E. Clark, Valerie J. Haines, and George M. Diekhoff. *Sociological Inquiry*, 60(2).

This report examines instances of self-reported cheating engaged in by college students, fifty-four percent of whom reported at least one incidence of cheating. Descriptive responses are analyzed in the context of techniques of neutralization. The neutralizing attitude held by these student cheaters suggests that situational ethics are involved. Although the respondents indicate disapproval of cheating, many students feel justified in cheating under certain circumstances.

Introduction

Studies have shown that cheating in college is epidemic, and some analysts of this problem estimate that fifty percent of college students may engage in such behavior (e.g., Pavela 1976; Baird 1980; Wellborn 1980; Haines, Diekhoff, LaBeff, and Clark 1986). Such studies have examined demographic and social characteristics of students such as age, sex, academic standing, major, classification, extracurricular activity, level of test anxiety, degree of sanctioned threat, and internal social control. Each of these factors has been found to be related, to some extent, to cheating although the relationship of these factors varies considerably from study to study (Bonjean and McGee 1965; Harp and Taietz 1966; Stannord and Bowers 1970; Fakouri 1972; Johnson and Gormly 1972; Bronzaft, Stuart, and Blum 1973; Tittle and Rowe 1973; Liska 1978; Baird 1980; Leming 1980; Barnett and Dalton 1981; Eve and Bromley 1981; Newhouse 1982; Singhal 1982; Haines et al. 1986).

In our freshmen classes, we often informally ask students to discuss whether they have cheated in college and, if so, how. Some students have almost bragged about which of their methods have proven most effective including writing notes on shoes and caps and on the backs of calculators. Rolling up a tiny cheat sheet into a pen cap was mentioned. And one student said he had "incredibly gifted eyes" which allowed him to see the answers of a smart student four rows in front of him. One female student talked about rummaging through the dumpsters at night close to final examination time looking for test dittos. She did find at least one examination. A sorority member informed us that two of her term papers in her freshman year were sent from a sister chapter of the sorority at another university, retyped and submitted to the course professor. Further, many of these students saw nothing wrong with what they were doing, although they verbally agreed with the statement that cheating was unethical.

It appears that students hold qualified guidelines for behavior which are situationally determined. As such, the concept of situational ethics might well describe this college cheating in that rules for behavior may not be considered rigid but depend on the circumstances involved (Norris and Dodder 1979, p. 545). Joseph Fletcher, in his well known philosophical treatise, *Situation Ethics: The New Morality* (1966), argues that this position is based on the notion that any action may be considered good or bad depending on the social circumstances. In other words, what is wrong in most situations might be considered right or acceptable if the end is defined as appropriate. This concept focuses on contextual appropriateness, not necessarily what is good or right, but what is viewed as fitting, given the circumstances. Central to this process is the idea that situations alter cases, thus altering the rules and principles guiding behavior (Edwards 1967).

Of particular relevance to the present study is the work of Gresham Sykes and David Matza (1957) who first developed the concept of neutralization to explain delinquent behavior. Neutralization theory in the study of delinquency expresses the process of situationally defining deviant behavior. In this view, deviance is based upon ". . . an unrecognized extension of defenses to crimes, in the form of justifications . . . seen as valid by the delinquent but not by . . . society at large" (Sykes and Matza 1957, p. 666). Through neutralization individuals justify violation of accepted behavior. This provides protection ". . . from self blame and the blame of others . . ." (Sykes and Matza 1957, p. 666). They do this before, during, and after the act. Such techniques of neutralization are separated into five categories: denial of responsibility, condemnation of condemners, appeal to higher loyalties, denial of victim, and denial of injury. In each case, individuals profess a conviction about a particular law but argue that special circumstances exist which cause them to violate the rules in a particular instance. However, in recent research, only Liska (1978) and Haines et al. (1986) found neutralization to be an important factor in college student cheating.

Methodology

The present analysis is based on a larger project conducted during the 1983–1984 academic year when a 49-item questionnaire about cheating was administered to students at a small southwestern university. The student body (N = 4950) was evenly distributed throughout the university's programs with a disproportionate number (twenty-seven percent) majoring in business administration. In order to achieve a representative sample from a cross-section of the university student body, the questionnaire was administered to students enrolled in courses classified as a part of the university's core curriculum. Freshmen and sophomores were overrepresented (eighty-four percent of the sample versus sixty percent of the university population). Females were also overrepresented (sixty-two percent of the sample versus fifty-five percent of the university population).

There are obvious disadvantages associated with the use of self-administered questionnaires for data-gathering purposes. One such problem is the acceptance of student responses without benefit of contest. To maximize the return rate, questionnaires were administered during regularly scheduled class periods. Participation was on a voluntary basis. In order to establish the validity of responses, students were guaranteed anonymity. Students were also instructed to limit their responses regarding whether they had cheated to the current academic year.

Previous analysis (e.g., Haines et al. 1986) focused on the quantitative aspects of the questionnaire. The present analysis is intended to assess the narrative responses to the incidence of cheating in three forms, namely on major examinations, quizzes, and class assignments, as well as the perceptions of and attitudes held by students toward cheating and the effectiveness of deterrents to cheating. Students recorded their experiences in their own words. Most students (eighty-seven percent) responded to the open-ended portion of the questionnaire.

Results

Of the 380 undergraduate students who participated in the spring survey, fifty-four percent indicated they had cheated during the previous six month period. Students were requested to indicate whether cheating involved examination, weekly quizzes, and/or homework assignments. Much cheating took the form of looking on someone else's paper, copying homework, and either buying term papers or getting friends to write papers for them. Only five of the 205 students who admitted cheating reported being caught by the professor. However, seven percent (n = 27) of the students reported cheating more than five times during the preceding six month period. Twenty percent (n = 76) indicated that most students openly approved of cheating. Only seventeen students reported they would inform the instructor if they saw another student cheating. Many students, especially older students, indicated they felt resentment toward cheaters, but most also noted that they would not do anything about it (i.e., inform the instructor).

To more fully explore the ways in which students neutralize their behavior, narrative data from admitted student cheaters were examined (n = 149). The narrative responses were easily classified into three of the five techniques described by Sykes and Matza (1957).

Denial of Responsibility

Denial of responsibility was the most often identified response. This technique involves a declaration by the offenders that, in light of circumstances beyond their control, they cannot be held accountable for their actions. Rather than identifying the behavior as "accidental," they attribute wrongdoing to the influence of outside forces. In some instances, students expressed an inability to withstand peer pressure to cheat. Responses show a recognition of cheating as an unacceptable behavior, implying that under different circumstances cheating would not have occurred. One student commented:

> I was working forty plus hours a week and we had a lot to read for that day. I just couldn't get it all in. . . . I'm not saying cheating is okay, sometimes you just have to.
>
> Another student explained her behavior in the following statement:
>
> . . . I had the flu the week before . . . had to miss several classes so I had no way of knowing what was going to be on the exam (sic). My grades were good up to that point and I hadn't cheated. . . . I just couldn't risk it.

It is noteworthy that these statements indicate the recognition that cheating is wrong under normal circumstances.

Other responses demonstrate the attempt by students to succeed through legitimate means (e.g., taking notes and studying) only to experience failure. Accordingly, they were left with no alternative but to cheat. One student commented:

> [E]ven though I've studied in the past, I've failed the exam (sic) so I cheated on my last test hoping to bring a better grade.
>
> Another student explained his behavior in the following manner:
>
> I studied for the exam (sic) and I studied hard but the material on the test was different from what I expected. . . . I had to make a good grade.

In some accounts, students present a unique approach to the denial of responsibility. Upon entering the examination setting, these students had no intention of cheating, but the opportunity presented itself. The following statement by one student provides a clear illustration of this point:

> I was taking the test and someone in another part of the room was telling someone else an answer. I heard it and just couldn't not (sic) write it down.

Although viewing such behavior as dishonest, the blame for any wrongdoing is quickly transferred to those who provide the answers. Another student justified her action in the following manner:

> I didn't mean to cheat but once you get the right answer it's hard, no impossible, not to. How could you ignore an answer that you knew was right?

In addition, some students reported accidentally seeing other students' test papers. In such instances, the cheaters chastised classmates for not covering up their answer sheets. As one student wrote, such temptation simply cannot be overcome:

> I studied hard for the exam (sic) and needed an A. I just happened to look up and there was my neighbor's paper uncovered. I found myself checking my answers against his through the whole test.

Appeal to Higher Loyalties

Conflict also arises between peer group expectations and the normative expectations of the larger society. When this occurs, the individual may choose to sacrifice responsibility, thereby maintaining the interest of peers. Such allegiance allows these individuals to supercede moral obligations when special circumstances arise.

Students who invoke this technique of neutralization frequently described their behavior as an attempt to help another. One student stated:

> I only cheated because my friend had been sick and she needed help. . . . [I]t (cheating) wouldn't have happened any other time.

Another student denied any wrongdoing on her part as the following statement illustrates:

> I personally have never cheated. I've had friends who asked for help so I let them see my test. Maybe some would consider that to be cheating.

These students recognize the act of cheating is wrong. However, their statements also suggest that in some situations cheating can be overlooked. Loyalty to a friend in need takes precedence over honesty in the classroom. Another student described his situation in the following manner:

I was tutoring this girl but she just couldn't understand the material. . . . I felt I had to help her on the test.

Condemnation of Condemners

Cheaters using this technique of neutralization attempt to shift attention from their own actions to the actions of others, most often authority figures. By criticizing those in authority as being unfair or unethical, the behavior of the offender seems less consequential by comparison. Therefore, dishonest behavior occurs in reaction to the perceived dishonesty of the authority figure. Students who utilize this technique wrote about uncaring, unprofessional instructors with negative attitudes who were negligent in their behavior. These incidents were said to be a precursor to their cheating behavior. The following response illustrates this view:

> The teachers here are boring and I dislike this school. The majority of teachers here don't care about the students and are rude when you ask them for help.

In other instances, students cite unfair teaching practices which they perceive to be the reason for their behavior. One student stated:

> Major exams (sic) are very important to your grade and it seems that the majority of instructors make up the exams (sic) to try and trick you instead of testing your knowledge.

In this case, the instructor is thought to engage in a deliberate attempt to fail the students by making the examinations difficult. Also within this category were student accounts which frequently express a complaint of being overworked. As one student wrote:

> One instructor assigns more work than anyone could possibly handle . . . at least I know I can't, so sometimes cheating is the answer.

Another student described his situation as follows:

> Sometimes it seems like these instructors get together and plan to make it difficult. . . . I had three major tests in one day and very little time to study

Although less frequently mentioned, perceived parental pressure also serves as a neutralizing factor for dishonesty. One student stated:

> During my early years at school my parents constantly pressured me for good grades. . . . [T]hey would have withheld money if grades were bad.

Another student blamed the larger society for his cheating:

> In America, we're taught that results aren't achieved through beneficial means, but through the easiest means.

Another stated:

> Ted Kennedy has been a modeling (sic) example for many of us. . . . This society teaches us to survive, to rationalize. . . . (it) is built on injustice and expediency.

This student went on to say that he cheated throughout a difficult science course so he could spend more time studying for major courses which he enjoyed.

Denial of Injury and Denial of the Victim

Denial of injury and denial of the victim do not appear in the student accounts of their cheating. In denial of injury, the wrongdoer states that no one was harmed or implies that accusations of injury are grossly exaggerated. In the second case, denial of the victim, those who violate norms often portray their targets as legitimate. Due to certain factors such as the societal role, personal characteristics, or lifestyle of the victim, the wrongdoer felt the victim "had it coming."

It is unlikely that students will either deny injury or deny the victim since there are no real targets in cheating. However, attempts to deny injury are possible when the one who is cheating argues that cheating is a personal matter rather than a public one. It is also possible that some students are cognizant of the effect their cheating activities have upon the educational system as a whole and, therefore, choose to neutralize their behavior in ways which allow them to focus on the act rather than the consequences of cheating. By observing their actions from a myopic viewpoint, such students avoid the larger issues of morality.

Conclusion

The purpose of this report was to analyze student responses to cheating in their college coursework. Using Sykes and Matza's model of techniques neutralization, we found that students rationalized their cheating behavior and do so without challenging the norm of honesty. Student responses fit three of the five techniques of neutralization. The most common technique is a denial of responsibility. Second, students tend to "condemn the condemners," blaming faculty and testing procedures. Finally, students "appeal to higher loyalties" by arguing that it is more important to help a friend than to avoid cheating. The use of these techniques of neutralization conveys the message that students recognize and accept cheating as an undesirable behavior which, nonetheless, can be excused under certain circumstances. Such findings reflect the prevalence of situational ethics.

The situation appears to be one in which students are not caught and disciplined by instructors. Additionally, students who cheat do not concern themselves with overt negative sanctions from other students. In some groups, cheating is planned, expected, and often rewarded in that students may receive better grades That leaves a student's ethical, internalized control as a barrier to cheating. However, the neutralizing attitude allows students to sidestep issues of ethics and guilt by placing the blame for their behavior elsewhere. Neutralization allows them to state their belief that in general cheating is wrong, but in some circumstances cheating is acceptable, even necessary.

Given such widespread acceptance of cheating in the university setting, it may be useful to further test the salience of neutralization and other such factors in more diverse university environments. This study is limited to a small state university. It is important also to extend the research to a wider range of institutions including prestigious private colleges, large state universities, and church-related schools.

Cross-cultural studies of cheating may also prove useful for identifying broader social and cultural forces which underlie situational ethics and cheating behavior. In this regard, the process involved in learning neutralizing attitudes could be integrated with work in the field of deviance in order to expand our understanding of rule breakers along a continuum of minor to major forms of deviance.

DISCUSSION QUESTIONS

1. How does the context in which deviance takes place affect whether a behavior is defined as deviant? Are there people you would openly discuss cheating with but others you would not? What is different about these groups?

2. How might these techniques of neutralization be used by someone who steals office supplies, time, or other things of value from his or her place of work?
3. Do you think that there might be cross-cultural variations in techniques of neutralization? Or might there be more techniques of neutralization from your culture that you could add to this list? How else do we justify deviant acts in ourselves or others?
4. Is sharing work and coordinating intellectual effort with other students always deviant? Under what circumstances is this not only accepted but also encouraged by your teacher?
5. Is not wearing a mask during the COVID-19 pandemic when in public or around others deviant? What does this depend on? Are these techniques of neutralization ever used as justification for not following health and safety recommendations?

REFERENCES

Baird, John S. 1980. "Current Trends in College Cheating." *Psychology in the Schools* 17:512–522.

Barnett, David C., and Jon C. Dalton. 1981. "Why College Students Cheat." *Journal of College Student Personnel* 22:545–551.

Bonjean, Charles M., and Reece McGee. 1965. "Undergraduate Scholastic Dishonesty: A Comparative Analysis of Deviance and Control Systems." *Social Science Quarterly* 65:289–296.

Bronzaft, Arline L., Irving R. Stuart, and Barbara Blum. 1973. "Test Anxiety and Cheating on College Examinations." *Psychological Reports* 32:149–150.

Edwards, Paul. 1967. *The Encyclopedia of Philosophy*, Vol. 3, edited by Paul Edwards. New York: Macmillan Company and Free Press.

Eve, Raymond, and David G. Bromley. 1981. "Scholastic Dishonesty Among College Undergraduates: A Parallel Test of Two Sociological Explanations." *Youth and Society* 13:629–640.

Fakouri, M. E. 1972. "Achieving Motivation and Cheating." *Psychological Reports* 31:629–640.

Fletcher, Joseph. 1966. *Situation Ethics: The New Morality*. Philadelphia: The Westminster Press.

Haines, Valerie J., George Diekhoff, Emily LaBeff, and Robert Clark. 1986. "College Cheating: Immaturity, Lack of Commitment, and the Neutralizing Attitude." *Research in Higher Education* 25:342–354.

Harp, John, and Philip Taietz. 1966. "Academic Integrity and Social Structure: A Study of Cheating Among College Students." *Social Problems* 13:365–373.

Johnson, Charles D., and John Gormly, 1972. "Academic Cheating: The Contribution of Sex, Personality, and Situational Variables." *Developmental Psychology* 6:320–325.

Leming, James S. 1980. "Cheating Behavior, Subject Variables, and Components of the Internal-External Scale Under High and Low Risk Conditions." *Journal of Education Research* 74:83–87.

Liska, Allen. 1978. "Deviant Involvement, Associations, and Attitudes: Specifying the Underlying Causal Structures." *Sociology and Social Research* 63:73–88.

Newhouse, Robert C. 1982. "Alienation and Cheating Behavior in the School Environment." *Psychology in the Schools* 19:234–237.

Norris, Terry D., and Richard A. Dodder. 1979. "A Behavioral Continuum Synthesizing Neutralization Theory, Situational Ethics and Juvenile Delinquency." *Adolescence* 55:545–555.

Pavela, Gary. 1976. "Cheating on the Campus: Who's Really to Blame?" *Time* 107 (June 7):24.

Singhal, Avinash C. 1982. "Factors in Student Dishonesty." *Psychological Reports* 51:775–780.

Stannord, Charles, I., and William J. Bowers. 1970. "College Fraternity as an Opportunity Structure for Meeting Academic Demands." *Social Problems* 17:371–390.

Sykes, Gresham, and David Matza. 1957. "Techniques of Neutralization: A Theory of Delinquency." *American Sociological Review* 22:664–670.

Tittle, Charles, and Alan Rowe. 1973. "Moral Appeal, Sanction Threat, and Deviance: An Experimental Test." *Social Problems* 20:448–498.

Wellborn, Stanley N. 1980. "Cheating in College Becomes Epidemic" *U.S. News and World Report* 89 (October 20):39–42.

READING

11

The New Jim Crow

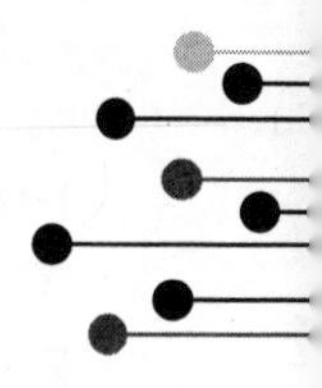

Michelle Alexander

A caste is a rigid system of stratification within a society. One of the most well-known caste systems is that associated with the Hindu religion, where belief in reincarnation shapes beliefs about how society should be organized. Children inherit the exact same position in society as their parents, without the opportunity for social mobility. Options for education, work, friendship, and romantic partners are controlled by strict social sanctions that ensure the members of each caste stay "in their place."

The concept of a caste system is the antithesis to what is commonly referred to as the American Dream—that there is equal opportunity for all Americans and that how far you go in life and where you wind up on the socioeconomic ladder is a reflection of individual ability and effort. The saying "pull yourself up by your bootstraps" is a colloquial way of referring to the idea behind the American Dream.

In a caste system, some segments of the population are not allowed to have bootstraps, or for that matter—boots. The ability to move up (or down) the socioeconomic ladder in a society is, by design, not available to them. In this reading, legal scholar Michelle Alexander argues that the American criminal justice system has created a caste system based on race, re-creating the overt legal and social barriers faced by African Americans in the Jim Crow era between 1896 and 1965. The problem today is subtler—politicians and those working in the criminal justice system tend to vociferously deny that race plays any role in arrests, incarceration rates, or treatment of criminals after they have served their time. Alexander shows that there are clear statistical and anecdotal biases based on race, and that even the laws surrounding how charges of racial bias can be brought to courts for consideration have contributed to the systematic discrimination and disenfranchisement of blacks in American society. The end result is a racial caste system that is quite the opposite of the American Dream.

Her work is even more relevant in light of the police killings of unarmed black citizens and the #blacklivesmatter protests that are an ongoing response. As you read, think about how the problems with the criminal justice system she describes also contribute to some segments of the population dismissing the concerns of Black Lives Matter protestors.

"The New Jim Crow," by Michelle Alexander, from *The American Prospect* (2010). https://prospect.org/special-report/new-jim-crow/. Reprinted with permission.

How Mass Incarceration Turns People of Color into Permanent Second-Class Citizens

The first time I encountered the idea that our criminal-justice system functions much like a racial caste system, I dismissed the notion. It was more than 10 years ago in Oakland when I was rushing to catch the bus and spotted a bright orange sign stapled to a telephone pole. It screamed in large, bold print: "The Drug War is the New Jim Crow." I scanned the text of the flyer and then muttered something like, "Yeah, the criminal-justice system is racist in many ways, but making such an absurd comparison doesn't help. People will just think you're crazy." I then hopped on the bus and headed to my new job as director of the Racial Justice Project for the American Civil Liberties Union of Northern California.

What a difference a decade makes. After years of working on issues of racial profiling, police brutality, and drug-law enforcement in poor communities of color as well as working with former inmates struggling to "re-enter" a society that never seemed to have much use for them, I began to suspect that I was wrong about the criminal-justice system. It was not just another institution infected with racial bias but a different beast entirely. The activists who posted the sign on the telephone pole were not crazy, nor were the smattering of lawyers and advocates around the country who were beginning to connect the dots between our current system of mass incarceration and earlier forms of racial control. Quite belatedly, I came to see that mass incarceration in the United States has, in fact, emerged as a comprehensive and well-disguised system of racialized social control that functions in a manner strikingly similar to Jim Crow.

What has changed since the collapse of Jim Crow has less to do with the basic structure of our society than with the language we use to justify severe inequality. In the era of colorblindness, it is no longer socially permissible to use race, explicitly, as justification for discrimination, exclusion, or social contempt. Rather, we use our criminal-justice system to associate criminality with people of color and then engage in the prejudiced practices we supposedly left behind. Today, it is legal to discriminate against ex-offenders in ways it was once legal to discriminate against African Americans. Once you're labeled a felon, depending on the state you're in, the old forms of discrimination—employment discrimination, housing discrimination, denial of the right to vote, and exclusion from jury service—are suddenly legal. As a criminal, you have scarcely more rights and arguably less respect than a black man living in Alabama at the height of Jim Crow. We have not ended racial caste in America; we have merely redesigned it.

More than two million African Americans are currently under the control of the criminal-justice system—in prison or jail, on probation or parole. During the past few decades, millions more have cycled in and out of the system; indeed, nearly 70 percent of people released from prison are re-arrested within three years. Most people appreciate that millions of African Americans were locked into a second-class status during slavery and Jim Crow, and that these earlier systems of racial control created a legacy of political, social, and economic inequality that our nation is still struggling to overcome. Relatively few, however, seem to appreciate that millions of African Americans are subject to a new system of control—mass incarceration—which also has a devastating effect on families and communities. The harm is greatly intensified when prisoners are released. As criminologist Jeremy Travis has observed, "In this brave new world, punishment for the original offense is no longer enough; one's debt to society is never paid."

The scale of incarceration-related discrimination is astonishing. Ex-offenders are routinely stripped of essential rights. Current felon-disenfranchisement laws bar 13 percent of African American men from casting a vote, thus making mass incarceration an effective tool of voter suppression—one reminiscent of the poll taxes and literacy tests of the Jim Crow era. Employers routinely discriminate against an applicant based on criminal history, as do landlords. In most states, it is also legal to make ex-drug offenders ineligible for food stamps. In some major urban areas, if you take into account prisoners—who are excluded from poverty and unemployment statistics, thus masking the severity of black disadvantage—more than half of working-age African American men have criminal records and are thus subject to legalized discrimination for the rest of their lives. In Chicago, for instance, nearly 80 percent of working-age African American men had criminal records in 2002. These men are permanently locked into an inferior, second-class status, or caste, by law and custom.

The official explanation for this is crime rates. Our prison population increased sevenfold in less than 30 years, going from about 300,000 to more than 2 million, supposedly due to rising crime in poor communities of color.

Crime rates, however, actually have little to do with incarceration rates. Crime rates have fluctuated during the past 30 years and today are at historical lows, but incarceration rates have consistently soared. Most sociologists and criminologists today will acknowledge that crime rates and incarceration rates have moved independently of each other; incarceration rates have skyrocketed regardless of whether crime has gone up or down in any particular community or in the nation as a whole.

What caused the unprecedented explosion in our prison population? It turns out that the activists who posted the sign on the telephone pole were right: The "war on drugs" is the single greatest contributor to mass incarceration in the United States. Drug convictions accounted for about two-thirds of the increase in the federal prison system and more than half of the increase in the state prison system between 1985 and 2000—the period of the U.S. penal system's most dramatic expansion.

Contrary to popular belief, the goal of this war is not to root out violent offenders or drug kingpins. In 2005, for example, four out of five drug arrests were for possession, while only one out of five were for sales. A 2007 report from Sentencing Project found that most people in state prison for drug offenses had no history of violence or significant selling activity. Nearly 80 percent of the increase in drug arrests in the 1990s, when the drug war peaked, could be attributed to possession of marijuana, a substance less harmful than alcohol or tobacco and at least as prevalent in middle-class white communities and on college campuses as in poor communities of color.

The drug war, though, has been waged almost exclusively in poor communities of color, despite the fact that studies consistently indicate that people of all races use and sell illegal drugs at remarkably similar rates. This is not what one would guess by peeking inside our nation's prisons and jails, which are overflowing with black and brown drug offenders. In 2000, African Americans made up 80 percent to 90 percent of imprisoned drug offenders in some states.

The extraordinary racial disparities in our criminal-justice system would not exist today but for the complicity of the United States Supreme Court. In the failed war on drugs, our Fourth Amendment protections against unreasonable searches and seizures have been eviscerated. Stop-and-frisk operations in poor communities of color are now routine; the arbitrary and discriminatory police practices the framers aimed to prevent are now commonplace. Justice Thurgood Marshall, in a strident dissent in the 1989 case of *Skinner v. Railway Labor Executive Association*, felt compelled to remind the Court that there is "no drug exception" to the Fourth Amendment. His reminder was in vain. The Supreme Court had begun steadily unraveling Fourth Amendment protections against stops, interrogations, and seizures in bus stops, train stations, schools, workplaces, airports, and on sidewalks in a series of cases starting in the early 1980s. These aggressive sweep tactics in poor communities of color are now as accepted as separate water fountains were several decades ago.

If the system is as rife with conscious and unconscious bias, many people often ask, why aren't more lawsuits filed? Why not file class-action lawsuits challenging bias by the police or prosecutors? Doesn't the 14th Amendment guarantee equal protection of the law?

What many don't realize is that the Supreme Court has ruled that in the absence of conscious, intentional bias—tantamount to an admission or a racial slur—you can't present allegations of race discrimination in the criminal-justice system. These rulings have created a nearly insurmountable hurdle, as law-enforcement officials know better than to admit racial bias out loud, and much of the discrimination that pervades this system is rooted in unconscious racial stereotypes, or "hunches" about certain types of people that come down to race. Because these biases operate unconsciously, the only proof of bias is in the outcomes: how people of different races are treated. The Supreme Court, however, has ruled that no matter how severe the racial disparities, and no matter how overwhelming or compelling the statistical evidence may be, you must have proof of conscious, intentional bias to present a credible case of discrimination. In this way, the system of mass incarceration is now immunized from judicial scrutiny for racial bias, much as slavery and Jim Crow laws were once protected from constitutional challenge.

As a nation, we have managed to create a massive system of control that locks a significant percentage of our population—a group defined largely by race—into a permanent, second-class status. This is not the fault of one political party. It is not merely the fault of biased police, prosecutors, or judges. We have all been complicit in the emergence of mass incarceration in the United States. In the so-called era of colorblindness, we have become blind not so much to race as to the re-emergence of caste in America. We have turned away from those labeled "criminals," viewing them as "others" unworthy of our concern. Some of us have been complicit by remaining silent, even as we have a sneaking suspicion that something has gone horribly wrong. We must break that silence and awaken to the human-rights nightmare that is occurring on our watch.

We, as a nation, can do better than this.

DISCUSSION QUESTIONS

1. What role does language play in allowing the striking racial disparities in the criminal justice system to cause little concern in wider American society?
2. After those convicted of a crime serve their sentences, what additional obstacles do they face? What are the arguments for and against keeping these additional sanctions?
3. How are crime rates and rates of incarceration related? What explains this relationship?
4. What role has the "war on drugs" played in the mass incarceration of African Americans?
5. If the criminal justice system has such widespread racial disparities, why don't activists and lawyers simply bring their evidence to the courts to try to change the system?

Calling the Shots

Why Parents Reject Vaccines

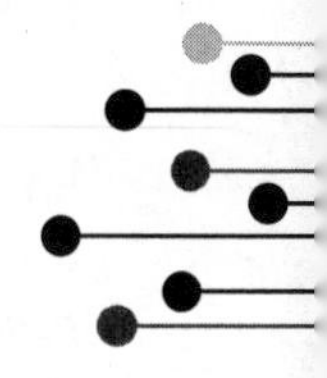

Jennifer A. Reich

One of the things that makes sociology such a powerful tool for understanding the world is its emphasis on trying to understand the social world from the point of view of others. Beliefs and behaviors that we find mystifying, infuriating, and dangerous become less so when we can understand the point of view of the person or people involved. Whether we want to try to be more compassionate, change our own mind, or find information that can be used to try to change someone else's beliefs and behaviors, sociology is the ideal tool for unlocking and understanding how other people experience the social world. This reading about parents who chose not to vaccinate their children exemplifies the kinds of insights that sociological research can provide.

Jennifer Reich outlines how parents' decisions about whether and when to vaccinate their children are shaped by their worldview, and in particular an emphasis on the very American ideology of individualism. Arguments and ire directed at parents who choose not to vaccinate their children often assume that they are poorly educated or don't understand the science of how vaccines work. But that is not the case—the vast majority of parents who intentionally forgo some or all of their children's vaccinations are wealthy, white, and well educated. The parents she studied carefully considered the perceived costs and benefits of vaccinations, often with extensive research. What differentiated them from parents who do vaccinate is their perception of the risks involved and their individualistic orientation toward health. They prioritized individual well-being over collective well-being, and often explicitly acknowledged that by not vaccinating their children, they were putting others at risk, but they saw that as their right, and indeed obligation in order to be a good parent.

Near the beginning of this reading, Reich proposes that "disagreements about vaccines raise larger questions. To what degree are we obligated to protect the most vulnerable members of our community? Where are the limitations of our individual liberty?[. . .] Who counts as experts? What do we owe to each other? These questions do not reside on the political left or right. They surround us always, but largely remain unheard." She was writing in 2016 about parents

---

Excerpt from *Calling the Shots: Why Parents Reject Vaccines* by Jennifer A. Reich. New York: New York University Press © 2016.

who choose not to vaccinate their children, but her words are eerily applicable to debates about wearing masks in public and social distancing during the COVID-19 pandemic in 2020, when these questions were no longer unheard, and were decidedly linked to the political spectrum.

As you read, think about how the challenges that public health faces related to vaccines are similar to the challenges of getting people to wear masks, and how much the decisions that individuals make in both these regards are linked to their larger worldview.

Minutes before the phone rang that Sunday evening, Tim was feeling good. His three-year-old daughter, Maggie, who had been diagnosed with leukemia months before, had survived multiple rounds of chemotherapy, lumbar punctures, and surgery to implant her port to make the next two years of treatment easier. Treatment had not been easy, with six hospital admissions, weeks in a local children's hospital, missed holidays, and the pain of the treatment itself. Now she had a three-week break from treatment to stay home with her parents and ten-month-old brother. Tim was excited about what he called the "vacation from chemotherapy." But then the phone rang.

A few days before, Maggie had been at a local hospital with her mother and brother for a lab test. Another patient at the hospital had been infected with measles, and unknowingly exposed those around her to the disease. The patient, a woman in her forties, had been infected by a stranger during a winter trip to Disneyland. As we now know, that outbreak infected about 150 people from twenty states and the District of Columbia, as well as travelers from Mexico and Canada (who subsequently infected more than 150 others in their home countries). Although Maggie had been vaccinated before her cancer diagnosis, her immune system was indisputably compromised; she was also most vulnerable to serious complication. Her baby brother was simply too young to be immunized. The next two weeks would be a process of watching, waiting, and avoiding contact with others—not the "vacation" they had hoped for.

Tim and his wife, Anna, were panicked. "My biggest fear is that I'll lose my child, or that she'll become deaf," Anna explained at the time. "My family has been through enough with cancer. I don't want her to go through anything else." Focusing her frustration on the large number of unvaccinated people implicated in the Disneyland outbreak, Anna imagined for a moment what she would say if she were facing a parent who opted not to vaccinate her children and increased risk to kids like Maggie: "Your children don't live in a little bubble. They live in a big bubble and my children live inside that big bubble with your children. If you don't want to vaccinate your children, fine, but don't take them to Disneyland."

Tim, a pediatrician, went further. Rather than imagining what he would tell a parent who rejects vaccines, he penned an open letter, "To the Parent of the Unvaccinated Child Who Exposed My Family to Measles," in which he expressed his frustration that both of his children were exposed to a disease that had been deemed eradicated from the United States in 2000. Written initially for the blog he keeps about his daughter's care, it was passed along to others by a nurse and subsequently reprinted multiple times, shared more than 1.3 million times on social media, and widely read. Some even felt compelled to reply.

Megan was one. A self-described naturopath, writer, stay-at-home mom, and cofounder and president of a nonprofit organization that focuses "on orphan care and poverty alleviation in Africa," Megan says she has "developed the habit of researching everything from the toothpaste we use to the toilet paper we wipe our butts with." Her blog describes how her information gathering "prompted us to throw out our microwave, ditch the gluten, sugar, milk, pork, and genetically modified foods, burn our medicine cabinet, wear our kids, breastfeed our babies, recycle our trash, up the probiotics, unschool our kids, and rip up the CDC's vaccination schedule."

Speaking directly to Tim, but citing "the creators of the hysteria" and "measles propaganda," Megan described the reasons for her frustration with Tim: "That you do not respect my choices, that you think my unvaccinated child is the only one who threatens yours, and that you would insinuate that my child should be sacrificed on the altar for your child." Calling vaccines artificial immunity that has upset the natural order of disease and naturally occurring immunity, Megan reiterated that she has the right to decide what is best for her children and what risks she and other parents might choose to take:

> When we take our child to a place like Disneyland, or any other public place for that matter (including a hospital), we assume the risk that we might come into contact with a sick person, someone who hasn't washed their hands, a kid who has picked their nose, or rides that have not been properly sanitized between each use.

Megan replied directly to Anna and Tim's insistence that as members of a community, children live in the same large bubbles, retorting, "It is not fair to require that my child get vaccinated for the benefit of yours or to force my child to live in a bubble so that yours doesn't have to."

Other parents shared her view, some more vocally than others. Jack, a cardiologist and father of two unvaccinated children, was among the loudest. Addressing Tim and Anna, he insisted, "It's not my responsibility to inject my child with chemicals in order for [a child like Maggie] to be supposedly healthy. . . . I'm not going to sacrifice the well-being of my child. My child is pure." Jack too challenged claims that vaccines promote health, arguing instead that disease is good for people: "We should be getting measles, mumps, rubella, chickenpox, these are the rights of our children to get it. . . . We do not need to inject chemicals into ourselves and into our children in order to boost our immune system." Also responding specifically to the notion of shared responsibility and individual parental rights, Jack made clear that he is comfortable in his commitment to rejecting vaccines, even if his child were to infect another child who became gravely ill. "It's an unfortunate thing that people die, but people die. I'm not going to put my child at risk to save another child."

The measles outbreak at Disneyland in December 2014 and the subsequent online feuds about the vulnerability of one child and the rights of parents of other children reflect many of the existing tensions about vaccines. As Megan's and Jack's responses illustrate, parents who reject vaccines distrust claims of safety and necessity, believe that disease is natural in a way vaccines are not, and identify their primary role of parents as superseding obligations to others. They also make clear that they are experts on their own children—able to assess and manage risk—and thus uniquely qualified to decide what their children need.

For the past decade, I have followed vaccine refusal from the perspectives of those who distrust vaccines and the corporations that make them, as well as the health providers and policy makers who see them as essential to ensuring community health. In an effort to tell the story of vaccines and explore the tensions between these views, I sought out a variety of key perspectives. I started with parents, and was careful to include those who opted out of vaccines completely and others who consented to select vaccines on a schedule of their own choosing. Children whose parents challenge vaccine recommendations are most likely to be white, have a college-educated mother, and a family income over $75,000. For the most part, this is what the parents in this study look like too. Only about 15 percent of parents in this study are fathers, since children's healthcare decisions are overwhelmingly maternal terrain.

Disagreements about vaccines raise larger questions. To what degree are we obligated to protect the most vulnerable members of our communities? Where are the limitations of our individual liberty? What defines good parenting? What counts as expertise? What do we owe others? These questions do not reside on the political left or right. They surround us always, but largely remain unheard. The parents I studied question, modify, or outright reject vaccines because they see them as unnatural, as tainted by the profit motives of big pharma, as inadequately tested and regulated, or as unnecessary for illness prevention. These parents engage in what we might call individualist parenting, expending immense time and energy strategizing how to keep their children healthy while often ignoring the larger, harder-to-solve questions around them. They tend to focus on the subjects of their own expertise: their own children. In the 1970s, when most of these parents were children, schools required vaccination against seven vaccine-preventable illnesses. By 2014, evidence of vaccination against thirteen vaccine-preventable illnesses became required for kindergarten attendance, with more recommended in adolescence. As the number of recommended vaccines has increased, resulting in more boosters and as many as two dozen shots by age two, even parents who don't reject vaccines altogether have started to question their safety and necessity and seek modifications of the schedule.

Vaccines as Public Health

Vaccines are a cornerstone of U.S. public health policy, which aims to protect the health and well-being of an entire population. Understanding public health requires a keen understanding of the points where individuals have compatible or conflicting interests and needs. One such point is "herd immunity" against infectious disease. When a person receives a vaccination, she has a far greater chance of being protected from that illness—receiving individual benefit—but also helps to protect others in the community who are vulnerable to infection. Some vaccines benefit only the individual, like that for tetanus, which is a disease that is not contagious but results from exposure to a toxin in the environment that causes neurological damage and death and is difficult to treat. However, the majority of required vaccines do not just protect the child who receives inoculation, but also prevents exposure of life-threatening illnesses in the disabled, the aged, the immune-compromised, the infants too young to be vaccinated, and the pregnant women whose fetuses could be devastated by these illnesses, as well as those few individuals who did not gain immunity from a vaccine they received.

The Uneven Landscape of Parental Choice

Public health scholars divide children who have not received all vaccines required for school attendance (but who do not have a medical reason to avoid vaccines) into two groups. On one side, there are the children who are undervaccinated because they lack consistent access to medical care. These children are more likely to be children of color, have a younger mother who is unmarried and does not have a college degree, and live in a household near the poverty line. Children on the other side—those who are unvaccinated because of parental choice—look significantly different. They are more likely to be white, have a mother who is married and college-educated, and to live in a household with an income over $75,000; they also tend to be geographically clustered. What this means is that the choice to opt out of vaccines is almost exclusively made by families with the most resources and represents a fairly privileged parenting practice. These differences reflect broader schisms in how families with different resources have access to choices.

Parents try to consider the possible risks and benefits for their individual children. They make what they understand to be the best choices they can for their children's health, with the information they have. They assess the risk of exposure to the disease and feared adverse reactions. They weigh those against the potential benefits of vaccines, as they understand them. This process of evaluating risk and benefit is an example of what the sociologist Deborah Lupton calls "lifestyle risk discourse," which places responsibility on the individual "to avoid health risks for the sake of his or her own health as well as the greater good of society." The discourse of health promotion and illness avoidance, that is, managing risk to avoid sickness, frames health as an individual pursuit. This focus on the individual undermines the collective nature of vaccine policy, where individuals might absorb some small amount of risk for the good of others. It also reminds consumers that they—and not their physicians or vaccine researchers—are the experts on their own needs, their own risks, and their own children. By closely examining parents' perceptions of risks and benefits, we can better understand their insistence that they hold unique expertise that makes them best qualified to make vaccine choices for their children.

Evaluating Potential Benefits of Vaccines

The sociologist Jacob Heller usefully describes what he calls the "vaccine narrative" in the United States. Noting that a master narrative is "an overarching storyline or sequence of events that anticipates and therefore reinforces our established expectations," Heller explains that, regarding vaccines, Americans have little experience with the diseases vaccines work to prevent and few have technical knowledge to understand how vaccines work, but support for vaccines remains high nonetheless. He argues that the reason for "vaccines' continued public support is that vaccination works; the technical knowledge has been transformed into lay knowledge, something people can grasp without the baggage of scientific jargon and data." Most parents accept that vaccines are necessary, with U.S. vaccine rates remaining around 90 percent for most childhood diseases. These parents most often trust their health provider or have a parent or grandparent or other trusted source that successfully communicates the horrors of infectious disease before vaccines.

For parents who reject vaccine recommendations, the process of considering necessity is more complex and draws on cultural information that challenges the vaccine narrative that vaccines are always intrinsically good. Anyone who questions that narrative by calling vaccine safety, necessity, or beneficence into question, Heller notes, is seen as a "crackpot."

We know from other contexts that for individuals to be motivated to seek health interventions for their own benefit, they must believe that they are susceptible to a particular health problem, that it is serious, that a treatment or medication will reduce the harm of that condition, and that there must be few barriers to accessing the treatment. Those who would seek out health interventions must also find ways that the prescribed treatment fits their lives and matches their goals, and they must also fear a negative outcome should they refuse that intervention. In deciding whether to consent to vaccines, parents engage in a process of evaluating the benefits of vaccines. First, parents consider the likelihood that their children will encounter disease. Second, they assess how badly the children would be affected if they were to become sick. These assessments drive their decisions.

Likelihood and Severity of Disease

In this cost-benefit analysis, parents weigh minute risks of vaccines against the small risks of infection of diseases that are rarely seen in the United States. For example, parents are often aware that wild-virus polio has not been seen in the United States since 1979 and in the Western Hemisphere since 1991. Citing this information, they suggest that public policy's insistence on subjecting young children to a vaccine against a disease they are unlikely to encounter is unreasonable and introduces potential harm to their children unnecessarily.

Parents also understand the relative benefit of vaccination in terms of the seriousness of the disease the vaccine prevents. They often dismiss vaccines for diseases that they understand to be minor. Anna Chase, a mother of two, spends a great deal of time considering vaccines. She is a former public health worker and now a part-time acupuncturist, and as such, she considers the meanings of health deeply.

Anna laboriously parses out the logic of different vaccines. She considers how severe infection would be for her children should they become ill, and how that would vary depending on her children's age and gender. With confidence in her own research, she defines specific strategies for her children, rather than the approach to disease prevention universally recommended by the healthcare community. She explains,

> The vaccines that I think make sense are tetanus. Diphtheria is kind of a nasty thing to get; totally believe in polio. I think that

> for boys it's probably better that they, you know, either get the mumps when they're little or if they don't get it when they're little then they have it before they're a teenager, because if they get it then they're at risk of sterilization. German measles, don't really care about. Regular measles for boys, I don't care about. Girls, if I had a girl, I'd want her to have the measles when she's little, or if not, to have the vaccine by the time she's a teen, because if she got it when she was pregnant, it'd be very sort of life-threatening to her fetus. So measles I think for girls makes sense.

By managing vaccine choices in a "cafeteria" fashion, Anna articulates a strategy that illustrates parents' efforts to separate out the risk of disease and potential benefit of vaccines as they vary depending on the individual child and include the variable long-term effects of exposure, perceived probability of exposure, and severity of the disease. In this way, risk and benefit remain situated in the individual, and might shift as her children grow. Because risk lies in the body, boys don't need to be vaccinated against diseases that can cause, for example, fetal demise, even as they may choose to be involved with women who could be pregnant or might encounter women in their neighborhoods or communities as they grow. Rather, Anna's children are the center of her assessment. She considers the reproductive capabilities of her children, but not others they may encounter.

Landscapes of Risk and Choice: Katie Reynolds

Thus far, I have shown how parents weigh risk and benefits of disease and vaccines and make individual decisions about vaccines for each of their children. Often, critics of those who opt out of vaccines portray parents as either wholly disapproving of vaccines or as underestimating the risks of diseases. The choice not to vaccinate is seen in isolation from the other strategies parents adopt. I find instead that the vaccine choice is one choice among a broad landscape of other choices parents make: about schools, religion, nutrition, neighborhood, youth sports, or discipline in the broader context of their children's lives. In the following section, I take one parent's explanation of her anxiety about vaccines to illustrate the many factors at play as parents strategize vaccine choices. Katie is a forty-one-year-old mother of two. Her son, Julian, is five years old and in kindergarten and her daughter, Maya, is two years old and home with her full-time. Katie has a master's degree in economics and when she could not find a job in her field, became a freelance financial writer. Katie recalls questioning vaccines when her son was due for his first round:

> I'm one of those people who researches everything to death, and reads every book I can read, so it was like the night before he was getting his first round of immunizations and I [felt like] I made the decision to give him—I mean, I just felt like I had made a lot of decisions without really researching them.

Being Good Parents

Much of the culture of individualist parenting demands that parents maintain vigilance in considering their children's needs and advocating for them with institutions. This has in many ways become the cornerstone of concerted cultivation, where investing in children's well-being demands intense resources to ensure that children have optimal outcomes. The parents in this study take these duties to heart. They conduct research, share information on listservs and in online forums with other parents, discuss their children's care with friends and providers, and consider the ways their children are unique.

As parents weigh risk and make vaccine choices, they do so in ways that illustrate how the mandates of public health and informed consent lie in tension. The narrative that vaccines are beneficent and should be accepted without question undermines the tenets of informed consent, which require providers to communicate potential risk and benefit so patients can decide whether and when they want an intervention. Although public health officials who develop vaccine schedules would disagree with the process that leads these parents to opt out, it is clear that parents thoughtfully consider the meanings of each vaccine, even if their understandings of science, risk, and benefit are different from expert views. In understanding risk and benefit, parents must believe that the risk of illness is significant and that vaccinating will mitigate that risk. Healthcare providers and policymakers might identify the statistical likelihood of infection, or of a significant injury from vaccination, but in order to choose to vaccinate, parents must perceive that those risks apply to their own children and that the vaccine will prevent those specific and identifiable risks while not causing other harm to their vulnerable children.

Some of these parents believe that vaccines work in general but believe that they are unnecessary or too risky; others do not accept that they are necessary and effective for their children at all. What is common to all of the parents in this study is the view of their children as individuals with unique bodies, immune systems, vulnerabilities, and lifestyles that predict different vaccine needs for their own health. In contrast to public health, which looks at immunity and efficacy at a population level, these parents evaluate their own children's lifestyle, diet, nutrition, social networks, and health to evaluate vaccines and then reject or accept them accordingly.

Conclusion: What Do We Owe Each Other?

Children who do not receive all their vaccines on the schedule set by federal advisory groups pose a challenge for public health systems. Although this book examines parents who deliberately reject or delay vaccines for their children, the most common reason that children are not fully vaccinated nationally is not vaccine refusal, but missed appointments or lack of access.

One pediatrician describes her publicly insured patients who are undervaccinated: "They might not know the schedule and not know when to come in. Or their [child] has been hospitalized forever so they missed it, or that they're just going—for families who have lots of social issues, or they can't afford to make it here travel-wise." These children remain at increased risk of infection, have higher rates of in-patient admission to hospitals when they become sick—even more than children who are unvaccinated by choice—and may have families least able to afford the time needed to care for sick children.

The parents in this book are not these parents. The parents in this book are the ones who have resources, who never forget about vaccinations because they devote a great deal of time and resources to thinking about them. Yet the children whose parents intentionally refuse vaccinations live in the same communities as the larger group of children who lack access or fall behind because of parental limitations in time, money, access, or information. The undervaccinated, rather than the unvaccinated by choice, are already most vulnerable to health challenges and perhaps become even more so when they share grocery stores, malls, parks, community spaces, or schools with an increasing number of unimmunized children. These different children are inevitably connected as members of communities share risk of disease as well as benefits of immunization, even in ways that are not always visible.

Free Choice and Free-Riding

Parents who refuse vaccines perceive risk to their own children to be measurable and manageable, which makes claims that their children increase risk to other children seem illogical. Despite public claims that an outbreak is only "a plane ride away" as vaccine rates drop below herd immunity levels, the parents in this study continue to see vaccines as an individual choice. One mother insists, "If those kids that are vaccinated are truly protected, what chance—why would you be threatened by my child who is not vaccinated?"

This kind of response—that if you think vaccines work and vaccinate your own children, then unvaccinated children pose no threat—is ubiquitous among parents who reject the logic of public health and instead see vaccines as a technology each parent can freely choose or reject. This view ignores the reality that some children are unvaccinated because they lack access, are medically fragile, or are too young. It also denies our interdependence.

Also hidden is the reality that children who are unvaccinated by choice benefit from others' immunity. Public health officials refer to the "free-rider" phenomenon as one that allows a portion of children to reject vaccines without risk of infection because they are essentially protected by the herd—the large segment of the population that is vaccinated. Parents who opt out are often confronted by those who disapprove of them, who erroneously assume that they are unaware of their role as free-riders, but would assume greater shared responsibility if only they knew. In fact, many of the parents I spoke with (although not all) are aware of their families' status as free-riders, but insist that their responsibility to their own children takes precedence.

Some are upset by the accusations that their children are free-riders, claims that violate their sense of themselves as good people. Consistently, that guilt is assuaged by a belief that they are protecting their children. One mother explains, "I know that if nobody had their children vaccinated, there would be polio and there would be diphtheria and there would be everything else, and I recognize that, but at the same time I feel like my children, for whatever reason, [would] have some kind of adverse reaction to vaccines."

Many parents acknowledge that the ability to opt out is a luxury, and recognize that it would be riskier to do so if everyone made the same choice. Yet concern for their children outweighs concerns for herd immunity. One mother explains how she weighed free-riding against shared responsibility:

> I think that ultimately my husband and I felt like we were making a little bit of an elitist decision, meaning that we're banking on the fact that most of the rest of the country is vaccinated. . . . If you believe that there is a potential adverse effect of vaccinations, then you're riding off the fact that everybody else is exposing their kid to those potential adverse effects. So your kid no longer really is at risk. . . . That was the most compelling of the counterarguments we heard, for sure.

There must be a balance between efforts to promote population health, from which we all benefit, and support for the concepts of consent, bodily integrity, and individual choice in healthcare. These issues are complex and representative of a wide array of public health issues, not just vaccines. Yet they are central to understanding when and how we assume risk to support the most vulnerable among us. What do we owe each other? Our privilege to participate in civil society is arguably inextricably linked to our obligation to protect that community, even at some personal potential cost. Vaccine resistance then represents an individual sense of entitlement to use public resources without shared responsibility to others. As parents claim individual expertise and the right to make their own choices, they do so while continuing to claim that their children are entitled to public resources like publicly funded education or use of public spaces like parks, while opting out of public obligation. At heart, the willingness to be free riders while demanding access to community resources may be one reason why parents who opt out experience high levels of vitriol and disapproval from others. Expecting resources without contributing to community health represents a certain breach of responsibility. One vaccine policy researcher and pediatrician suggests that there is social significance in these individual choices and supports parents' rights to exercise them. However, she also argues that children who opt out of community health programs like vaccination are not entitled to community participation, including public schools:

> This is a social contract. There are things provided to you and things you have to do. I don't know where that got lost. I think that's a very important thing to understand, whether these people don't perceive or how they don't perceive it applies to them, particularly vis-à-vis public school. Why should kids who are unimmunized be in public school? I have a problem with that. I actually don't have a problem with saying, "You know what? If you're not immunized, you're not going to be in public school. You can homeschool and we'll help you." To me, that's a reasonable statement. Why are you allowed to put other people's kids at risk? I think that it's a complicated situation, but I actually think the whole idea of the social contract is being lost.

The rhetoric of a social contract was common, but not without contention. As one opponent of vaccines announced to a cheering audience of like-minded people at a national meeting in opposition to vaccine mandates, "I don't remember signing a contract!"

Outside the vaccine context, there are few places where our social contract with each other is debated so regularly and openly. We seldom hear reference to social contract when discussing school funding, votes on bonds, taxes, traffic safety, public assistance, fracking, social security, or environmental policy. Even the significant public health programs that limit smoking in community spaces are more often framed as efforts to protect individual rights, rather than an expression of our communal investment in one another's well-being. Yet proponents of vaccines on all sides and ideologies insist we have a social contract that vaccine refusers violate. Even the libertarian-leaning Cato Institute references our social contract:

> There is no reason to be vaccinated against non-communicable diseases if you don't want to. If you believe that your small chance of getting tetanus isn't worth the (very, very) much smaller risk of crippling Guillain-Barré syndrome after the vaccination, that's your business. But vaccination for communicable diseases is part of a social contract that maintains civil society with a general ethic that no one has the right to harm someone without serious provocation. The fact that someone else may avoid vaccination gives no license to avoidably infect that person, however foolhardy he or she might be.

Parents most certainly should advocate for their children, but taking advantage of opportunities involves obligations to invest in others' children too, obligations that are arguably higher for those who have the best access to high-quality food, healthcare, schools, housing, and resources. Vaccines highlight the interplay between community risk and benefit, even as these same extensions of a social contract exist more broadly.

DISCUSSION QUESTIONS

1. Who did you find yourself siding with in the opening story about Tim's open letter to parents who don't vaccinate and Megan's response to him? Did your opinion of either parent change as you read the rest of the article?
2. What is individualistic parenting? How is it related to the concept of *concerted cultivation* from reading 22, "Unequal Childhoods"?
3. What is the vaccine narrative?
4. What groups are at risk from unvaccinated children? How does the refusal to vaccinate perpetuate health inequalities related to social class?
5. Do you get a flu vaccine each yet? Why or why not? If you don't, are your reasons similar to or different from those of the parents interviewed in this

research? If you do, is your motivation primarily to protect yourself or others? Did this reading make you feel differently about your decision?

6. Author Jennifer Reich shares more details about why parents don't vaccinate their children and the social consequences of that decision in the TEDx Talk "What I learned from parents who don't vaccinate their kids," available at https://www.youtube.com/watch?v=CTj_xoCuhPU from 2020. What is the take-home message from her talk, and how can it help us think about the challenges public health official face in getting sufficient numbers of Americans vaccinated for COVID-19 to achieve herd immunity?

READING 13

American Policing and the Danger Imperative

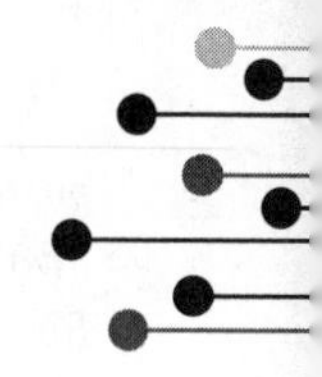

Michael Sierra-Arévalo

[Warning: This reading continues descriptions of violence and death]

The Black Lives Matter movement was well established in America's cultural landscape when George Floyd, an unarmed African American man, was killed by police officer Derek Chauvin during an arrest for allegedly passing a counterfeit $20 bill in May 2020. After a video of Chauvin kneeling on Floyd's neck for almost eight minutes while Floyd pleaded that he couldn't breathe went viral, there were widespread protests against police brutality across the country and calls to radically cut police budgets and reallocate resources to community-based organizations, social workers, and mental health professionals among others (sometimes referred to as "defunding" the police.) As the protests continued in June and July 2020, police began clashing with largely peaceful protestors in increasingly violent fashion. In Portland, Oregon, mothers wearing bike helmets formed a self-proclaimed "Wall of Moms" to protect protestors from police and federal agents, and protestors routinely appeared on the news and social media to describe being assaulted, pepper sprayed, shot at, shoved, and otherwise physically harmed by police while breaking no law and peacefully exercising their right to free speech.

In June 2020, two police officers who were part of the Buffalo, New York, Police Department's Emergency Response Team shoved an unarmed 75-year-old man to the ground as he attempted to talk to one of the officers. The man, peace activist Martin Gugino, lay bleeding from his head on the concrete. As another officer moved toward Gugino to check on him, he was pulled back by others

---

Excerpts from Sierra-Arévalo, M. (2021, Forthcoming). American Policing and the Danger Imperative. *Law & Society* Review 55(1). URL: https://osf.io/preprints/socarxiv/yrw65/

Acknowledgments: This project was supported by the Institution for Social and Policy Studies, the Justice Collaboratory at the Yale Law School, and the Macarthur Foundation (15-108050-000-USP). The author would like to thank Andrew Papachristos, Tracey Meares, Joscha Legewie, Frederick Wherry, Joshua Page, Jooyoung Lee, Nicholas Occhiuto, Tony Cheng, Colleen Berryessa, participants at workshops in the Yale Department of Sociology, the Deconstructing Ferguson Working Group, and three anonymous reviewers for their generous insights and comments. My thanks as well to the officers of the EPD, WPD, and SPD, without whom this research would not have been possible.

on the team. After video of the incident went viral, the two officers directly involved in the incident were suspended, and all 57 members of the Emergency Response Team resigned in protest in a show of support for the two officers who shoved Gugino.

Police brutality such as that described above is often explained at an individual and psychological level. Individual officers must be racist, violence-prone, trigger happy, or callous human beings or some combination thereof. Certainly some police are, but many more are not. The analogy of police who commit brutality as "bad apples" captures the psychological and individual level thinking that is most commonly used to explain such behavior. But the bad apple approach doesn't explain why those bad apples are not held accountable for their behavior by the "good" apples. A better analogy and a more sociological approach to the problem would be to talk about bad orchards. What are the social and cultural conditions that "grow" police who commit violence against the citizens they are supposed to protect? And how do those same social and cultural conditions lead to bystanders and others who know about brutality to not just turn a blind eye, but to support those who commit violent acts against citizens?

In this article, sociologist Michael Sierra-Arévalo answers these precise questions as he turns a sociological eye on police departments by doing participant observations and interviews with police officers from three urban police departments across the country. He finds that through their training in the police academy and on the job, officers learn what he calls the danger imperative—the idea that no matter what type of interaction they are having while on the job, they are always in danger of being killed. As he points out, policing is a dangerous occupation, but it is nowhere near as dangerous as police perceive it to be and it is notably safer as an occupation than it was 50 years. As Ruth Simpson pointed out in Reading 11 on the social construction of danger, what we perceive to be dangerous and how much danger we are actually in tend to be quite far apart, and policing is no exception.

As you read about the training scenarios officers go through and the various reminders of the potential dangers they face, think about how this type of socialization and the culture it creates can help explain not just why a police officer might kill an unarmed citizen, but why other officers and those in charge of departments are so loathe to admit and punish those who make such mistakes.

Introduction

In testimony to the President's Task Force on 21st Century Policing, the President of the Fraternal Order of Police warned, "now more than ever, we see our officers in the cross-hairs of these criminals" (Canterbury 2015). However, trends in violence against police suggest that policing is growing *safer* over time. Felonious officer deaths have decreased for half a century (White, Dario, and Shjarback 2019) and recent analyses find no significant change in patterns of fatal or non-fatal assault on police officers (Maguire, Nix, and Campbell 2017; Shjarback and Maguire 2019; Sierra-Arévalo and Nix 2020). Despite this measurable decrease in line-of-duty death and injury over the past half century, officers' concern with the mortal danger of their work continues to shape police socialization, culture, and practice (Ingram, Terrill, and Paoline 2018; Sierra-Arévalo 2019b). The understanding of policing as profoundly dangerous, in turn, encourages behaviors that damage the legitimacy of police, harm the public, and perpetuate inequalities in the criminal legal system.

Existing research, however, does little to elucidate the consequences of policing's preoccupation with danger beyond its deleterious effects on the targets of coercive control. Though a large and ever-growing body of research documents inequalities in policing and its negative effects on marginalized communities (Armenta 2017; Rios 2011; Stuart 2016), there is scarce consideration of how police culture and its related behaviors can also lead to unexpected, damaging consequences for police officers themselves. This analytic exclusion of officers likely underestimates the total costs of behavior oriented by the assumption of constant danger and frustrates consideration of how culturally-mediated behavior aimed at keeping officers safe can, in fact, lead to officer injuries and deaths.

To elucidate the origins of such safety-enhancing behaviors and their often unseen negative externalities, I leverage insights from research on police, culture, organizations, and the social construction of risk to advance the concept of the *danger imperative*—a cultural frame that emphasizes violence and the need to provide for officer safety. Drawing on ethnographic observations and interviews with officers in three urban police departments in the United States, I provide an empirical account of officers' formal and informal socialization into the danger imperative and how experience mediated through this frame encourages both policy-compliant and policy-deviant behaviors to ensure officer safety. I then highlight policy-deviant behaviors like unauthorized high-speed driving with neither emergency lights nor seatbelts which, though justified as necessary to ensure officer safety, contribute to the injury and death of police officers in high-speed car crashes. Following this analysis of the unintended and counterproductive behaviors shaped by the danger imperative, I consider the broader implications of policing's focus on officer safety for police and the public. Beyond the harm to citizens and police officers resulting from vehicle crashes, I consider how seemingly mundane policy deviant behaviors are a reflection of assumptions within police culture that also undergird policing practices that damage public wellbeing and perpetuate broader inequalities in the U.S. criminal legal system.

Policing, Danger, and Deviance

Recognizing the marked historical changes in the structure and implementation of police work (Manning 2011), policing is still work that pits "ordinary men" against the "extraordinary strains...and threats" posed by suspects who may violently resist arrest by police (Westley 1970:xvii).[1] Though policing ranks well below logging, mining, and construction in terms of worker deaths and death rates (Bureau of Labor Statistics 2014), "policing is unique in that injury and death come not just from accidents, but from job performance" (Moskos 2009:1). Unlike the miner claimed by a tunnel collapse or the construction worker slain in a fall from a roof, officers contend with the extraordinary threat posed by violent assailants.

Given the centrality of crime and potentially dangerous suspects to the professional mandate of police (Manning 1978), it is unsurprising that officers' concern with violence pervades the policing literature, as does the emphasis on officer safety enshrined in decades of police procedure, policy, and law (Stoughton 2014b). Scholars for over half a century have noted the emphasis placed by police on the danger of their work and the role of danger in shaping police training, how officers interact with one another, and how they interact with the public (Skolnick 2011 [1966]; Van Maanen 1978b; Westley 1970). More recent scholarship confirms that danger continues to be a "ubiquitous cultural theme" in policing (Crank 2014:160), and that the necessity of ensuring officer safety at all times is a pervasive philosophy "reinforced at all levels of the police organization" (Moskos 2009:22). Today, the danger of police work continues to occupy a "prominent position within [the] occupational consciousness" of police officers (Loftus 2010:13).

The emphasis on violence and the danger of patrol is disseminated to officers though formal and informal mechanisms within the police department. In the police academy, defensive tactics and weapons training make up the largest part of academy curricula (Reaves 2015), and these lessons are supplemented with "war stories" from senior officers about the danger recruits will face (Van Maanen 1978a:297–98). The possibility—even inevitability—of violence is further emphasized in field training. This field training, in addition to assigning experienced field training officers (FTOs) to guide rookie officers, is a mechanism for the transmission of informal norms and practices that are necessary to reconcile inflexible regulation with the uncertainty and limited resources that officers encounter on patrol (Engelson 1999). Outside academy and field training, officers' broader occupational environment is replete with symbols and cultural artifacts that perpetuate the cultural salience of danger in police work. Rare but devastating line-of-duty deaths are commemorated through cultural artifacts like memorial walls, tattoos, and funeral pamphlets, amplifying the danger of policing across time and space (Sierra-Arévalo 2019b).

Together, these various facets of police socialization propagate the prominence of danger in police culture, in turn, shaping officers' understanding and practice of their work. Danger is a key driver of the loyalty and cohesion at the core of policing's esprit de corps, yielding the unwavering support between officers needed to ensure one another's safety on patrol (Bittner 1970:63). This intragroup solidarity is part of the "working personality" of police and structures how police interact with the public, fostering suspicion of community members (Skolnick 2011 [1966]), and support for aggressive enforcement tactics associated with "traditional" police culture (Ingram et al. 2018). Unfortunately, though solidarity can serve protective functions in the face of danger, it is also implicated in decidedly problematic phenomena like the "blue wall" or "code of silence" that hampers police accountability and helps officers avoid punishment for wrongful acts (Skolnick 2002). What's more, strong in-group ties and a collective emphasis on danger can manifest in aggressive, enforcement-centric practices that characterize a "warrior" approach to policing linked to deviant behaviors ranging from rudeness to the use of excessive and illegal force (Ouellet et al. 2019; Skolnick and Fyfe 1994; Stoughton 2014a). The persistence of such damaging police deviance are part and parcel of departmental socialization designed to keep officers alive.[2]

However, narrowing analytic attention to these outward-facing acts of police deviance restricts our understanding of danger's effect on police practice to behaviors whose negative consequences directly affect public well-being. As a result, how the foundational preoccupation with violence might mute attention to other dangers in officers' occupational environment is unexplored by existing research on danger and police behavior. To better understand how police officers come to focus on and protect against particular dangers, as well as the inadvertent and even counterproductive consequences of supposedly safety-enhancing strategies, research on police, danger, and culture must be brought into conversation with research on the perception and construction of risk.

Risk, the Collective Construction of Danger, and Normalized Deviance

Despite my preference for the term "danger" up to this point, terminological clarity between "danger" and the more general term "risk" is warranted. There is no such field as "danger studies" but instead a constellation of managerially-oriented fields encompassing risk assessment, management, and analysis. These fields, largely dominated by economists, define risk with an array of probabilistic curves of potential gains and losses (see discussion by Short 1984). In this quantified paradigm, human behavior and decision made under conditions of "risk" boil down to a balancing act of probability and potential harm.

What is missed in the world of probabilistic risk is that people do not dread or avoid probabilities; people fear *things* and what those *things* may cause. As Desmond (2006) discusses in his study of wildland firefighting, prior accounts of risk and individual risk-taking ignore the lived, visceral nature of decisions made when confronting imminent harm. Just as probabilities matter little to a firefighter trying to survive amidst billowing smoke and burning trees, the statistical rarity of death is immaterial to a police officer who is taught to "treat every individual they interact with as an armed threat and every situation as a deadly force encounter in the making" (Stoughton 2014a:228). In this spirit, I use "danger" to capture the individuals and their actions that stand to do physical harm to officers—the suspects and violence at the core of policing's professional mandate.

This operationalization of danger is useful for considering how culture—the norms, values, and patterned action of individuals embedded in groups—influences collective understanding of what constitutes a threat and appropriate strategies for addressing it. Which dangers are to be confronted, ignored, or avoided (and how to do so) does not exist a priori and is instead shaped by a group's environment. Firefighters learn and practice the use of their bodies and axes to fight roaring flame; police officers socialized to survive their shift practice perpetual suspicion attuned to "signs indicating a potential for violence and lawbreaking" (Skolnick 2011:41 [1966]). In short, the interplay of culture and context influences group members' perception, their collective definition of what defines danger, and subsequent action of group members aimed at protecting themselves and the group from harm (Douglas and Wildavsky 1983).

For police, the nexus of culture and occupational context is also embedded within the organizational environment of the police department. As with organizations more broadly, collectively-defined understandings of danger among police are influenced by organizational norms and values that set bounds for what is a reasonable solution to an organizational problem (DiMaggio and Powell 1983; Vaughan 1996). As police address issues ranging from low-level misdemeanors to violent crimes, they must negotiate the tension between their need to keep themselves safe from violence and the organizational constraints of limited time, large call loads, and departmental policy (Lipsky 1980). Officers' shared conceptions of danger, the harsh realities of the street, and the demands of the police organization engender perceptual and behavioral strategies that officers believe allow them to meet the cultural, occupational, and organizational requirements of their work (Van Maanen and Barley 1984).

However, police officers balancing these varied demands amidst conditions of uncertainty will deviate from organizational rules and engage in "normalized deviance" to solve a collectively-defined problem (Vaughan

1996). The threat of violence is one such problem that frustrates adherence to departmental policies:

> Danger typically yields self-defensive conduct, conduct that must strain to impulsive because danger arouses fear and anxiety. [...] As a result, procedural requirements take on a "frilly" character, or at least tend to be reduced to a secondary position in the face of circumstances seen as threatening (Skolnick 2011:62 [1966]).

Normalized deviance aimed at solving the exigencies of the moment, like all individual action, comes with downstream consequences often unforeseen by individuals whose decisions are a response to problems "located in one context of time and space" (Giddens 1986:14). As a result, both sanctioned and deviant behavior focused on addressing a specific danger necessarily ignore others and leave individuals imperfectly protected from the full range of environmental dangers (Kasperson et al. 1988). And though prior research shows that officers alter their behavior in response to the threat of potential violence, research on police officers' normalized deviance and their behavioral responses to danger does not consider how normalized police deviance, in addition to breaking organizational rules, might unintentionally expose officers to danger other than that posed by violent individuals.

Conceptualizing the Danger Imperative

To address this gap in our understanding of danger and its effects on police behavior, there is need for a concept flexible enough to account for the danger on which officers focus their attention and action, that which is ignored or minimized, and the unintended consequences of these behaviors. The cultural frame, defined as a lens through which individual experience is filtered to "highlight certain aspects and hide or block others" (Lamont and Small 2008:80), provides such flexibility. I propose that police officers employ such a frame—what I term the *danger imperative*—that emphasizes potential violence and the need to provide for officer safety at all times. Unlike past research that centers on officers' use of cognitive categories or schemas to differentiate potentially lethal threats from harmless civilians or run-of-the-mill "asshole[s]" (Skolnick 2011 [1966]; Van Maanen 1978b), the danger imperative frame provides analytic leverage for understanding how officers are socialized to practice their work as dangerous in particular ways and not in others.

Though a cultural frame does not cause behavior, it filters perception as to make certain behaviors more or less likely given a set of social facts (Lamont and Small 2008). For police officers, the danger imperative's emphasis on violence mediates perception in a way that encourages particular safety-enhancing behaviors, (re)constructing an organizational culture and lived experience that highlight the mortal peril faced by officers on patrol. As officers engage in behaviors tailored to protect them from violence, their behaviors are observed, learned, and echoed by other officers socialized into shared appreciation for the need to ensure officer safety. Officers who perceive their world through the danger imperative are thus more likely to orient their attention and action to address violence rather than other environmental dangers, increasing exposure to these unmitigated threats.

In addition to skewing officers' attention toward violence and away from other dangers, perception mediated through the danger imperative can encourage individual behavior that conflicts with organizational rules. Similar to the adaptive use of violence to ensure personal safety in communities often distrustful of police (Anderson 1999; Kirk and Papachristos 2011), perception that highlights the threat of violence can normalize deviant behavior seen as necessary to survive the "collectively constructed cultural reality" of dangerous police work (Vaughan 1996:65). Viewing their occupational environment through the danger imperative, officers participate in and reproduce the cultural reality of work that can devolve into violence at any moment. In turn, deviant rule-breaking is relabeled as a necessary police practice that allows officers to navigate the constraints of their work and the police organization.

Field Sites and Fieldwork

Ethnographic observations and interviews were gathered across three urban police departments in the United States. Table 1 provides descriptive information on the police departments in Elmont (EPD), West River (WPD), and Sunshine (SPD).[3] The three departments included in this study are located in unique regions of the U.S. Elmont is a small city of less than 150,000 along the eastern seaboard, West River is home to some 400,000 on the west coast, and Sunshine is a city of approximately 500,000 in the arid Southwest. Although these departments vary in terms of size, they are all within the top 1 percent of local police departments in the United States by number of sworn, full-time officers they employ: the Elmont Police Department has approximately 500 sworn officers, the West River Police Department close to 700, and the Sunshine Police Department has nearly 900. All three departments are overwhelmingly male, reflecting the gender imbalance of policing in the U.S. writ large (FBI 2019b). Finally, these departments differ in their racial and ethnic makeup, with West River being the most diverse department and Sunshine being the least diverse of the three.[4]

Table 1 Field Site Characteristics							
Site	Region	Officers	% White	% Black	% Latino	% Asian	% Female
Elmont	Northeast	500	50	25	20	.5	15
West River	West	700	40	15	25	15	12
Sunshine	Southwest	900	70	2	25	2	15

Ethnographic observations and interviews were predominantly gathered in the course of "ride-alongs" in which I accompanied officers on patrol. Following the example of recent sociolegal scholarship (Hureau and Braga 2018; Sierra-Arévalo 2019a, 2019b; Stuart 2016), this study also collected "ethnographic interviews" that follow the style of an "informal conversation [...] infused with ethnographic elements" (Hureau and Braga 2018:520; Spradley 1979). These ethnographic interviews were recorded via smartphone or audio recorder with participant consent and subsequently transcribed. In contrast to more formal interview methods with a pre-determined protocol, this interview method allows for the content of interviews to be molded to the unique positionality or experiences of an individual and their immediate context. This fluid style of ethnographic interview is especially useful for studying police as they allow the researcher the flexibility to engage in informal conversations and build rapport, a decided advantage given police officers' weariness of outsiders (Rojek, Smith, and Alpert 2012).

The following presentation of results weaves observations and interactions recorded in field notes with audio recorded interviews. Following the example of other ethnographic work that combines similar data (Contreras 2012; Sierra-Arévalo 2019a, 2019b), I denote interactions and conversations recorded in field notes with the use of italics and leave data from interview transcripts in plain text.

Formal Socialization and Policy-Compliant Behaviors

Formal, organizationally-mandated training is an important mechanism for the socialization of police officers. For recruits, the police academy is their official introduction to the culture, regulations, and practice of policing. Following graduation and being "cut loose" on the street, periodic in-service training provides officers a refresher on underlying assumptions of dangerous police work and the tangible skills officers can (and should) deploy to stay safe on patrol. Such tactics comply with department policies that set the bounds for organizationally-approved strategies to ensure officer safety.

Training Danger

Nowhere is the role of formal training in officers' socialization into the danger imperative clearer than in use-of-force training. During Sunshine in-service training, I observed officers go through scenarios in the PRISim judgement and use-of-force simulator, a "shoot-don't-shoot" simulation system that projects pre-recorded footage of call-for-service scenarios that range from a suspicious person to an armed hostage taker. Each scenario has multiple "branches" that can be selected by a training officer to dynamically alter scenarios that, per the PRISim's manufacturer, expose officers to the "judgement calls, indecision, sudden fear, partial understanding, blind side surprise and eye-blink response [...] that condition[] the trainee for survival" (Cubic Defence UK 2019).

I observed Officer Stuart (SPD) take part in one scenario that was controlled by Officer Baker, the academy training instructor in charge of administering PRISim training. In the scenario, Officer Stuart arrived on scene to a landlord-tenant dispute between two men outside a one-story house. Raising his voice over the argument concerning rent, Stuart told both men to calm down and then instructed the tenant at the bottom of the steps to come with him and step away from the porch. As Stuart continued to call to the tenant, the cowboy-booted landlord barked, "*Deal with this guy, because if you don't deal with him I will!*" The landlord stormed back into the house and Stuart commanded him to come back out immediately. A few moments later the man reappeared on the porch, only this time carrying a shotgun. The tenant fled at the sight of the weapon and Stuart immediately unholstered his pistol and took aim at the landlord, yelling, "*Drop the gun!*" Less than two seconds later and without further command, Stuart fired several shots that struck the landlord.

The image on the screen froze, two blue dots showing where Stuart's infra-red pistol shots landed and where bullet holes would've blossomed had he been firing his department-issued Glock. I asked Officer Stuart what he was thinking when he chose to shoot:

> *He made the choice to go back in and back out with a gun. Him walking out with a gun is already a threat. I gave him a verbal command to drop it, he didn't, and at that point I would fear for my life.*

Officer Baker, who had been in control of the PRISim scenario's branches, concurred with Stuart's explanation and viewed his decision to use lethal force as a "*reasonable*" (i.e. legal) response. This assessment was especially notable given that Baker, unbeknownst to Officer Stuart, had already selected a branch in which the landlord would *not* raise his weapon and would, instead, surrender and place his shotgun on the ground. Baker explained:

> *I don't have a real problem with that [shooting]. The idea on this scenario is that the guy doesn't pick the gun up at you, but then again, who walks in when two cops are standing out there, grabs a shotgun, and walks back out again? With a gun?*

Though it was not the one selected, the other scenario branch—in which the landlord *does* raise his weapon—represents a potential outcome that officers must plan for and safeguard against at all times. That the landlord did not raise his weapon does not change that he *could* have raised it and fired at any moment. In Baker's eyes, this deadly possibility further justified Stuart's decision to use lethal force.

> *[The scenario] can go two different ways. When he pulls the shotgun up, how long does it take? Not even a half a second. It's about a quarter to a half a second for him to go from that position to getting that shotgun downrange ... I won't critique that shot. That was reasonable.*

Officers also learn to appreciate the deadly stakes of their work in training not explicitly geared towards the use of force, such as in training scenarios that use academy instructors to play drivers or suspects with whom trainees interact. After a 10-hour shift in late-July, I met Officers Alonzo and Diggler (SPD) for some Saturday night beers. I mentioned a video I had seen in which a South Carolina State Trooper shot an unarmed, Black motorist who leaned into his car to retrieve his driver's license. Officer Diggler, an academy instructor, suggested that this seeming overreaction is tied to academy training that teaches recruits that "*Everybody wants to murder you.*"[5]

He described one such training scenario in which he played the driver of a vehicle that contained a "*sims gun*" (simulation pistol) in plain view. Though ostensibly designed as a simple car stop, the scenario's deeper goal is to teach trainees to be aware of the contents of all vehicles they stop, to address the presence of weapons, and the costs of not doing so. As Diggler explained, "*If [the trainee] doesn't see [the gun] you kill the cop... if he doesn't see the gun, when he walks back to his car you get out and you fucking murder him. . . . But the problem is that you put them into that mindset.*" Alonzo, seated next to me, distilled this mindset concisely: if you do not heed your training and plan for violence, "*You're gonna die.*"

Virtual and real-world simulations teach officers to view their work through a lens that emphasizes the possibility of violence, be it in a confrontation with an armed suspect or in the course of a routine traffic stop. Though in a controlled environment, such training is vital to a socialization process that inculcates and perpetuates collective understanding of the unpredictable danger of patrol. Interpreting their work through the frame of the danger imperative, officers understand that survival on the street demands their assiduous preoccupation with violence and constant consideration of the worst possible outcome of interactions with the public.

Video and Vicarious Danger

Formal socialization into the danger imperative also uses body or dashboard camera video of real-life fights, shootings, and car stops "gone bad." As one EPD officer explained, these videos are intentionally graphic, painting a grim picture for recruits:

> *We see a lot of videos of officers dying, officers calling out for help. Their mic is keyed in and we're hearing their last breaths, their last words. It hits home.*

On a bitterly cold graveyard shift in mid-January, Officer Michaelson (EPD) had a similar explanation for the videos he was shown in the academy.

> *They show a bunch of videos of stops—dash cams, body cameras—to show you how things can go wrong really quickly. They show you videos to…I don't know…I guess to show you not to make any assumptions. To not let your guard down.*

He provided a detailed description of a dashcam video of a traffic-stop he was shown years ago:

> *… it's a state trooper or a sheriff, I don't remember. But the guy gets out of his car, he's dancing in the middle of the street telling the officer to shoot him, and then he gets up in the officer's face screaming at him. If you get up in my face like that, being aggressive, I'm going hands on. But this officer didn't and the suspect goes back to his car and starts loading a rifle. The whole time the officer is screaming at him to stop, to get down, but the guy won't listen. Then he comes back with a rifle out, the officer is telling him to put it down, and then the guy starts firing. The officer tries to take cover but the suspect keeps shooting. He eventually reloads then comes around the back of the car and executes the officer. It was crazy.*[6]

This video—described in a popular police magazine as "forever seared in the minds of police officers across the world" (Law Officer 2017)—is of the 1998 murder of Kyle Dinkheller, a deputy of the Laurens County Sheriff's Office in rural Georgia. Multiple officers across the EPD, WPD, and SPD recalled seeing this video even though the incident occurred over two decades ago and many hundreds of miles away. Despite this temporal and geographic distance, Deputy Dinkheller's murder provides officers with a poignant and vicarious experience of the brutal speed with which the mundane parts of police work can snap to lethal violence. Though officers today have no direct connection to this more than 20-year-old murder, videos of such line-of-duty deaths emphasize the violence that *all* officers, regardless of where they patrol or when, must always be prepared to face. Officers are also shown videos during lineup as part of "lineup training" that periodically occurs before officers are sent out on patrol. During one lineup in West River, the lieutenant acting as watch commander announced she was going to show officers a video of an incident in another southwestern city. She instructed the room, *"Pay attention to issues of officer safety. What can we learn from it? Pay attention to everyone involved."*

What media accounts say began as a dispute in a Walmart bathroom between a customer and Walmart employee eventually culminated in both a suspect and an officer non-fatally shot, one suspect killed.[7] The video was utter chaos, the audio a mixture of screams, grunts, curses, and "Get on the ground!" as punches, pepper spray, TASERs, and eventually firearms were used by officers to gain control of the situation. My field notes from that lineup read: "By the end [of the video] I couldn't even see if someone had been shot, much less who did the shooting."

At the conclusion of the video, the lieutenant summarized the events shown, emphasizing that this incident could have been avoided if officers had properly utilized tactics learned in academy training: *"Control the situation, keep people separated. These officers didn't and look what happened: a brawl."* She concluded lineup the way watch commanders always did before officers went out on patrol: *"Be safe."*[8]

Importantly, lineup training differs from academy training in that it does not focus entirely on recruits; from the newest officer still in field training to the saltiest veteran, everyone who will be answering calls that shift is present for lineup. The presentation of such videos to a multi-generational police audience underlines that socialization into the danger imperative is not restricted to an officer's time in the academy. On the contrary, rookies and veterans alike receive formal, organizationally-backed reminders that reinforce the necessity of interpreting their work through the danger imperative. These reminders make clear that the cost of not doing so is simply too high. As stated by Officer Gutierrez (EPD) while driving around the city between calls for service, *"Always expect the unexpected. It could be an ambush. You never know. The smallest BS call could end up going bad. When you're not alert, that's when you get hurt."*

Informal Training and Policy-Deviant Behavior

Many of the safety-enhancing tactics used by police are relatively mundane and unlikely to harm the officers or citizens involved. Leaving a fingerprint on a car's trunk, keeping one's firearm away from a suspect, and letting dispatchers know where a stop is occurring are relatively low-cost, policy-compliant tactics for ensuring officer safety. Supplementing these formally taught techniques are informally learned behaviors that directly contravene departmental policy. Such policy-deviant behaviors are meant to help officers keep themselves and their fellow officers safe but, in fact, contribute to injuries and deaths on patrol.

Unauthorized Code 3 and Providing Backup

Though the threat of violence is front and center in police socialization and practice, the policing profession has increasingly come to recognize the risk of injury and death as a result of vehicle crashes during high-speed driving. As a result, contemporary police departments frequently employ policies to restrict high-speed vehicle pursuits and non-pursuit emergency driving (Walker and Archbold 2013). In what is known more commonly as driving "code 3," officers exceed the speed limit and utilize their lights and sirens to quickly reach calls in which there is an immediate threat to life, such as a robbery or shooting in progress. The policies of Elmont, West River, and Sunshine restrict code 3 responses to when officers are expressly dispatched to an emergency call or, if officers are not assigned to that call, when officers request and receive a superior's approval.

Despite these policy restrictions, officers frequently drive code 3 without approval. Officer Morales (SPD) explained his department's policy to me in detail but also admitted it is no guarantee of officers' compliance:

> By GOs, general orders, you're able to go code 3 if you come up on the radio and say, "I'll be en route code 3." But you cannot go code 3 to anything if there's already two units going code 3; it's only max two units code 3 to a scene. Same thing in a vehicle pursuit: you've got a lead car, back car, and that's it, going code 3, lights and sirens. Does that happen? *[Laughs]* No.

On the way to drop off Officer Roland on his walking beat in Elmont, Officer Vance explained that he flouts the code 3 policy in the interest of getting to serious "priority 1" calls quickly. "*Yeah, you're supposed to [get approval], but I don't. There's different rules for it. If it's a serious call, a priority 1,*

I'll go code 3...I mean, if it's a priority 1 that's really far away I might come on the radio [to notify dispatch]." Chiming in from the back seat, Roland gave his own perspective, "*I go [code] three to all priority 1 [calls]; I never ask for approval. I might get jammed up if I get in a 22 [vehicle collision] but that's on me.*" I asked him why he would knowingly break the policy if he knew it might mean discipline in the event of a car accident. He responded, "*Seconds matter if it's a hot call. Getting there fast can keep someone alive and you'd want your buddies to come back you up if it were you, right?*"

In officers' view, that they could be the difference between life and death for another officer overrides the potential disciplinary consequences of driving code 3 without approval and the significant danger such driving poses to them, other officers, and other motorists. As officers navigate work viewed through the danger imperative, they reify the collective responsibility for ensuring officer safety and affirm unauthorized code 3 driving as a useful, policy-deviant strategy to stay safe.

I asked Officer Cisneros, an EPD academy instructor, why officers willfully ignore policies designed to protect them. He explained that officers' in-the-moment assessment of safety-related exigencies produce tension between departmental policy and officers' collective need to protect one another:

> I think officers to a degree are looking at the immediate, you know. I need to protect my brother or sister officers. We're the thin blue line. We're the ones that are on the front line. We're not behind a desk, we're at the front line. If this goes wrong, this is going to affect me and him [fellow officer]. I can make that change.

Despite potential punishment for flouting departmental policy and the danger of a catastrophic car crash, perception filtered through the danger imperative biases officers' behavioral calculations to focus on the threat of violence. In lieu of adherence to organizational rules, officers engage in policy-deviant behaviors like unauthorized code 3 driving to ensure they provide speedy backup to other officers from whom they expect the same aid. Unfortunately, this collective responsibility for officer safety and its associated policy-deviant behaviors, though intended to protect officers, place them in harm's way.

Seatbelts as Safety Concerns

In addition to the unauthorized code 3 driving, officers also engage in the policy-deviant behavior of not wearing their mandated seatbelt. This behavior specifically endangers officers, in large part because it exacerbates the danger of their frequent high-speed driving.

During patrol with Officer Estacio (EPD), officers in another district reported they were following a car that fled when they attempted to stop it for a traffic violation. *"Let's see if we can get in the mix,"* said Estacio, and immediately sped off toward where radio traffic indicated a potential chase was developing. Without wearing his seatbelt, Estacio accelerated to speeds upwards of 60 miles per hour through residential areas, past a hospital, park, and school. Within a few minutes a supervisor came over the radio and, when officers could not articulate probable cause that the driver was guilty of anything more than a traffic violation, denied permission to continue the pursuit.

After the would-be pursuit, Estacio explained why he, like most officers, does not wear his seatbelt.

> *I'd say 90% of us don't wear our seatbelts. It's just too much for us. Tactically, some places the cops wear the vests or the carriers that have all their gear in the front or on their chest, then it's easier to wear the seatbelt. But here, look at where my holster is [points to pistol holster that is obstructing the seatbelt buckle]: it's too much. I'd say only 10% actually wear [a seatbelt].*

Implicit in this rationalization is the belief born of perception through the danger imperative that, at a moment's notice, an officer might need to defend their lives. In anticipation of this violent hypothetical, officers like Estacio leave their seatbelt off to improve access to their firearm.

This policy deviant solution to the problem of officer safety is not attributable to individual-level nonconformity alone. Instead, such policy-deviant behavior is perpetuated through informal interactions among officers that transmit and maintain the "hidden curriculum" of policing (Engelson 1999). In West River, Officer Garner explained that though she now wears her seatbelt after being reprimanded by a sergeant many years ago, a veteran officer informally taught her early in her career to not wear her seatbelt.

Garner: *It's an officer safety issue. The seatbelt might prevent you from being able to get to your gun or your spray, or it could snag on your belt if you're trying to get out of your car quickly to chase a suspect.*

AUTHOR: *And you were taught this in training?*

Garner: *Well, not officially. Department policy is we always wear our seatbelts, but unofficially we're told not to. First day on the street it was "Forget it."*

Other female officers eschew their seatbelts based on the same officer safety concerns voiced by male officers. For example, Officer Herrera (SPD) leaves off her seatbelt because, ". . . it takes a really long amount of time to unbuckle your seatbelt and jump out of the vehicle. [...] If someone's gonna shoot me, they're gonna shoot me while I'm getting out of the vehicle." Officer Willis (WPD) explained she does not wear her seatbelt because, "*you don't want to get stuck in your car. If I need to get out quickly the seatbelt can get caught, or it can get in the way if I have to get to my weapon.*" Similarly, seatbelt usage did not map neatly onto differences in age, race, or police experience. For example, Herrera is a 26-year-old Latina with three years on patrol and Willis is a Black woman in her late 30s with nearly 15 years of law enforcement experience. The link between officers' preoccupation with violence and their decision to break departmental policy requiring a seatbelt was consistent across multiple departments and officers of varying demographic characteristics.

Unintended Consequences of the Danger Imperative

Though intended to protect officers from the threat of violence, the policy-deviant behaviors described contribute to the grievous injury and death of police officers. Just before 3am in West River, Officer Jenkins—a rookie officer who I met before he entered the WPD academy—responded at high speed and without lights and sirens to a report of suspicious persons. While racing to the location listed in the call text, he collided with another vehicle, lost control of his patrol car, and careened into a parked semi-truck. The impact obliterated the front end of the patrol car and trapped him inside.

After being extricated by firefighters, he was rushed to a local hospital for emergency surgery and placed in a medically induced coma. At the time of this article's writing, Jenkins is able to open his eyes and sporadically track movement. His family has transferred him to a long-term medical facility and is raising money to pay for neurological rehabilitation not covered by his insurance. Despite the severe injuries sustained by Officer Jenkins in this crash, one officer I spoke with confirmed that he and other officers in the department continue to ignore departmental policy requiring seatbelt use, even when driving at high speeds.

In Elmont, Assistant Chief Altidore described a high-speed crash that left one officer comatose and another dead as they responded to a domestic violence call.

> The reason why the officer died is because he wasn't wearing a seatbelt. He got ejected and his own car ran over him, rolled over. [...] It wasn't a pretty sight. [...] I was there. I arrived there, he was still hanging out the door. And the car was back upright, landed back on its four wheels. [...] It was Reggie Tagliano. Reggie, you alright? You don't realize, no, he's not alright because

> the car just rolled over him. . . . Had he been wearing his seatbelt, he would have survived that crash. Probably not the other officer who's a vegetable now [. . .] but [Reggie] would have survived that. Definitely.

Though it is impossible to know exactly why Tagliano chose to not wear his seatbelt in this particular case, the consistent justifications of officers in Elmont, West River, and Sunshine for not wearing theirs suggest that Tagliano's death, though tragic, is unremarkable in the factors that contributed to it. Injuries like Jenkins's and deaths like Tagliano's are the unfortunate and unintended outcomes of behaviors stemming from officers' perceptions of their work through the danger imperative.

Because of the emphasis placed on protecting themselves from violence, officers make what they conceive as strategic choices to ensure their safety while preserving their ability to chase or fight. In these efforts, officers choose to disregard departmental policy restricting high-speed driving and requiring seatbelts that they believe create unacceptable officer safety concerns. These policy-deviant behaviors, though justified as a way for officers to stay safe from the threat of violence, increase the probability of serious injury during the high-speed driving that they engage in far more often than life or death battles with armed suspects.

Discussion and Conclusion

This article joins a growing body of contemporary sociolegal research on the street-level practices of police officers and provides needed insight into the role of danger and threat in police behavior. My findings from the Elmont, West River, and Sunshine Police Departments show that the cultural frame of the danger imperative—the perceptual preoccupation with violence and the provision of officer safety—shapes officer behaviors intended to ensure survival on the street. Unlike policy-compliant behaviors like calling for backup or touching the trunk of a stopped vehicle, policy-deviant behaviors like unauthorized high-speed driving, code 2½ driving, and failure to use a seatbelt during high-speed driving, though intended to keep them safe from violence, lead to the injury and death of police officers.

As a complement to research that links officers' preoccupation with danger to deviant behaviors ranging from corruption to brutality and excessive force, this study also allows us to see that some supposedly safety-enhancing police behaviors endanger both the public *and* the police. Namely, officers' attempts to avoid violent victimization can also directly contribute to the vehicle crashes that represent the leading cause of accidental death in policing and the second most common cause of line-of-duty deaths overall (FBI 2019a). What's more, this high-speed driving also contributes to the injury and death of community members. One analysis finds that police pursuits between 1979 and 2013 claimed the lives of more than 5,000 bystanders or passengers and injured tens of thousands more (Frank 2015). Though policy-deviant behaviors like not wearing a seatbelt or unauthorized high-speed driving may appear mundane in comparison to high-profile police shootings, this article shows that danger and its influence on officers' behavior have grave consequences for police and the public they serve.

The danger imperative's emphasis on violence in the line of duty also has implications for the link between police behavior, public well-being, and police legitimacy. For example, the danger imperative is closely related to the "warrior mentality" and its emphasis on aggressive enforcement. "Warrior" officers approach interactions under the assumption that any contact with the public could erupt into violence at any moment. Those looking to "maintain the edge" over suspects will engage in pre-emptive uses of force seen as necessary to ensure control over a situation and head-off resistance (Van Maanen 1974; Stoughton 2014a). Indeed, the vast majority of force used by police occurs *before* there is physical resistance from a suspect (Stoughton 2014b:866–68). Even though such force is very often legal, within departmental policy, and in line with officer training, these dominance-based interactions are precisely those liable to escalate into violence that harms both police and the public (Stoughton 2014a:229–30; Garrett and Stoughton 2017:250–51). Even if an interaction does not result in physical violence, aggressive and antagonistic police behavior in the name of officer safety can still create interactions that reinforce distrust of police, further damage police legitimacy, and increase the risk of future encounters escalating (Gau and Brunson 2010).

Officers' preoccupation with violence and officer safety is also implicated in cases of excessive force. In keeping with the state's interest in allowing police to forcefully protect their lives (Harmon 2008), officers regularly cite safety concerns as a reason for their use of force. When deploying their TASERs, for example, officers will justify such force on the grounds that it enhances their safety, even in cases where fellow officers view the use of force as plainly excessive (Sierra-Arévalo 2019a). Similar justifications are used in cases of excessive lethal force, including rare cases in which an officer is convicted of a criminal offense, such as in the police killings of Walter Scott and Laquan McDonald (Crepeau and St. Clair 2018; Schmidt and Apuzzo 2015). More often, this justification is given in cases that do not result in criminal convictions, such as in the police killing of Philando Castille (Ingraham 2017), and in cases where no charges are filed, such as in the police killings of Michael Brown and Tamir Rice (Haag 2018; Sanburn 2014). Whether a use of force is found to be reasonable, criminal, against department policy, or some combination thereof, it is clear that the preoccupation with violence and officer safety is closely tied to officers' use of force, including the high-profile police killings that are at the heart of U.S. policing's current crisis of legitimacy (Cobbina 2019; Weitzer 2015).

Crucially, neither aggressive, dominance-based policing, police violence, nor the consequences of such police action are equally distributed across the population. Instead, longstanding associations between race, place, violence, and criminality perpetuate the funneling of police into disadvantaged minority communities (Anderson 2012; Capers 2009). These communities continue to disproportionately experience police stops, searches, arrests, and uses of force (Epp, Maynard-Moody, and Haider-Markel 2014; Gaston 2019; Kramer and Remster 2018), virtually guaranteeing that those most likely to be perceived as suspicious, violent, and criminal will be those most likely to encounter police primed for threat (Eberhardt et al. 2004; Goff et al. 2014). In turn, the concentration of police in marginalized communities contributes to decreased mental and physical health (Sewell and Jefferson 2016; Sugie and Turney 2017), lower educational attainment (Legewie and Fagan 2019), and disengagement from social institutions like banks, hospitals, and schools (Brayne 2014).

Of course, the ethnographic and interview data presented in this analysis cannot, in and of themselves, confirm the direct effect of officers' preoccupation with danger on behaviors like stops, searches, arrests, or uses of force, nor on deviance that ranges from low-level policy violations to wanton brutality. To better delineate this perceptual-behavioral chain, researchers might build on research that finds culturally shared distrust of the public and support for aggressive patrol tactics predict both officers' use of force and complaints filed against them (Ingram et al. 2018). Future inquiry might employ survey methods to create individual and group-level measures of perceived danger, then combine these constructs with individual-level data on deviant and non-deviant officer behavior. In conjunction, cultural measures and fine-grained data on officer behavior would enable exploration of danger's individual and collective effects on the full range of discretionary police action. Knowing that police behavior is strongly tied to officers' local environment and the features of their interactions with citizens (Gaston 2019; Klinger et al. 2016), future research might also incorporate data on neighborhood demographics, crime, violence, and situational-level measures to better elucidate how the cultural preoccupation with violence interacts with micro-level context to shape police behavior.

Finally, policing's pervasive preoccupation with violence and officer safety is implicated in the police profession's resistance to reform and its efforts to expand police power. Officer safety is often used by police advocates, especially police unions, as a shield against reform efforts. The New York City Police Benevolent Association, for example, has for years fought against the release of NYPD misconduct data on the grounds that these data will enable retaliatory violence against officers (Rayman 2020; Taggart and Hayes 2018). More broadly, police union contracts across the nation commonly require misconduct and disciplinary records to be destroyed after a period of time, further frustrating efforts to enhance transparency and accountability (Rushin 2017).

The danger of police work is also explicitly leveraged to expand police power and protections. In recent years, some have claimed that the United States is in the grip of a "war on cops" characterized by growing disrespect and violence directed at police (Mac Donald 2016). Though scholars have found no evidence of a significant increase in violence toward police in recent years (Shjarback and Maguire 2019; Sierra-Arévalo and Nix 2020; White et al. 2019), concerns over officer safety undergird new "Blue Lives Matter" laws that seek increased punishment for attacks on police (Craven 2017). This increased punitiveness is supported by officials at the highest levels of the federal government. In a speech to the Fraternal Order of Police, a police advocacy organization with more than 354,000 members, Attorney General William P. Barr claimed increasing violence against police officers and promised to introduce federal legislation to fast track the death penalty for those who kill a police officer (Barr 2019). While the ultimate outcomes of this rhetoric and proposed changes are as of yet unknown, evidence strongly suggests that these developments—rooted in policing's preoccupation with violence and officer safety—will further expand police power, increase legal punitiveness, and frustrate reform efforts.

DISCUSSION QUESTIONS

1. What is the danger imperative? How does it shape decisions that police make about how to act?
2. On page 166, the author states, "Which dangers are to be confronted, ignored, or avoided (and how to do so) does not exists a priori and is instead shaped by a group's environment." How does this statement related to the reading "*Neither Clear nor Present?*"
3. How are the dangers faced by police similar to those faced by firefighters? How are they different?
4. What is "line up" training and who participates in it? What purpose does line up training serve?
5. Violence against innocent civilians is one consequence of the danger imperative; what are the consequences to police themselves?
6. The risks of being harmed by police are particularly high for African Americans. Look at the results of this recent Gallup poll and think about how race plays a role in even mundane interactions with police.

https://news.gallup.com/poll/316247/black-americans-police-encounters-not-positive.aspx

REFERENCES

Anderson, Elijah. 1999. *Code of the Street: Decency, Violence, and the Moral Life of the Inner City*. New York: Norton.

Anderson, Elijah. 2012. "The Iconic Ghetto." *The ANNALS of the American Academy of Political and Social Science* 642(1):8–24.

Armenta, Amada. 2017. *Protect, Serve, and Deport: The Rise of Policing as Immigration Enforcement*. Oakland: University of California Press.

Barr, William P. 2019. "Attorney General William P. Barr Delivers Remarks at the Grand Lodge Fraternal Order of Police's 64th National Biennial Conference." *The United States Department of Justice*. Retrieved August 13, 2019 (https://www.justice.gov/opa/speech/attorney-general-william-p-barr-delivers-remarks-grand-lodge-fraternal-order-polices-64th).

Bittner, Egon. 1970. *The Functions of the Police in Modern Society: A Review of Background Factors, Current Practices, and Possible Role Models*. National Institute of Mental Health, Center for Studies of Crime and Delinquency.

Brayne, Sarah. 2014. "Surveillance and System Avoidance: Criminal Justice Contact and Institutional Attachment." *American Sociological Review* 79(3):367–91.

Brayne, Sarah. 2017. "Big Data Surveillance: The Case of Policing." *American Sociological Review* 82(5):977–1008.

Bureau of Labor Statistics. 2014. *National Census of Fatal Occupational Injuries in 2013 (Preliminary Results)*. Washington, D.C.: Bureau of Labor Statistics, U.S. Department of Labor.

Canterbury, Chuck. 2015. *Testimony before the President's Task Force on 21st Century Policing*. Washington, D.C.

Capers, I. Bennett. 2009. "Policing, Race, and Place." *Harvard Civil Rights-Civil Liberties Law Review* 44(1):43–78.

Cobbina, Jennifer E. 2019. *Hands Up, Don't Shoot: Why the Protests in Ferguson and Baltimore Matter, and How They Changed America*. NYU Press.

Contreras, Randol. 2012. *The Stickup Kids: Race, Drugs, Violence, and the American Dream*. University of California Press.

Crank, John P. 2014. *Understanding Police Culture*. Routledge.

Craven, Julia. 2017. "32 Blue Lives Matter Bills Have Been Introduced Across 14 States This Year." *Huffington Post*, March 1.

Crepeau, Megan, and Stacy St. Clair. 2018. "Will Van Dyke Testify? Defense Begins Presenting Evidence Monday." *Chicago Tribune*, September 22.

Cubic Defence UK. 2019. "PRISim Suite Judgement Trainer." *Cubic Defense UK*. Retrieved January 8, 2019 (http://www.ais-solutions.co.uk/training-simulators/prisim-suite/judgement-trainer.php).

Desmond, Matthew. 2006. "Becoming a Firefighter." *Ethnography* 7(4):387–421.

DiMaggio, Paul J., and Walter W. Powell. 1983. "The Iron Cage Revisited: Institutional Isomorphism and Collective Rationality in Organizational Fields." *American Sociological Review* 48(2):147–60.

Douglas, Mary, and Aaron Wildavsky. 1983. *Risk and Culture*. Berkeley: University of California Press.

Eberhardt, Jennifer L., Phillip Atiba Goff, Valerie J. Purdie, and Paul G. Davies. 2004. "Seeing Black: Race, Crime, and Visual Processing." *Journal of Personality and Social Psychology* 87(6):876–93.

Engelson, Wade. 1999. "The Organizational Values of Law Enforcement Agencies: The Impact of Field Training Officers in the Socialization of Police Recruits to Law Enforcement Organizations." *Journal of Police and Criminal Psychology* 14(2):11–19.

Epp, Charles R., Steven Maynard-Moody, and Donald P. Haider-Markel. 2014. *Pulled Over: How Police Stops Define Race and Citizenship*. Chicago, IL: University of Chicago Press.

FBI. 2019a. "About LEOKA." *FBI*. Retrieved January 13, 2020 (https://ucr.fbi.gov/leoka/2018/resource-pages/about-leoka).

FBI. 2019b. "Full-Time Law Enforcement Employees by Population Group, Percent Male and Female, 2018." *FBI*. Retrieved January 30, 2020 (https://ucr.fbi.gov/crime-in-the-u.s/2018/crime-in-the-u.s.-2018/tables/table-74/table-74.xls).

Frank, Thomas. 2015. "High-Speed Police Chases Have Killed Thousands of Innocent Bystanders." *USA TODAY*. Retrieved (http://www.usatoday.com/story/news/2015/07/30/police-pursuits-fatal-injuries/30187827/).

Garrett, Brandon, and Seth Stoughton. 2017. "A Tactical Fourth Amendment." *Virginia Law Review* 103(2):211–308.

Gaston, Shytierra. 2019. "Producing Race Disparities: A Study of Drug Arrests across Place and Race." *Criminology* 57(3):424–451.

Gau, Jacinta M., and Rod K. Brunson. 2010. "Procedural Justice and Order Maintenance Policing: A Study of Inner-City Young Men's Perceptions of Police Legitimacy." *Justice Quarterly* 27(2):255–79.

Goff, Phillip Atiba, Matthew Christian Jackson, Brooke Allison Lewis Di Leone, Carmen Marie Culotta, and Natalie Ann DiTomasso. 2014. "The Essence of Innocence: Consequences of Dehumanizing Black Children." *Journal of Personality and Social Psychology* 106(4):526–45.

Haag, Matthew. 2018. "Cleveland Officer Who Killed Tamir Rice Is Hired by an Ohio Police Department." *The New York Times*, October 8.

Harmon, Rachel A. 2008. "When Is Police Violence Justified?" *Northwestern University Law Review* 102:1119–88.

Hureau, David M., and Anthony A. Braga. 2018. "The Trade in Tools: The Market for Illicit Guns in High-Risk Networks." *Criminology* 56(3):510–45.

Ingraham, Christopher. 2017. "Officer Who Shot Philando Castile Said Smell of Marijuana Made Him Fear for His Life." *Washington Post*, June 21.

Ingram, Jason R., William Terrill, and Eugene A. Paoline. 2018. "Police Culture and Officer Behavior: Application of a Multilevel Framework." *Criminology* 56(4): 780–811.

Kasperson, Roger E., Ortwin Renn, Paul Slovic, Halina S. Brown, Jacque Emel, Robert Goble, Jeanne X. Kasperson, and Samuel Ratick. 1988. "The Social Amplification of Risk: A Conceptual Framework." *Risk Analysis* 8(2):177–87.

Kirk, David S., and Andrew V. Papachristos. 2011. "Cultural Mechanisms and the Persistence of Neighborhood Violence." *American Journal of Sociology* 116(4):1190–1233.

Klinger, David, Richard Rosenfeld, Daniel Isom, and Michael Deckard. 2016. "Race, Crime, and the Micro-Ecology of Deadly Force." *Criminology & Public Policy* 15(1):193–222.

Kramer, Rory, and Brianna Remster. 2018. "Stop, Frisk, and Assault? Racial Disparities in Police Use of Force During Investigatory Stops." *Law & Society Review* 52(4):960–93.

Lamont, Michèle, and Mario Small. 2008. "How Culture Matters: Enriching Our Understanding of Poverty." Pp. 76–102 in *The Colors of Poverty: Why Racial and Ethnic Disparities Persist*, edited by A. L. Harris and D. Harris. New York: Russel Sage Foundation.

Law Officer. 2017. "The Kyle Dinkheller Murder Shows Us Why There Is More to the Tulsa Incident." *Law Officer*. Retrieved October 5, 2016 (http://lawofficer.com/2016/09/the-kyle-dinkheller-murder-shows-us-why-there-is-more-to-the-tulsa-incident/).

Legewie, Joscha, and Jeffrey Fagan. 2019. "Aggressive Policing and the Educational Performance of Minority Youth." *American Sociological Review* 0003122419826020.

Lipsky, Michael. 1980. *Street-Level Bureaucracy: Dilemmas of the Individual in Public Services*. 30th anniversary expanded ed. New York: Russell Sage Foundation.

Mac Donald, Heather. 2016. *The War on Cops: How the New Attack on Law and Order Makes Everyone Less Safe*. New York: Encounter Books.

Maguire, Edward R., Justin Nix, and Bradley A. Campbell. 2017. "A War on Cops? The Effects of Ferguson on the Number of U.S. Police Officers Murdered in the Line of Duty." *Justice Quarterly* 34(5):739–58.

Manning, Peter K. 1978. "The Police: Mandate, Strategies, and Appearances." Pp. 7–31 in *Policing: A View from the Street*, edited by Peter K. Manning and John Van Maanen. New York: Random House.

Manning, Peter K. 2011. *The Technology of Policing: Crime Mapping, Information Technology, and the Rationality of Crime Control*. New York; Chesham: NYU Press.

Moskos, Peter. 2009. *Cop in the Hood: My Year Policing Baltimore's Eastern District*. Princeton, N.J.: Princeton University Press.

Ouellet, Marie, Sadaf Hashimi, Jason Gravel, and Andrew V. Papachristos. 2019. "Network Exposure and Excessive Use of Force." *Criminology & Public Policy* 18(3): 675–704.

Perkins, Gráinne. 2018. "Danger and Death: Organisational and Occupational Responses to the Murder of Police in South Africa—a Case Study." 1–276.

Rayman, Graham. 2020. "Cops, Fire, Correction Unions Sue de Blasio Administration over Release of Disciplinary Records." *New York Daily News*, July 15.

Reaves, Brian A. 2015. *Local Police Departments, 2013: Equipment and Technology*. NCJ 248767. Washington, D.C.: Bureau of Justice Statistics.

Rios, Victor M. 2011. *Punished: Policing the Lives of Black and Latino Boys*. New York: NYU Press.

Rojek, Jeff, Hayden P. Smith, and Geoffrey P. Alpert. 2012. "The Prevalence and Characteristics of Police Practitioner-Researcher Partnerships." *Police Quarterly* 1098611112440698.

Rushin, Stephen. 2017. "Police Union Contracts." *Duke Law Journal* 66(6):1191–1266.

Sanburn, Josh. 2014. "All The Ways Darren Wilson Described Being Afraid of Michael Brown." *Time*, November 25.

Schmidt, Michael S., and Matt Apuzzo. 2015. "South Carolina Officer Is Charged With Murder of Walter Scott." *The New York Times*, April 7.

Sewell, Abigail A., and Kevin A. Jefferson. 2016. "Collateral Damage: The Health Effects of Invasive Police Encounters in New York City." *Journal of Urban Health* 93(1):42–67.

Shjarback, John A., and Edward R. Maguire. 2019. "Extending Research on the 'War on Cops': The Effects of Ferguson on Nonfatal Assaults Against U.S. Police Officers." *Crime & Delinquency* 0011128719890266.

Short, James F. 1984. "The Social Fabric at Risk: Toward the Social Transformation of Risk Analysis." *American Sociological Review* 49(6):711–25.

Sierra-Arévalo, Michael. 2019a. "Technological Innovation and Police Officers' Understanding and Use of Force." *Law & Society Review* 53(2):420–51.

Sierra-Arévalo, Michael. 2019b. "The Commemoration of Death, Organizational Memory, and Police Culture." *Criminology* 57(4):632–58.

Sierra-Arévalo, Michael, and Justin Nix. 2020. "Gun Victimization in the Line of Duty: Fatal and Nonfatal Firearm Assaults on Police Officers in the United States, 2014–2019." *Criminology & Public Policy* 1745-9133.12507.

Skolnick, Jerome H. 2002. "Corruption and the Blue Code of Silence." *Police Practice and Research* 3(1):7–19.

Skolnick, Jerome H. 2011. *Justice Without Trial: Law Enforcement in Democratic Society*. 4th edition. New Orleans, LA: Quid Pro Quo Books.

Skolnick, Jerome H., and James J. Fyfe. 1994. *Above the Law: Police and the Excessive Use of Force*. New York; Toronto: Free Press.

Spradley, James P. 1979. *The Ethnographic Interview*. New York: Holt, Rinehart and Winston.

Stoughton, Seth W. 2014a. "Law Enforcement's Warrior Problem." *Harvard Law Review Forum* 128:225–34.

Stoughton, Seth W. 2014b. "Policing Facts." *Tulane Law Review* 88:847–98.

Stuart, Forrest. 2016. *Down, Out, and Under Arrest: Policing and Everyday Life in Skid Row*. Chicago ; London: University Of Chicago Press.

Sugie, Naomi F., and Kristin Turney. 2017. "Beyond Incarceration: Criminal Justice Contact and Mental Health." *American Sociological Review* 82(4):719–43.

Taggart, Kendall, and Mike Hayes. 2018. "Police Union Tried to Block Publication of NYPD Database." *BuzzFeed News*. Retrieved August 25, 2020 (https://www.buzzfeednews.com/article/kendalltaggart/police-union-tried-to-block-publication-of-nypd-database).

Van Maanen, John. 1974. "Working the Street: A Developmental View of Police Behavior." Pp. 83–130 in *The Potential for Reform of Criminal Justice*, edited by H. Jacob. Beverly Hills, CA: Sage Publications.

Van Maanen, John. 1978a. "Observations on the Making of a Policeman." Pp. 292–308 in *Policing: A View from the Street*, edited by Peter K. Manning and John Van Maanen. New York, NY: Random House.

Van Maanen, John. 1978b. "The Asshole." Pp. 221–37 in *Policing: A View from the Street*, edited by P. K. Manning and J. Van Maanen. New York, NY: Random House.

Van Maanen, John, and Stephen R. Barley. 1984. "Occupational Communities: Culture and Control in Organizations." Pp. 287–365 in *Research in Organizational Behavior*. Vol. 6, edited by B. M. Staw and L. L. Cummings. Greenwood, CT: JAI Press.

Vaughan, Diane. 1996. *The* Challenger *Launch Decision: Risky Technology, Culture, and Deviance at NASA*. Chicago, IL: University of Chicago Press.

Weitzer, Ronald. 2015. "American Policing Under Fire: Misconduct and Reform." *Society* 52(5):475–80.

Westley, William A. 1970. *Violence and the Police: A Sociological Study of Law, Custom, and Morality*. Cambridge, MA: The MIT Press.

White, Michael D., Lisa M. Dario, and John A. Shjarback. 2019. "Assessing Dangerousness in Policing: An Analysis of Officer Deaths in the United States, 1970–2016." *Criminology & Public Policy* 18(1):11–35.

NOTES

1. The use of "men" in older literature predates increased gender diversity in U.S. policing. However, FBI Police Employee Data indicate the continued underrepresentation of women in policing—less than 13% of officers in the U.S. are female (FBI 2019b).

2. The term "deviance" includes "misconduct" (e.g. brutality or corruption) that is at least partially measured in citizen complaint data, as well as less grave violations of departmental norms or policies that are "committed during the course of 'normal' work activities" (Barker 1977, p. 356).

3. In addition to pseudonyms for officers, I use city pseudonyms and approximate city and department statistics to prevent identification of my

field sites. These steps are taken in line with this study's IRB-approved protocol and my guarantee of anonymity to officers.

4. The American Community Survey estimates that 79 percent of U.S. officers in 2016 were White, suggesting that the EPD and WPD are markedly more racially/ethnically diverse than the average police department. Similarly, though women are underrepresented in these departments relative to the U.S. population, overall, the EPD and SPD show greater gender diversity than the average police department—less than 13 percent of sworn officers are female (FBI 2019b).
5. The video can be found here: https://www.youtube.com/watch?v=RBUUO_VFYMs
6. Officers in all three departments recalled having seen this video, which can be found here: https://www.youtube.com/watch?v=mssNOhv1UMc (Retrieved January 17, 2015).
7. Video link: https://www.youtube.com/watch?v=zv5Cbgn4TOU (Retrieved June 1, 2015).
8. Departments' local context informed how officers discussed the threat of violence. For example, the 2014 ambush of NYPD officers Wenjian Liu and Rafael Ramos was geographically proximal to Elmont; EPD officers were required to patrol with a partner for several weeks after the ambush in case of copycats. Sunshine was closest to the U.S. Mexico border and officers discussed violence tied to transnational drug cartels. WPD officers were sensitive to the threat posed by violent West River gangs. Across all departments, however, the salient concern for officers was being violently attacked on patrol.

PART

IV

Gender

Doing Gender

Candace West and Don H. Zimmerman

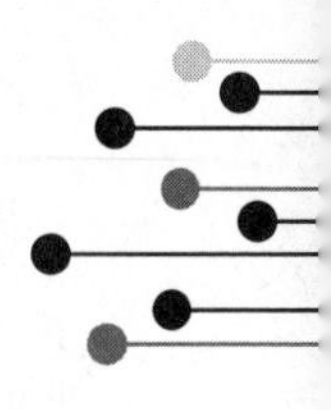

Gender is one of the central organizing features of social life. While we have many different roles we play in different contexts (employee, student, friend, significant other), and we each have personality traits that we may turn up in some situations and down in others (shyness, sense of humor, talkativeness), we are always gendered beings. While there is a movement toward socially supporting those who wish to pick their gender or remain gender-neutral in their identity, there is also a fierce social backlash against this social change.[1]

It is still the predominant view in American society to think of gender as a trait that someone simply has, much like eye color. On the other hand, many sociologists see gender as a role that people learn rather than something they have. In this reading, West and Zimmerman argue that gender should be thought of not as a role that we learn but as an accomplishment, something that we actively do and that is a product of our interactions. This outcome of gender is usually seen as justification of institutional arrangements that separate the genders, but West and Zimmerman argue that in fact by doing gender, we create through social interaction the very differences that we think of as being natural and normal. For example, public restrooms, even those with single stalls, are gender segregated, and this is seen as a necessity because of the natural biological differences between men and women. Yet bathrooms in homes are not segregated, and men and women quite happily share the same bathrooms with the same setup in their private lives. In outdoor public spaces, men and women routinely share port-a-potties. We don't have separate stalls for women in indoor public bathrooms because women biologically need them, we think women need them because *there are separate stalls. As you read, think about your own gender performance each day and how it reinforces existing institutional arrangements between men and women.*

Our purpose in this article is to propose an ethnomethodologically informed, and therefore distinctively sociological, understanding of gender as a routine, methodical, and recurring accomplishment. We contend that the "doing" of gender is undertaken by women and men whose

---

Excerpt from "Doing Gender," by C. West and D. H. Zimmerman. *Gender and Society* (1987), 1(2), pp. 125–151. Reprinted with permission.

competence as members of society is hostage to its production. Doing gender involves a complex of socially guided perceptual, interactional, and micropolitical activities that cast particular pursuits as expressions of masculine and feminine "natures."

When we view gender as an accomplishment, an achieved property of situated conduct, our attention shifts from matters internal to the individual and focuses on interactional and, ultimately, institutional arenas. In one sense, of course, it is individuals who "do" gender. But it is a situated doing, carried out in the virtual or real presence of others who are presumed to be oriented to its production. Rather than as a property of individuals, we conceive of gender as an emergent feature of social situations: both as an outcome of and a rationale for various social arrangements and as a means of legitimating one of the most fundamental divisions of society.

To advance our argument, we undertake a critical examination of what sociologists have meant by *gender*, including its treatment as a role enactment in the conventional sense and as a "display" in Goffman's (1976) terminology. Both *gender role* and *gender display* focus on behavioral aspects of being a woman or a man (as opposed, for example, to biological differences between the two). However, we contend that the notion of gender as a role obscures the work that is involved in producing gender in everyday activities, while the notion of gender as a display relegates it to the periphery of interaction. We argue instead that participants in interaction organize their various and manifold activities to reflect or express gender, and they are disposed to perceive the behavior of others in a similar light.

To elaborate our proposal, we suggest at the outset that important but often overlooked distinctions be observed among *sex*, *sex category*, and *gender*. Sex is a determination made through the application of socially agreed upon biological criteria for classifying persons as females or males.[2] The criteria for classification can be genitalia at birth or chromosomal typing before birth, and they do not necessarily agree with one another. Placement in a *sex category* is achieved through application of the sex criteria, but in everyday life, categorization is established and sustained by the socially required identificatory displays that proclaim one's membership in one or the other category. In this sense, one's sex category presumes one's sex and stands as proxy for it in many situations, but sex and sex category can vary independently; that is, it is possible to claim membership in a sex category even when the sex criteria are lacking. *Gender*, in contrast, is the activity of managing situated conduct in light of normative conceptions of attitudes and activities appropriate for one's sex category. Gender activities emerge from and bolster claims to membership in a sex category.

We argue that gender is not a set of traits, nor a variable, nor a role, but the product of social doings of some sort. What then is the social doing of gender? It is more than the continuous creation of the meaning of gender through human actions (Gerson and Peiss 1985). We claim that gender itself is constituted through interaction.[3]

Sex, Sex Category, and Gender

Garfinkel's (1967, pp. 118–40) case study of Agnes, a transsexual raised as a boy who adopted a female identity at age 17 and underwent a sex reassignment operation several years later, demonstrates how gender is created through interaction and at the same time structures interaction. Agnes, whom Garfinkel characterized as a "practical methodologist," developed a number of procedures for passing as a "normal, natural female" both prior to and after her surgery. She had the practical task of managing the fact that she possessed male genitalia and that she lacked the social resources a girl's biography would presumably provide in everyday interaction. In short, she needed to display herself as a woman, simultaneously learning what it was to be a woman. Of necessity, this full-time pursuit took place at a time when most people's gender would be well-accredited and routinized. Agnes had to consciously contrive what the vast majority of women do without thinking. She was not "faking" what "real" women do naturally. She was obliged to analyze and figure out how to act within socially structured circumstances and conceptions of femininity that women born with appropriate biological credentials come to take for granted early on. As in the case of others who must "pass," such as transvestites, Kabuki actors, or Dustin Hoffman's "Tootsie," Agnes's case makes visible what culture has made invisible—the accomplishment of gender.

Garfinkel's (1967) discussion of Agnes does not explicitly separate three analytically distinct, although empirically overlapping, concepts—sex, sex category, and gender.

Sex

Agnes did not possess the socially agreed upon biological criteria for classification as a member of the female *sex*. Still, Agnes regarded herself as a female, albeit a female with a penis, which a woman ought not to possess. The penis, she insisted, was a "mistake" in need of remedy (Garfinkel 1967, pp. 126–27, 131–32). Like other competent members of our culture, Agnes honored the notion that there are "essential" biological criteria that unequivocally distinguish females from males. However, if we move away from the commonsense viewpoint, we discover that the reliability of these criteria is not beyond question (Money and Brennan 1968; Money and Ehrhardt 1972; Money and Ogunro 1974; Money and Tucker 1975). Moreover, other cultures have acknowledged the existence of "cross-genders" (Blackwood 1984; Williams 1986) and the possibility of more than two sexes (Hill 1935; Martin and Voorheis 1975, pp. 84–107; but see also Cucchiari 1981, pp. 32–35).

More central to our argument is Kessler and McKenna's (1978, pp. 1–6) point that genitalia are conventionally hidden from public inspection in everyday life; yet we continue through our social rounds to "observe" a world of two naturally, normally sexed persons. It is the *presumption* that essential criteria exist and would or should be there if looked for that provides the basis for sex categorization. Drawing on Garfinkel, Kessler and McKenna argue that "female" and "male" are cultural events—products of what they term the "gender attribution process"—rather than some collection of traits, behaviors, or even physical attributes. Illustratively they cite the child who, viewing a picture of someone clad in a suit and a tie, contends, "It's a man, because he has a pee-pee" (Kessler and McKenna 1978, p. 154). Translation: "He must have a pee-pee [an essential characteristic] because I see the *insignia* of a suit and tie." Neither initial sex assignment (pronouncement at birth as a female or male) nor the actual existence of essential criteria for that assignment (possession of a clitoris and vagina or penis and testicles) has much—if anything—to do with the identification of sex category in everyday life. There, Kessler and McKenna note, we operate with a moral certainty of a world of two sexes. We do not think, "Most persons with penises are men, but some may not be" or "Most persons who dress as men have penises." Rather, we take it for granted that sex and sex category are congruent—that knowing the latter, we can deduce the rest.

Sex Categorization

Agnes's claim to the categorical status of female, which she sustained by appropriate identificatory displays and other characteristics, could be *discredited* before her transsexual operation if her possession of a penis became known and after by her surgically constructed genitalia (see Raymond 1979, pp. 37, 138). In this regard, Agnes had to be continually alert to actual or potential threats to the security of her sex category. Her problem was not so much living up to some prototype of essential femininity but preserving her categorization as female.

This task was made easy for her by a very powerful resource, namely, the process of commonsense categorization in everyday life.

The categorization of members of society into indigenous categories such as "girl" or "boy," or "woman" or "man," operates in a distinctively social way. The act of categorization does not involve a positive test, in the sense of a well-defined set of criteria that must be explicitly satisfied prior to making an identification. Rather, the application of membership categories relies on an "if-can" test in everyday interaction (Sacks 1972, pp. 332–35). This test stipulates that if people *can be seen* as members of relevant categories, *then categorize them that way.* That is, use the category that seems appropriate, except in the presence of discrepant information or obvious features that would rule out its use. This procedure is quite in keeping with the attitude of everyday life, which has us take appearances at face value unless we have special reason to doubt (Bernstein 1986;

Garfinkel 1967, pp. 272–77; Schutz 1943).[4] It should be added that it is precisely when we have special reason to doubt that the issue of applying rigorous criteria arises, but it is rare, outside legal or bureaucratic contexts, to encounter insistence on positive tests[5] (Garfinkel 1967, pp. 262–83; Wilson 1970).

Agnes's initial resource was the predisposition of those she encountered to take her appearance (her figure, clothing, hair style, and so on), as the undoubted appearance of a normal female. Her further resource was our cultural perspective on the properties of "natural, normally sexed persons." Garfinkel (1967, pp. 122–28) notes that in everyday life, we live in a world of two—and only two—sexes. This arrangement has a moral status, in that we include ourselves and others in it as "essentially, originally, in the first place, always have been, always will be, once and for all, in the final analysis, either 'male' or 'female'" (Garfinkel 1967, p. 122).

Consider the following case:

> This issue reminds me of a visit I made to a computer store a couple of years ago. The person who answered my questions was truly a salesperson. I could not categorize him/her as a woman or a man. What did I look for? (1) Facial hair: She/he was smooth skinned, but some men have little or no facial hair. (This varies by race, Native Americans and Blacks often have none.) (2) Breasts: She/he was wearing a loose shirt that hung from his/her shoulders. And, as many women who suffered through a 1950s' adolescence know to their shame, women are often flat-chested. (3) Shoulders: His/hers were small and round for a man, broad for a woman. (4) Hands: Long and slender fingers, knuckles a bit large for a woman, small for a man. (5) Voice: Middle range, unexpressive for a woman, not at all the exaggerated tones some gay males affect. (6) His/her treatment of me: Gave off no signs that would let me know if I were of the same or different sex as this person. There were not even any signs that he/she knew his/her sex would be difficult to categorize and I wondered about that even as I did my best to hide these questions so I would not embarrass him/her while we talked of computer paper. I left still not knowing the sex of my salesperson, and was disturbed by that unanswered question (child of my culture that I am). (Diane Margolis, personal communication)

What can this case tell us about situations such as Agnes's (cf. Morris 1974; Richards 1983) or the process of sex categorization in general? First, we infer from this description that the computer salesclerk's identificatory display was ambiguous, since she or he was not dressed or adorned in an unequivocally female or male fashion. It is when such a display *fails* to provide grounds for categorization that factors such as facial hair or tone of voice are assessed to determine membership in a sex category. Second, beyond the fact that this incident could be recalled after "a couple of years," the customer was not only "disturbed" by the ambiguity of the salesclerk's category but also assumed that to acknowledge this ambiguity would be embarrassing to the salesclerk. Not only do we want to know the sex category of those around us (to see it at a glance, perhaps), but we presume that others are displaying it for us, in as decisive a fashion as they can.

Gender

Agnes attempted to be "120 percent female" (Garfinkel 1967, p. 129), that is, unquestionably in all ways and at all times feminine. She thought she could protect herself from disclosure before and after surgical intervention by comporting herself in a feminine manner, but she also could have given herself away by overdoing her performance. Sex categorization and the accomplishment of gender are not the same. Agnes's categorization could be secure or suspect, but did not depend on whether or not she lived up to some ideal conception of femininity. Women can be seen as unfeminine, but that does not make them "unfemale." Agnes faced an ongoing task of *being* a woman—something beyond style of dress (an identificatory display) or allowing men to light her cigarette (a gender display). Her problem was to produce configurations of behavior that would be seen by others as normative gender behavior.

Agnes's strategy of "secret apprenticeship," through which she learned expected feminine decorum by carefully attending to her fiancé's criticisms of other women, was one means of masking incompetencies and simultaneously acquiring the needed skills (Garfinkel 1967, pp. 146–47). It was through her fiancé that Agnes learned that sunbathing on the lawn in front of her apartment was "offensive" (because it put her on display to other men). She also learned from his critiques of other women that she should not insist on having things her way and that she should not offer her opinions or claim equality with men (Garfinkel 1967, pp. 147–48). (Like other women in our society, Agnes learned something about power in the course of her "education.")

Popular culture abounds with books and magazines that compile idealized depictions of relations between women and men. Those focused on the etiquette of dating or prevailing standards of feminine comportment are meant to be of practical help in these matters. However, the use of any such source *as a manual of procedure* requires the assumption that doing gender merely involves making use of discrete, well-defined bundles of behavior that can simply be plugged into interactional situations to produce recognizable enactments of masculinity and femininity. The man "does" being masculine by, for example, taking the woman's arm to guide her across a street, and she "does" being feminine by consenting to be guided and not initiating such behavior with a man.

Agnes could perhaps have used such sources as manuals, but, we contend, doing gender is not so easily regimented (Mithers 1982; Morris 1974). Such sources may list and describe the sorts of behaviors that mark or display gender, but they are necessarily incomplete (Garfinkel 1967, pp. 66–75; Wieder 1974, pp. 183–214; Zimmerman and Wieder 1970, pp. 285–98). And to be successful, marking or displaying gender must be finely fitted to situations and modified or transformed as the occasion demands. Doing gender consists of managing such occasions so that, whatever the particulars, the outcome is seen and seeable in context as gender-appropriate or, as the case may be, gender-inappropriate, that is, *accountable*.

Resources for Doing Gender

Doing gender means creating differences between girls and boys and women and men, differences that are not natural, essential, or biological. Once the differences have been constructed, they are used to reinforce the "essentialness" of gender. In a delightful account of the "arrangement between the sexes," Goffman (1977) observes the creation of a variety of institutionalized frameworks through which our "natural, normal sexedness" can be enacted. The physical features of social setting provide one obvious resource for the expression of our "essential" differences. For example, the sex segregation of North American public bathrooms distinguishes "ladies" from "gentlemen" in matters held to be fundamentally biological, even though both "are somewhat similar in the question of waste products and their elimination" (Goffman 1977, p. 315). These settings are furnished with dimorphic equipment (such as urinals for men or elaborate grooming facilities for women), even though both sexes may achieve the same ends through the same means (and apparently do so in the privacy of their own homes). To be stressed here is the fact that:

> The *functioning* of sex-differentiated organs is involved, but there is nothing in this functioning that biologically recommends segregation; *that* arrangement is a totally cultural matter . . . toilet segregation is presented as a natural consequence of the difference between the sex-classes when in fact it is a means of honoring, if not producing, this difference. (Goffman 1977, p. 316)

Standardized social occasions also provide stages for evocations of the "essential female and male natures." Goffman cites organized sports as one such institutionalized framework for the expression of manliness. There, those qualities that ought "properly" to be associated with masculinity, such as endurance, strength, and competitive spirit, are celebrated by all parties concerned—participants, who may be seen to demonstrate such traits, and spectators, who applaud their demonstrations from the safety of the sidelines (1977, p. 322).

Assortative mating practices among heterosexual couples afford still further means to create and maintain differences between women and men. For example, even though size, strength, and age tend to be normally distributed among females and males (with considerable overlap between them), selective pairing ensures couples in which boys and men are visibly bigger, stronger, and older (if not "wiser") than the girls and women with whom they are paired. So, should situations emerge in which greater size, strength, or experience is called for, boys and men will be ever ready to display it and girls and women, to appreciate its display (Goffman 1977, p. 321; West and Iritani 1985).

Gender may be routinely fashioned in a variety of situations that seem conventionally expressive to begin with, such as those that present "helpless" women next to heavy objects or flat tires. But, as Goffman notes, heavy, messy, and precarious concerns can be constructed from *any* social situation, "even though by standards set in other settings, this may involve something that is light, clean, and safe" (Goffman 1977, p. 324). Given these resources, it is clear that *any* interactional situation sets the stage for depictions of "essential" sexual natures. In sum, these situations "do not so much allow for the expression of natural differences as for the production of that difference itself" (Goffman 1977, p. 324).

Many situations are not clearly sex categorized to begin with, nor is what transpires within them obviously gender relevant. Yet any social encounter can be pressed into service in the interests of doing gender. Thus, Fishman's (1978) research on casual conversations found an asymmetrical "division of labor" in talk between heterosexual intimates. Women had to ask more questions, fill more silences, and use more attention-getting beginnings in order to be heard. Her conclusions are particularly pertinent here:

> Since interactional work is related to what constitutes being a woman, with what a woman *is*, the idea that it *is* work is obscured. The work is not seen as what women do, but as part of what they are. (Fishman 1978, p. 405)

We would argue that it is precisely such labor that helps to constitute the essential nature of women *as* women in interactional contexts (West and Zimmerman 1983, pp. 109–11; but see also Kollock, Blumstein, and Schwartz 1985).

Individuals have many social identities that may be donned or shed, muted or made more salient, depending on the situation. One may be a friend, spouse, professional, citizen, and many other things to many different people—or, to the same person at different times. But we are always women or men—unless we shift into another sex category. What this means is that our identificatory displays will provide an ever-available resource for doing gender under an infinitely diverse set of circumstances.

Some occasions are organized to routinely display and celebrate behaviors that are conventionally linked to one or the other sex category. On such occasions, everyone knows his or her place in the interactional scheme of things. If an individual identified as a member of one sex category engages in behavior usually associated with the other category, this routinization is challenged. Hughes (1945, p. 356) provides an illustration of such a dilemma:

> [A] young woman . . . became part of that virile profession, engineering. The designer of an airplane is expected to go up on the maiden flight of the first plane built according to the design. He [sic] then gives a dinner to the engineers and workmen who worked on the new plane. The dinner is naturally a stag party. The young woman in question designed a plane. Her co-workers urged her not to take the risk—for which, presumably, men only are fit—of the maiden voyage. They were, in effect, asking her to be a lady instead of an engineer. She chose to be an engineer. She then gave the party and paid for it like a man. After food and the first round of toasts, she left like a lady.
>
> On this occasion, parties reached an accommodation that allowed a woman to engage in presumptively masculine behaviors. However, we note that in the end, this compromise permitted demonstration of her "essential" femininity, through accountably "ladylike" behavior.

Hughes (1945, p. 357) suggests that such contradictions may be countered by managing interactions on a very narrow basis, for example, "keeping the relationship formal and specific." But the heart of the matter is that even—perhaps, especially—if the relationship is a formal one, gender is still something one is accountable for. Thus, a woman physician (notice the special qualifier in her case) may be accorded respect for her skill and even addressed by an appropriate title. Nonetheless, she is subject to evaluation in terms of normative conceptions of appropriate attitudes and activities for her sex category and under pressure to prove that she is an "essentially" feminine being, despite appearances to the contrary (West 1984, pp. 97–101). Her sex category is used to discredit her participation in important clinical activities (Lorber 1984, pp. 52–54), while her involvement in medicine is used to discredit her commitment to her responsibilities as a wife and mother (Bourne and Wikler 1978, pp. 435–37). Simultaneously, her exclusion from the physician colleague community is maintained and her accountability *as a woman* is ensured.

In this context, "role conflict" can be viewed as a dynamic aspect of our current "arrangement between the sexes" (Goffman 1977), an arrangement that provides for occasions on which persons of a particular sex category can "see" quite clearly that they are out of place and that if they were not there, their current troubles would not exist. What is at stake is, from the standpoint of interaction, the management of our "essential" natures, and from the standpoint of the individual, the continuing accomplishment of gender. If, as we have argued, sex category is omnirelevant, then any occasion, conflicted or not, offers the resources for doing gender.

We have sought to show that sex category and gender are managed properties of conduct that are contrived with respect to the fact that others will judge and respond to us in particular ways. We have claimed that a person's gender is not simply an aspect of what one is, but, more fundamentally, it is something that one *does*, and does recurrently, in interaction with others.

Gender, Power, and Social Change

Let us return to the question: Can we avoid doing gender? Earlier, we proposed that insofar as sex category is used as a fundamental criterion for differentiation, doing gender is unavoidable. It is unavoidable because of the social consequences of sex-category membership: the allocation of power and resources not only in the domestic, economic, and political domains but also in the broad arena of interpersonal relations. In virtually any situation, one's sex category can be relevant, and one's performance as an incumbent of that category (i.e., gender) can be subjected to evaluation. Maintaining such pervasive and faithful assignment of lifetime status requires legitimation.

But doing gender also renders the social arrangements based on sex category accountable as normal and natural, that is, legitimate ways of organizing social life. Differences between women and men that are created by this process can then be portrayed as fundamental and enduring dispositions. In this light, the institutional arrangements of a society can be seen as responsive to the differences—the social order being merely an accommodation to the natural order. Thus if, in doing gender, men are also doing dominance and women are doing deference (cf. Goffman 1967, pp. 47–95), the resultant social order, which supposedly reflects "natural differences," is a powerful reinforcer and legitimator of hierarchical arrangements. Frye observes:

> For efficient subordination, what's wanted is that the structure not appear to be a cultural artifact kept in place by human decision or custom, but that it appear *natural*—that it appear to be quite a direct consequence of facts about the beast which are beyond the scope of human manipulation. . . . That we are trained to behave so differently as women and men, and to behave so differently toward women and men, itself contributes mightily to the appearance of extreme dimorphism, but also, the *ways* we act as women and men, and the *ways* we act toward women and men, mold our bodies and our minds to the shape of subordination and dominance. We do become what we practice being. (Frye 1983, p. 34)

If we do gender appropriately, we simultaneously sustain, reproduce, and render legitimate the institutional arrangements that are based on sex category. If we fail to do gender appropriately, we as individuals—not the institutional arrangements—may be called to account (for our character, motives, and predispositions).

Social movements such as feminism can provide the ideology and impetus to question existing arrangements, and the social support for individuals to explore alternatives to them. Legislative changes, such as that proposed by the Equal Rights Amendment, can also weaken the accountability of conduct to sex category, thereby affording the possibility of more widespread loosening of accountability in general. To be sure, equality under the law does not guarantee equality in other arenas. As Lorber (1986, p. 577) points out, assurance of "scrupulous equality of categories of people considered essentially different needs constant monitoring." What such proposed changes *can* do is provide the warrant for asking why, if we wish to treat women and men as equals, there needs to be two sex categories at all (see Lorber 1986, p. 577).

The sex category/gender relationship links the institutional and interactional levels, a coupling that legitimates social arrangements based on sex category and reproduces their asymmetry in face-to-face interaction. Doing gender furnishes the interactional scaffolding of social structure, along with a built-in mechanism of social control. In appreciating the institutional forces that maintain distinctions between women and men, we must not lose sight of the interactional validation of those distinctions that confers upon them their sense of "naturalness" and "rightness."

Social change, then, must be pursued both at the institutional and cultural level of sex category and at the interactional level of gender. Such a conclusion is hardly novel. Nevertheless, we suggest that it is important to recognize that the analytical distinction between institutional and interactional spheres does not pose an either/or choice when it comes to the question of effecting social change.

DISCUSSION QUESTIONS

1. What do the authors mean when they say that gender is something that we "do"?
2. How do the ideas in this article relate to those in Goffman's *Presentation of Self* article from the last section?
3. How does the act of "doing" gender in face-to-face interactions support and legitimize institutionalized gender differences?
4. Are the authors arguing that gendered differences in interactions are reflections of natural differences between men and women or that gendered differences in interactions have the effect of making what are really social differences appear natural?
5. What is the difference between sex, sex category, and gender? Why do the authors argue these distinctions are important?
6. Can you think of an example of an "institutionalized framework" (p. 149) that facilitates or demands that people "do" gender?
7. How do the institutional arrangements that support a dichotomous gender system (men and women) affect the social interactions of those who do not clearly identify with either gender?

REFERENCES

Bernstein, Richard. 1986. "France Jails 2 in Odd Case of Espionage." *New York Times* (May 11).

Blackwood, Evelyn. 1984. "Sexuality and Gender in Certain Native American Tribes: The Case of Cross-Gender Females." *Signs: Journal of Women in Culture and Society* 10:27–42.

Bourne, Patricia G. and Norma J. Wikler. 1978. "Commitment and the Cultural Mandate: Women in Medicine." *Social Problems* 25:430–40.

Cucchiari, Salvatore. 1981. "The Gender Revolution and the Transition from Bisexual Horde to Patrilocal Band: The Origins of Gender Hierarchy." In: *Sexual Meanings: The Cultural Construction of Gender and Sexuality*, edited by S. B. Ortner and H. Whitehead. New York: Cambridge, pp. 31–79.

Fishman, Pamela. 1978. "Interaction: The Work Women Do." *Social Problems* 25:397–406.

Frye, Marilyn. 1983. *The Politics of Reality: Essays in Feminist Theory*. Trumansburg, NY: The Crossing Press.

Garfinkel, Harold. 1967. *Studies in Ethnomethodology*. Englewood Cliffs, NJ: Prentice Hall.

Gerson, Judith M. and Kathy Peiss. 1985. "Boundaries, Negotiation, Consciousness: Reconceptualizing Gender Relations." *Social Problems* 32:317–31.

Goffman, Erving. 1967 (1956). "The Nature of Deference and Demeanor." In *Interaction Ritual*. New York: Anchor/Doubleday, pp. 47–95.

Goffman, Erving. 1976. "Gender Display." *Studies in the Anthropology of Visual Communication* 3:69–77.

Goffman, Erving. 1977. "The Arrangement Between the Sexes." *Theory and Society* 4:301–31.

Henley, Nancy M. 1985. "Psychology and Gender." *Signs: Journal of Women in Culture and Society* 11:101–119.

Hill, W. W. 1935. "The Status of the Hermaphrodite and Transvestite in Navaho Culture." *American Anthropologist* 37:273–79.

Hughes, Everett C. 1945. "Dilemmas and Contradictions of Status." *American Journal of Sociology* 50:353–59.

Jaggar, Alison M. 1983. *Feminist Politics and Human Nature*. Totowa, NJ: Rowman & Allanheld.

Kessler, Suzanne J. and Wendy McKenna. 1978. *Gender: An Ethnomethodological Approach*. New York: Wiley.

Kollock, Peter, Philip Blumstein, and Pepper Schwartz. 1985. "Sex and Power in Interaction." *American Sociological Review* 50:34–46.

Lorber, Judith. 1984. *Women Physicians: Careers, Status and Power*. New York: Tavistock.

Lorber, Judith. 1986. "Dismantling Noah's Ark." *Sex Roles* 14:567–80.

Martin, M. Kay and Barbara Voorheis. 1975. *Female of the Species*. New York: Columbia University Press.

Mithers, Carol L. 1982. "My Life as a Man." *The Village Voice* 27 (October 5):1ff.

Money, John. 1974. "Prenatal Hormones and Postnatal Sexualization in Gender Identity Differentiation." In *Nebraska Symposium on Motivation*, Vol. 21, edited by J. K. Cole and R. Dienstbier. Lincoln: University of Nebraska Press, pp. 221–95.

Money, John and John G. Brennan. 1968. "Sexual Dimorphism in the Psychology of Female Transsexuals." *Journal of Nervous and Mental Disease* 147:487–99.

Money, John and Anke A. Ehrhardt. 1972. *Man and Woman/Boy and Girl*. Baltimore: Johns Hopkins University Press.

Money, John and Charles Ogunro. 1974. "Behavioral Sexology: Ten Cases of Genetic Male Intersexuality with Impaired Prenatal and Pubertal Androgenization." *Archives of Sexual Behavior* 3:181–206.

Money, John and Patricia Tucker. 1975. *Sexual Signatures*. Boston: Little, Brown.

Morris, Jan. 1974. *Conundrum*. New York: Harcourt Brace Jovanovich.

Raymond, Janice G. 1979. *The Transsexual Empire*. Boston: Beacon.

Richards, Renée (with John Ames). 1983. *Second Serve: The Renée Richards Story*. New York: Stein and Day.

Sacks, Harvey. 1972. "On the Analyzability of Stories by Children." In *Directions in Sociolinguistics*, edited by J. J. Gumperz and D. Hymes. New York: Holt, Rinehart & Winston, pp. 325–45.

Schutz, Alfred. 1943. "The Problem of Rationality in the Social World." *Economics* 10:130–49.

West, Candace. 1984. "When the Doctor Is a 'Lady': Power, Status and Gender in Physician-Patient Encounters." *Symbolic Interaction* 7:87–106.

West, Candace and Bonita Iritani. 1985. "*Gender Politics in Mate Selection: The Male-Older Norm.*" Paper presented at the Annual Meeting of the American Sociological Association, August, Washington, DC.

West, Candace and Don H. Zimmerman. 1983. "Small Insults: A Study of Interruptions in Conversations Between Unacquainted Persons." In *Language, Gender and Society*, edited by B. Thorne, C. Kramarae, and N. Henley. Rowley, MA: Newbury House, pp. 102–17.

Wieder, D. Lawrence. 1974. *Language and Social Reality: The Case of Telling the Convict Code*. The Hague: Mouton.

Williams, Walter L. 1986. *The Spirit and the Flesh: Sexual Diversity in American Indian Culture*. Boston: Beacon.

Wilson, Thomas P. 1970. "Conceptions of Interaction and Forms of Sociological Explanation." *American Sociological Review* 35:697–710.

Zimmerman, Don H. and D. Lawrence Wieder. 1970. "Ethnomethodology and the Problem of Order: Comment on Denzin." In *Understanding Everyday Life*, edited by J. Denzin. Chicago: Aldine, pp. 287–95.

NOTES

1. http://www.dailymail.co.uk/news/article-1389593/Kathy-Witterick-DavidStocker-raising-genderless-baby.html
2. This definition understates many complexities involved in the relationship between biology and culture (Jaggar 1983, pp. 106–13). However, our point is that the determination of an individual's sex classification is a *social* process through and through.
3. This is not to say that gender is a singular "thing," omnipresent in the same form historically or in every situation. Because normative conceptions of appropriate attitudes and activities for sex categories can vary across cultures and historical

moments, the management of situated conduct in light of those expectations can take many different forms.

4. Bernstein (1986) reports an unusual case of espionage in which a man passing as a woman convinced a lover that he/she had given birth to "their" child, who, the lover, thought, "looked like" him.

5. For example, in 2009, South African track star Caster Semenya was required to undergo what was dubbed a "gender test" after her appearance and performance in the 800-meter world championships raised doubts about her sex.

Authors' Note: *This article is based in part on a paper presented at the Annual Meeting of the American Sociological Association, Chicago, September 1977. For their helpful suggestions and encouragement, we thank Lynda Ames, Bettina Aptheker, Steven Clayman, Judith Gerson, the late Erving Goffman, Marilyn Lester, Judith Lorber, Robin Lloyd, Wayne Mellinger, Beth E. Schneider, Barrie Thorne, Thomas P. Wilson, and most especially, Sarah Fenstermaker Berk.*

Doing, Undoing, or Redoing Gender?

Learning From Transpeople in the Workplace

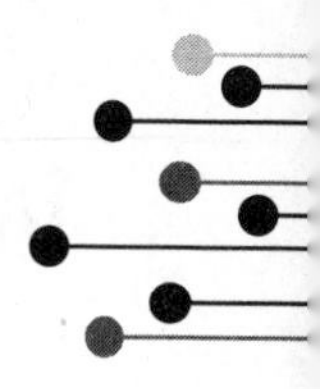

Catherine Connell

Transgender individuals have started to receive much more public acknowledgment in the past few years. At the forefront of this was Caitlyn Jenner, stepfather of Kim and Khloe Kardashian, who transitioned in 2015 and famously came out in part by being photographed for the cover of Vanity Fair *magazine. One criticism of the cover, showing Caitlyn in full makeup, a stereotypically feminine pose and wearing a white corset, is that she was reinforcing the gender binary—the idea that one can only be male or female—rather than challenging societal rules about what gender means and the range of identities that are available.*

In "Doing Gender" (Reading 14), West and Zimmerman argued that being only one of these two gender identities, male or female, is an unavoidable product of our interactions with each other, and they highlight that being genderless is not an option in contemporary American society. This reading questions whether a binary division of gender into male and female is inevitable, or if alternatives are possible. Drawing on interviews with trans individuals about their experiences in the workplace, Catherine Connell tries to understand where the gender identity work of transpeople fits (or doesn't) in West and Zimmerman's widely used theoretical framework about gender.

This reading is an excellent example of the collaborative nature of science in action, with one researcher drawing on and challenging the work of another. Connell's goal is not to prove that West and Zimmerman are wrong and therefore "win," but rather to add what her research tells us about meaningful ways to think about gender identity and push for modifications (or even rejection) of previously held beliefs if the evidence is sufficient. As you spend more time reading within a discipline, you'll start to see familiar names pop up in readings as the authors reference work that you are familiar with. It can be a very satisfying experience, much like bumping into a friend or acquaintance on the street whose company you particularly enjoy, when you first start encountering references to work that you've read. To set yourself up for that satisfying experience here, take a moment to skim over West and Zimmerman's article "Doing Gender" at the beginning of this section before you read this one.

Excerpt from "Doing, Undoing, or Redoing Gender" by Catherine Connell. *Gender & Society* (2010), 24(1): 31–55. Reprinted with permission.

West and Zimmerman developed their theory of "doing gender" (1987) to account for the reproduction of gender through interaction. Two decades later, the theory has reached near canonical status in the sociology of gender (Jurik and Simsen 2009). As doing gender has emerged as the hegemonic theoretical framework for understanding gender inequality, feminist scholars have begun to interrogate the theory's ability to account for social change. A central question in the debate is this: *is undoing gender possible*?

On one side of the debate are those who argue that the gender binary *can* be subverted in interaction (Deutsch 2007; Risman 2009). These scholars criticize the common deployment of doing gender to document the ways gender oppression is maintained, arguing that it is important also to highlight the "undoing" of gender to further the feminist project of dismantling gender inequality (Deutsch 2007). In response, West and Zimmerman (2009) have argued that gender can never be "undone," but might instead be "redone." They argue that the accountability structures that maintain gender may shift to accommodate less oppressive ways of doing gender, but are never entirely eradicated (West and Zimmerman 2009).

Thus far, this debate regarding the possibility of undoing gender has remained largely theoretical. This article offers an important contribution to this discussion by empirically investigating the workplace experiences of transgender-identified individuals. Transpeople disrupt the assumption that sex (designation at birth as either "male" or "female"), sex category (social designation as either "male" or "female" in everyday interactions), and gender (management of conduct based on one's assigned sex category) correspond with each other. While cispeople, or nontrans-identified individuals, are assigned a sex at birth, placed in the corresponding sex category, and held accountable to the corresponding gender norms (doing masculinity or doing femininity), the sex category and/or gender of transpeople does not match up as seamlessly with their sex. Theoretically, this disruption opens up an opportunity to undo or redo gender. Looking at transpeople's experiences allows us to ask the question: When sex, sex category, and gender do not match up, does this result in an undoing of gender? In other words, do transgender people subvert or undermine the gender binary in their daily interactions (Deutsch 2007; Risman 2009)? Alternatively, do transpeople redo gender by expanding or altering the norms associated with gender (West and Zimmerman 2009)?

I interviewed 19 transgender individuals about their negotiation and management of gendered interactions at work, and evaluated how the experiences they disclosed might contribute to doing, undoing, or redoing gender.

The term "transgender" entered the public discourse in the mid-1980s (Elkins and King 1996). It has generally replaced the earlier term "transsexual," which is now used to refer specifically to people who have had or desire surgical and medical procedures that will match their sex to their gender. *Transgender* usually refers to individuals who deliberately reject their original gender assignment. The term may be used regardless of surgical and medical status. Therefore, the category "transgender" includes transsexual individuals, but also encompasses a wider group than this. Transgender people sometimes label themselves transwomen (or male-to-female), transmen (or female-to-male), or genderqueer. *Genderqueer* generally refers to gender identification other than that of "man" or "woman." It often involves a politically motivated blending of gendered presentations, pronouns, and self-concepts. *Transpeople* has become the generic category used to describe everyone in these various categories.

Barbara Risman (2009, p. 82) suggests that we might think of "undoing gender" (Deutsch 2007) as occurring "when the essentialism of binary distinctions between people based on sex category is challenged" (Risman 2009, p. 83). In a response to Risman, West and Zimmerman (2009) take issue with the language of "undoing," claiming that it implies abandonment of accountability to sex category—an abandonment they treat as impossible. They argue that gender is "not so much *undone* as *redone*" (West and Zimmerman 2009, p. 118) through shifts in the accountability structures that sustain gender in interaction. In other words, accountability structures may shift to accommodate challenges to sex category. In this article, I consider whether transpeople's accounts of their gendered work experiences challenge the binary distinctions of sex category and, if so, what this might mean for West and Zimmerman's theory of doing gender. Through an analysis of these experiences, I consider whether transgender workers describe themselves as doing, undoing, or redoing gender.

Method

Because I am interested in questions of meaning making, a qualitative approach was necessary for this research (Esterberg 2002). Since transpeople are located in a variety of jobs, rather than concentrated in any one industry or workplace, ethnography was not suitable for this research project. Ethical concerns about drawing unwanted attention to trans employees by conducting on-the-job observations further precluded an ethnographic account of their individual workplaces. For these reasons, I chose in-depth interviews as my primary research method.

I sought participants from a wide range of racial, ethnic, and class backgrounds. However, my sample is primarily white and, to lesser degree, middle class. This is in part a function of my snowball sampling technique, which tends to produce demographically similar respondents (Esterberg 2002). Seven of the 19 respondents were involved in a local transgender advocacy group; the remaining 12 were referred through the study participants' personal networks. (Thus, the majority were not members of the advocacy group.)

In the semi-structured interviews, research participants were asked to outline their work histories from their first jobs to their current employment situations. If they transitioned on the job, we discussed that process. I also inquired about interactions with supervisors, coworkers, and clients. After all of the interviews were conducted and transcribed, I coded them by reading through each interview carefully and cataloging each theme. As I cataloged, I kept a journal of patterns, connections, interesting anecdotes, themes, and possible theoretical directions.

The transgender workers I interviewed negotiated their changing gender identities in a variety of ways. A few did "stealth," meaning that they did not identify themselves as transgender to their coworkers, nor were they perceived as such (as far as they could tell). Others either engaged in an open transition at work and/or made their transgender status evident through the process of dramatic realization (Goffman 1959), meaning they "came out" as trans.

The decision to be "out" as trans is one that must be individually negotiated based on a number of complex and sometimes contradictory financial, psychological, political, and personal considerations. It must be understood in the socioeconomic context of the individual's life, as well as in the historical context of the violence, stigma, and repression that transpeople have faced. How one navigates this decision in such a repressive environment is not merely a matter of free choice, just as is the case with the gay and lesbian "closet" (Seidman 2002).

My research suggests that the experiences of those performing stealth fit more or less within the theoretical paradigm of doing gender. Out transpeople, on the other hand, described experiences that fit better under either the rubric of undoing gender or of redoing gender. As I will show, they often attempted to meld together masculine and feminine gender performances. At the same time, however, open transpeople often felt they were gender disciplined and/or reinterpreted according to conventional gender norms. In the following section of this article, I will describe these different kinds of transgender experience and explain how they correspond to the processes of doing, undoing, and redoing of gender in the workplace.

Doing Gender at Work

Of the 19 research participants in this study, five performed "stealth" in the workplace, meaning that they did not identify themselves as transgender, nor were they (at least to their knowledge) "read" as transgender by their coworkers and clientele. These transpeople performed masculinity or femininity in a way that masked discordance between sex and sex category, leaving them subject to the same accountability structures of doing gender that cispeople must negotiate.

Mark, a 64-year-old white transman, had been identifying and living as a man for over 25 years. Because of the lack of legal and social protections at the time of his transition, Mark had always worked stealth. He was able to manage this by changing his name, Social Security information, and driver's license in 1985, before restrictive identification policies made this process more difficult (NCTE 2007). Coworkers questioned his gender early in his transition, because, he said, "as a middle-aged male, there were certain things I didn't know, because I hadn't been raised in the environment and so there were certain things that men expected me to know or be or react to that I didn't." Over time, however, Mark learned to do gender in an "appropriately" masculine way. He eventually "assimilate[d] some of that ["appropriate" masculinity] by being in that community, by having to work in that environment where we have to be one or the other." Here, Mark directly references the gender binary established through the application of sex category in interaction. Mark's on-the-job experiences as a stealth transman are consistent with conventional notions of "doing gender" (West and Zimmerman 1987).

Jessica, a 26-year-old Latina transwoman who works as a customer service representative, was also stealth at work. Unlike Mark, she was not motivated by fears of discrimination; in fact, she invoked her rights under new gender identity legal protections when asked what she would do if her coworkers found out about her transgender status, saying that she would "go straight to HR" with any discrimination or harassment concerns that might arise. Jessica defined her decision to remain stealth as a matter of privacy, explaining, "it's really nobody's business—it's not something that I'm ashamed to talk about, whatever, but in an environment with those people, with ignorant people, it's kind of like, there's no point." Because she felt that her "ignorant" coworkers would misunderstand her transgender status, Jessica chose not to identify herself as trans at work.

When asked how her work experience changed since her transition, which occurred before her current job, Jessica described a newfound accountability to the stringent appearance expectations placed on women in the workplace:

> I put more effort into what I wear. A lot. I mean, I think I always did, period, but I think now in particular it's like—like last night, oh my gosh! I was trying on different clothes and it took me like an hour and a half just to figure out what I want to wear today for work. Before that wouldn't usually happen. I'd just throw on whatever. Plus there's certain things I have to wear, to take into consideration, like—I want to wear pants, but I can't wear jeans because we're a business casual environment, and if I wear these pants, did I shave my legs? Do I need to shave my legs? Do I need to wear a skirt that doesn't make my tummy stand out too much or not flatter my butt?

Prior feminist analyses of doing gender at work have underscored the pervasive pressures working women face to conform to conventional standards of feminine beauty (Dellinger and Williams 1997). According to Jessica's experience, these same pressures are exerted on stealth transwomen at work. Mark's and Jessica's experiences, as well as those of the other stealth participants in the sample, suggest that transpeople who do not reveal their transgender status remain subject to the same gendered accountability structures as cispeople. From their perspectives, the disruption of sex, gender, and sex category is not apparent in their interactions with their coworkers; thus, they participate in the process of doing gender described by West and Zimmerman (1987).

Some of the "out" transgender people I interviewed also described experiences that fit under the rubric of doing gender. The process of transition can sometimes bring transpeople more into alignment with gender norms, thereby possibly easing the anxiety of coworkers and employers who were uncomfortable with their gender transgressive appearance pre-transition. Coming out as transgender sometimes mitigates, rather than incurs, ambiguity in gender presentation. This actually allows the transgender subject to be read as more gender normative, thereby making them feel more accepted by others.

This seemed particularly true for the transmen in my study who lived as masculine women before transitioning into men. For example, Bobby, a 47-year-old biracial transman, and Kyle, a 29-year-old white transman, related anecdotes from their previous experiences as women when they were chased out of women's bathrooms for appearing "too masculine" and thereby threatening to the women inside. In particular, Kyle spoke of his prior straggle to "pass" as a woman; work interactions felt easier once his sex category was in line with his gender. He said,

> I can just go to court, wear a suit, not have to worry about what bathroom I'm going to go to or what they're going to call me on the stand when I'm testifying, or how my client is going to react to that. I don't have to worry about it anymore—I wear a suit and it's good to go, no question.

Kyle believed that his transition eased tensions at work and smoothed over the possibility that his gender presentation might have a detrimental effect on his clients' court cases. Thus, Kyle's transition brought him back in line with the norms of gender presentation at his workplace. He felt that people were more accepting of him because he presented a less controversial spectacle.

Several of the out transpeople in my sample described feeling interpreted in a way that reinforced hegemonic gender dynamics at work. They felt that coworkers, clients, and supervisors often reinterpreted their self-presentations and reinforced hegemonic gender dynamics at work, often in spite of their more transgressive beliefs and practices regarding gender. For instance, Julie, a 31-year-old Latina transwoman, mentioned how, as a customer service representative, customers often tried to make sense of her masculine voice by hearing her name wrong. She explained, "When I said 'This is Julie' on the phone, they would repeat it back to me as 'Julian?' So I started saying 'Juliette' but they still changed it into a guy's name, even less related sounding—'George?' 'Jake?'" Julie felt that her customers were trying to make sense of her masculine vocal presentation by assuming that they misheard her feminine name and translating it into a similar sounding (and even not-so-similar sounding) man's name, thus making her accountable to doing gender. Julie's experiences imply interactional limitations to the possibility of undoing or redoing gender when other participants in the interaction uphold gender accountability by resisting or reinterpreting discordant gender cues.

After announcing his transition and presenting as a man at work, Kurt, a 62-year-old white transman, felt policed by other men in the workplace regarding "appropriate" gender behavior. He recalled, "This one guy—it's kinda funny sometimes, because I'll say, 'I'm gonna slap the crap out of you.' And he says, 'Men do not slap.' And he'll correct me on different things." Kurt's coworker drew the boundary lines for acceptable behavior for men by letting him know that "men do not slap." Consequently, Kurt couldn't express himself without immediately being held accountable to rigid standards of masculine language and actions. To feel accepted as a man, Kurt must learn these "lessons" and adjust himself accordingly. This unbidden "apprenticeship" is a unique consequence of open workplace transitions, in that coworkers feel compelled to teach transpeople the gender normative behaviors they were not socialized into from birth (Schilt and Connell 2007). The experiences of Julie, Kurt, and others suggest that out transpeople are subject to gender accountability in workplace interactions, perhaps even more than cispeople, who may be allowed more room for improvisation in their gender performance.

This finding suggests that simply *being* transgender does not necessarily disrupt doing gender. Those who embody conventional gender presentations find themselves subjected to the accountability structures of doing gender, while those who transgress the rules find themselves corrected or misinterpreted in ways that support the gender binary. However, as the next section of this article shows, the out transgender individuals I interviewed nevertheless resisted these expectations by intentionally disrupting the assumed relationships between sex, gender, and sex category in their workplace interactions. They attempted to undo or redo gender even as their coworkers and clients held them accountable to conventional gender practices.

Undoing or Redoing Gender at Work?

The 13 participants in my sample who were out as transgender intentionally sought to undermine gendered expectations as they began performing their new gender. They were not always successful, because they felt accountable to the conventional gendered practices demanded by their coworkers. However, I found that many resisted these pressures by adapting a hybrid gender style of interacting with others. These acts constitute moments of "chipping away" at the established gender order (Lucal 1999) and, as I will argue, can be interpreted either as "undoing" or "redoing" gender.

Several research participants indicated that they consciously held on to gendered characteristics that did not match their chosen gender presentations. Their reasons for this varied: Some felt that gender-blending had important political meaning, others wanted to maintain parts of themselves that felt authentic even if they didn't perfectly "match" their chosen gender, and still others articulated a combination of both motivations.

For example, Kyle made deliberate decisions to keep certain so-called "feminine" aspects of his work style in his employment as a corrections officer. He did this both to maintain a sense of authenticity and to mitigate the white male privilege that his transition bestowed on him. He described how the style of his interactions with clients differed from that of his male coworkers:

> I tend to take a more female route of "Tell me what you're feeling, tell me where you're at"—that kind of thing, where a lot of our male coworkers are kind of like, in, out, you know, just—these are the boxes I need to check, let's check them. Where I'm, again, I kind of dig into them a little bit more and try to figure out what really is going on. . . . And I know that my clients are just kind of like [eyebrow raised questioningly]. Usually when people meet me they stereotype me as just a straight, white man—but I still talk with my hands, I have a lot of female socialization things that I'm not really willing to compromise because they're part of who I am.

Kyle's relationships with his clients, both in style (talking with his hands) and substance (asking about their feelings), included aspects of his personality that he attributed to his socialization as a woman. Although he perceives these qualities as distinguishing him from other men, he is unwilling to eliminate them from his interactions because they are central to his self-concept. While Kyle's attributes are not innately "female," as he labels them here, they are attributes that are socially interpreted as such. By maintaining these attributes rather than erasing them wholesale in favor of a more masculine self-presentation, Kyle engages in a hybrid form of gender presentation.

Not only did Kyle maintain these attributes because "they're part of who [he is]," he also conceptualized this choice as a critique of white male domination. He recognized that he is read as a "straight white man," but he attempted to craft an alternative kind of masculinity that might mitigate the privilege this gave him.

The genderqueer participants in my research were especially committed to hybrid gender performances. For example, Jared, a 23-year-old white genderqueer teaching assistant, articulated an aspect of political critique and resistance in how ze does gender. (I refer to Jared throughout using the pronouns ze prefers—the gender-neutral "ze" and "hir.") Jared used a masculine name and dressed in men's clothing, yet hir embodiment (short, small, delicate facial features) prevented hir from being read exclusively as a man. As a genderqueer, ze saw this confusing presentation as important hir identity and political work. In fact, Jared noted that if ze were to become more gender normative (as a result of testosterone use), ze would enact other strategies to maintain the confusion:

> I do think about hormones and I wonder if I start taking hormones—I'm going to pass whether I want to or not . . . I'll get read maybe questioningly still, but I'll probably get read as man. So I suppose if I were to start hormones, I might do more fun, feminine things! . . . I've already told my girlfriend that, you know, if and when I ever get a beard, I'm stealing her skirt!

Rather than try to minimize gender confusion, Jared actively cultivated it because of the way it challenged gender assumptions. Jared's intentional challenge to the gender binary suggest that gender is being undone in hir interactions, according to Risman's (2009) definition of undoing gender. Alternately, Jared can be read as attempting to redo gender, or revising the strictly delineated expectations imposed on men and women.

Agape, a 28-year-old white transwoman, also played with gender ambiguity before and after transitioning. In the period when she worked as a man, she occasionally came into the office in a skirt or dress and wore a dress to the office Christmas party two years in a row. Because of her ambiguous presentation before transition, she noted that her transition was confusing for her coworkers:

> I think the manner of my transition made things harder for people, because it was smooth, rather than abrupt. It wasn't like one day I was male and the next day I was female. It was more like, one day I'm kind of vaguely male-ish, and already pretty androgynous, and then I switch to—from like, slightly masculine androgynous to slightly feminine androgynous. I think it just made it kind of blurry for people.

While she initially felt the need to dress "really girly for a few months," she gradually realized that this presentation was a "façade" and didn't fit her. She explained,

> I tried doing the whole girly girl thing, wearing makeup, wearing pretty clothes, and then I was like, "Eh, this is wrong, this isn't me." But it's a phase I had to go through to get to where I am now.

In both her ambiguous style of transition and her decision not to adhere to a "girly girl" style of gender presentation, Agape tried to demonstrate gender transgression for her coworkers. Her choice of a gender-neutral name (meaning "love") underscored her opposition to the gender binary, which may either undo or redo gender in her workplace interactions.

Carolina, a 35-year-old Latina transwoman, explained her self-presentation using the creative term "*transparency*." Carolina was preparing to leave her engineering career, where she openly identified as trans, to attend law school. When I asked Carolina, who said that she passes most of the time, if she would still be out as transgender in law school, she responded:

> Oh yeah, being out is important to me, period. The only way we'll ever change people's minds is for all of us to be out. It doesn't mean you walk around with a big "T" on your forehead, but you gotta let people know. There's an interesting term I heard recently called "*transparency*." I'm gonna be *trans*parent. . . . It means that you don't hide or deny who you are, but you don't wear a Transsexual Menace t-shirt everywhere you go. Yeah, it's less in your face, but you also don't deny or hide who you are. Because for me—who I am and where I come from is very important. I like myself, so why am I going to deny that? Why am I going to—there's this idea of "stealth" which is never telling anyone, making up stories about your past. I'm not going to do that, I like who I am.

Carolina refused to start over as stealth in her new life, even though she probably could do so without much difficulty. She said, "I'm going to make [being transgender] an issue. I'm going to always stand up, especially in law school—I'm going to stand up when we start talking about civil rights and challenge people." Carolina planned to use this strategy of transparency to critique legal and social inequalities.

Many of the transgender workers used "outness" as a strategy of political visibility and role modeling in the workplace. Some engaged in acts of dramatic realization (Goffman 1959) to make their trans status apparent in their interactions with others. These moments of dramatic realization can be subtle, such as Carolina's *trans*parency strategy, or they can be obvious, such as Jared's use of clashing gender displays to highlight hir genderqueer status.

This politicization of transgender, combined with the efforts at hybridity in their gender performances, could be interpreted as moments of undoing or redoing gender. By blending their current and former gender biographies and drawing attention to their disruption of the relationships between sex, gender, and sex category, these trans people interrupt the gender binary. This is what Risman (2009) would identify as a moment of undoing gender. In documenting these moments of undoing gender, Risman (2009, p. 84) would argue, feminist sociologists are providing guideposts for the ultimate political goal of "mov[ing] to a postgender society."

In contrast, West and Zimmerman (2009) might point to the heightened gender accountability that trans people describe as evidence for the impossibility of gender's undoing. As an alternative to undoing gender, they offer the concept of redoing gender, or revisions to gender accountability that "weaken its utility as a ground for men's hegemony" (West and Zimmerman 2009, p. 117). According to this perspective, by enacting a hybrid gender performance, these transpeople "redo" the accountability structures that maintain the rigid boundaries between men's and women's gender presentations. This redoing may challenge the essentialized notions of masculinity that shore up men's power in society, but it does not eliminate gender as a sorting device in interactional or organizational settings.

Conclusion

Drawing from the perspectives of transpeople, this article finds evidence that they experience the doing and the undoing/redoing of gender. Transpeople are tasked with making sense of a disconnect between sex, gender, and sex category, which they solve in a variety of ways, including through "stealth" representations and through a more transparent blending of characteristics from their former and current gender expressions. I call this constellation of interactive practices "doing transgender." Regardless of whether they are stealth or out, transgender positionality sensitizes transpeople to gender discrimination, thereby opening up possibilities for the "collective contestation" (Connell 2009) of gendered inequality by transpeople and cisfeminists.

While sociologists have often used doing gender theory to account for stability in gender relations (Deutsch 2007), these findings suggest that interactions may be a site for change as well as stability, at least for this particular group of individuals. This is not to say that all transpeople attempt to undo or redo gender, but rather that they are all always faced with the complex task of negotiating the discordance between sex, gender, and sex category. My interviews with transpeople show that this negotiation often results in moments of interactive resistance to gender stability that deserve careful attention. Future research might investigate other groups for these changes, as proponents of undoing gender have suggested (Deutsch 2007; Risman 2009). Transpeople are not necessarily the only social actors engaged in the undoing or redoing of gender; in fact, the more moments of challenging the gender binary that are identified, the more common ground is uncovered for transpeople and others to oppose gender inequality.

DISCUSSION QUESTIONS

1. What aspects of West and Zimmerman's "doing gender" idea does the author embrace? Which does she think we should reconsider?
2. What were the different ways that her study participants "did" gender at work? What was their motivation for each of these approaches?
3. Watch an episode of the Amazon show *Transparent*. Do you think Maura is "doing," "undoing," or "redoing" gender? What other kinds of social identities might be said to require "doing," "undoing," or "redoing"?

REFERENCES

Acker, Joan. 1990. "Hierarchies, Jobs, Bodies: A Theory of Gendered Organizations." *Gender & Society* 4(2):139–58.

Bolough, Roslyn W. 1992. "The Promise and Failure of Ethnomethodology from a Feminist Perspective: Comment on Rogers." *Gender & Society* 6(2):199–206.

Bornstein, Kate. 1995. *Gender Outlaw: On Men, Women, and the Rest of Us*. New York: Vintage.

Butler, Judith. 1990. *Gender Trouble: Feminism and the Subversion of Identity*. New York: Routledge.

Butler, Judith. 2000. *Undoing Gender*. New York: Routledge.

Collins, Patricia Hill. 2000. *Black Feminist Thought: Knowledge, Consciousness, and the Politics of Empowerment*. 2nd ed. New York: Routledge.

Connell, R.W. 2006. *Masculinities: Knowledge, Power, and Social Change*. Oxford, UK: Polity Press.

Connell, Raewyn. 2009. "Accountable Conduct: "Doing Gender" in Transsexual and Political Retrospect." *Gender & Society* 23(1):104–11.

Dellinger, K. and C. Williams. 1997. "Makeup at Work: Negotiating Appearance Rules in the Workplace." *Gender & Society* 11(2): 151–77.

Denzin, Norman. 1990. "Harold and Agnes: A Feminist Narrative Undoing." *Sociological Theory* 8(2):198–216.

Deutsch, Frances. 2007. "Undoing Gender." *Gender & Society* 21(2):106–27.

Dozier, Raine. 2005. "Beards, Breasts, and Bodies: Doing Sex in a Gendered World." *Gender & Society* 19(3):297–316.

Eichler, Margrit. 1987. "Sex Change Operations: The Last Bulwark of the Double Standard." In *Gender Roles: Doing What Comes Naturally?* edited by E. D. Salamon & N. Robinson. Toronto: Methuen.

Elkins, R. and D. King. 1996. *Blending Genders: Social Aspects of Cross-Dressing and Sex-Changing*. London and New York: Routledge.

Esterberg, Kristin. 2002. *Qualitative Methods in Social Research*. Boston: McGraw-Hill.

Garfinkel, Harold. 1967. *Studies in Ethnomethodology*. Englewood Cliffs, NJ: Prentice Hall.

Goffman, Erving. 1959. *Presentation of Self in Everyday Life*. New York: Doubleday.

Gorman, Elizabeth. 2005. "Gender Stereotypes, Same-Gender Preference, and Organizational Variation in the Hiring of Women: Evidence from Law Firms." *American Sociological Review* 70:702–28.

HRC. 2009. LGBT equality at the Fortune 500. *Human Rights Campaign*. http://www.hrc.org/issues/fortune500.htm (accessed July 17, 2009).

Irvine, Janice. 1990. *Disorder and Desire: Sex and Gender in Modern American Sexology*. Philadelphia: Temple University Press.

Jurik, N. C. and C. Simsen. 2009. "'Doing Gender' as Canon or Agenda: A Symposium on West and Zimmerman." *Gender & Society* 23(1): 72–75.

Kanter, Rosabeth M. 1977. *Men and Women of the Corporation*. New York: Basic Books.

Kessler, S. J. and W. McKenna. 1978. *Gender: An Ethnomethodological Approach*. Chicago: University of Chicago Press.

Lucal, Betsy. 1999. "What It Means to be Gendered Me: Life on the Boundaries of a Dichotomous Gender System." *Gender & Society* 13(6):781–97.

Martin, Patricia Yancey. 2003. "'Said and Done' versus 'Saying and Doing': Gendering Practices, Practicing Gender at Work." *Gender & Society* 17(3):342–66.

Merton, Robert K. 1972. "Insiders and Outsiders: A Chapter in the Sociology of Knowledge." *American Journal of Sociology* 78:9–47.

Meyerowitz, Joanne. 2002. *How Sex Changed: A History of Transsexuality in the United States*. Cambridge, MA: Harvard University Press.

Mills, C. W. 1940. "Situated Actions and Vocabularies of Motive." *American Sociological Review* 5:904–13.

Namaste, Viviane. 2002. *Invisible Lives: The Erasure of Transsexual and Transgender People*. Chicago: University of Chicago Press.

National Center for Transgender Equality (NCTE). 2007. Federal policy changes, http://www.nctequality.org/Issues/federal_documents.html (accessed July 17, 2009).

National Gay and Lesbian Task Force. 2007. One community. One ENDA. http://www.thetaskforce.org/enda07/enda07.html (accessed July 17, 2009).

Raymond, Janice. 1977. "Transsexualism: The Ultimate Homage to Sex-Role Power." *Chrysalis* 3:11–23.

Raymond, Janice. 1979. *The Transsexual Empire: The Making of the She-Male*. London: Women's Press.

Risman, Barbara. 2009. "From Doing to Undoing: Gender As We Know It." *Gender & Society* 23(1):81–84.

Rogers, Mary F. 1992. "They Were All Passing: Agnes, Garfinkel, and Company." *Gender & Society* 6(2):169–91.

Rudacille, Deborah. 2005. *The Riddle of Gender: Science, Activism, and Transgender Rights*. New York: Pantheon.

Schilt, Kristen. 2006. "Making Gender Visible: Transmen as "Outsiders-Within" in the Workplace." *Gender & Society* 20(4):465–90.

Schilt, K. and C. Connell. 2007. "Do Workplace Gender Transitions Make Gender Trouble?" *Gender, Work, and Organization* 14(6):596–618.

Seidman, Steven. 2002. *Beyond the Closet? The Transformation of Gay and Lesbian Life*. New York: Routledge.

Stone, Allucquére Rosanne. 1993. "The Empire Strikes Back: A Posttransexual Manifesto." *Camera Obscura* 10(2):150–76.

Stryker, Susan. 1987. "Identity Theory: Developments and Extensions." In *Self and Identity: Psychological Perspectives*, edited by K. Yardley and T. Holmes. New York: Wiley.

Stryker, Susan. 1995. "Transsexuality: The Postmodern Body and/as Technology." *Exposure: The Journal of the Society for Photographic Education* 30:38–50.

Vidal-Ortiz, Salvador. 2008. "The Figure of the Transwoman of Color through the Lens of 'doing gender.'" *Gender & Society* 23(10):99–103.

Vidal-Ortiz, Salvador. 2009. "Transgender and Transsexual Studies: Sociology's Influence and Future Steps." *Sociological Compass* 2(2):433–50.

West, C. and D. H. Zimmerman. 1987. "Doing Gender." *Gender & Society* 1(2):125–51.

West, C. and D. H. Zimmerman. 2009. "Accounting for Doing Gender." *Gender & Society* 23(1):112–22.

Williams, Christine. 1989. *Gender Differences at Work: Women and Men in Non-Traditional Occupations*. Berkeley: University of California Press.

Williams, Christine. 1995. *Still a Man's World*. Berkeley: University of California Press.

"Out" in the Club

The Down Low, Hip-Hop, and the Architexture of Black Masculinity

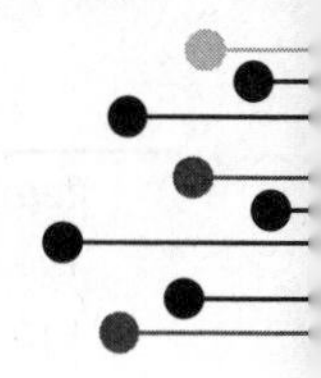

Jeffrey Q. McCune Jr.

Note: This reading contains repeated use of a racial slur

The term "coming out of the closet"—or in short, "coming out"—often refers to an LGBTQ individual making public some aspect of their gender or sexual identity. This is much more common today than it was in the past. American society has changed immensely in its acceptance of homosexuality over the past 30 years. The Diagnostic Statistical Manual (DSM) is the official list of mental disorders recognized by the American Psychiatric Association. The DSM II, published in 1968, listed homosexuality as a mental disorder. It remained in subsequent revisions to the DSM *until 1987. This is one reflection of the widespread attitudes and beliefs that Americans had at the time that homosexuality was immoral, unnatural, and deviant.*

Today, however, a majority of Americans are accepting of homosexuality, and it has lost its taboo, stigmatized status in many (though not all) areas of social life. In 2015, the landmark Supreme Court decision in Obergefell v. Hodges *legalized same-sex marriage in all 50 states, and a Pew Research poll in 2019 found that 61 percent of Americans supported same-sex marriage. That number hides some important differences however, with older people, conservatives, and certain religious groups tending to remain opposed.*

Just as different segments of society feel differently about homosexuality, so too do those who are gay often feel differently about their own sexuality. And as always, social characteristics shape the path that individuals must negotiate as they make their way in the world.

In this research, sociologist Jeffrey McCune explores the intersection of race and sexual identity for black men in a gay hip-hop club called The Gate. Negative stereotypes about black men's sexuality are ubiquitous and many who seek sexual relationships with other men but do not wish to make this desire public find the analogy of "the closet" to be problematic. Instead, they use the

---

Excerpt from "'Out' in the Club: The Down Low, Hip-Hop, and the Architexture of Black Masculinity," by Jeffrey Q. McCune Jr. *Text and Performance Quarterly* (2008), 28(3), pp. 298–314. Reprinted with permission from Taylor & Francis Ltd.

term "on the down low" or DL. Gay clubs are one place where they can take on the role (in Goffman's terms) of someone who enjoys sex with men to whatever extent they find comfortable. As McCune says, "Most men at The Gate are not 'coming out' but participating in a sort of 'comin' in.' They have arrived at a queer space that welcomes them, but does not require them to become official members" (see p. 229). As you read, think about other types of identities that may function in similar ways, become more or less salient depending on the geographic and social locations in which interactions unfold.

> For whom is outness a historically available and affordable option? Is there an unmarked class character to the demand for universal "outness"? Who is represented by which use of the term, and who is excluded? For whom does the term present an impossible conflict between racial, ethnic, or religious affiliation and sexual politics? What kinds of policies are enabled by what kinds of usages and which are backgrounded or erased from view? (Butler 1993, p. 227)

> DL offers a new-school remix of the old-school closet, an improvisation on the coming-out narrative that imagines a low-key way of being in the world. (King 2003, p. 1)

"Coming out of the closet" has been the contemporary niche phrase to articulate the universal threshold experience of sexual self-discovery and self-fulfillment. Recently, however, we have seen the emergence of black men who have discreet sex with other men, who engage in low-key queer activity and describe themselves as being on the "down low" (DL). These men challenge this overdetermination of the closet as a container of shame, pain, discomfort, and anxiety—offering a counter-narrative of discretion as a tactic of survival. As a queer ethnographer committed to understanding the meaning and making of communities, I contend that the closet may be an insufficient trope in critical discussions of the complex sexuality of men of color.[1]

The DL may offer an alternative to the closet—a space where much more happens than black men having sex with wives/girlfriends while having sex with other men—where men actively negotiate issues of race, gender, class, and sexuality. Indeed, if we must accept the idea that black men do play, dwell, or reside in the closet, it is indeed a *quare* one.[2] However, the closet's entanglement with "coming out" often jeopardizes its utility for men of color. As one DL man told me, "There is no closet for us [black men] to go in—neither is it necessary to come out." As these men dis-identify with dominant descriptors and performances of sexuality, their lives are often constructed as a black phenomenon of this contemporary moment, even though discreet sexual politics have historically been a part of black male constructions of sexual identity. The DL extends a historical black cultural practice of "quiet as kept" and "be still and know"—adages which have encouraged many black people to safeguard information, not for deceit but survival. DL men are new bodies dancing to an old song.

This essay maps DL presence within "The Gate,"[3] a known gay club in Chicago, and reveals that black masculinity with its diverse textures uniquely enables the possibility for discreet sexual desire. This essay highlights the minoritized subjects' use of masculinity within public space, without having to sacrifice notions of privacy, or the politics of sexual discretion. Here, DL men and black gay men re-mix the closet, in the act of *queer world-making*.

I focus on the case study, the experience of a twenty-two-year-old man named "Shawn." I met Shawn at a black fraternity informational—where he introduced himself and gave me his number, saying that he was going to "tell me all about the fraternity." Although I trusted his interest in sharing with me the logistics of black fraternal order, the quick passing of his number on a crumpled sheet of paper during our salutatory handshake exchange suggested otherwise. Our phone conversations, which began as an attempt on his part to pique my erotic interest, turned into a series of conversations around discreet sexual behavior and "stories of a DL Hotboi," as Shawn so humbly described his life story. Shawn's centrality in this essay is important, as he was the first of the men with whom I spoke who I witnessed at a queer club. I use his experiences to illuminate, complicate, and outline some of the contradictions and complexities that arise when a DL guy goes "out." These encounters prompted many questions: How do DL men negotiate their commitment to a heteronormative understanding of self, while participating in homonormative social and sexual activities? What is it about DL subjectivity that allows for such possibilities? What is it about the structures and textures of the club space that invites these performers of discreet sexual identity?

Black Queer World-Making: Going Inside the Gate

The Gate is a gay domain once a week—the Friday night queer outlet for a large hip-hop queer mass. While those who attend The Gate have the option of listening to house or hip-hop, all of the club's advertisements and publicity seems to highlight its hip-hop appeal. Together, those who "kick it" at The Gate partake in what Fiona Buckland describes as *queer world-making*—"a conscious, active way of fashioning the self and the environment, cognitively and physically, through embodied social practices moving through and clustered in the city" (2002, p. 19). While Buckland does not deny the possibility of a racialized subject engaging this practice, her research does not advance a theoretical application that accounts for racial subjectivity. The Gate's patrons were definitely participating in an act of black-queer-world making through their appropriation of a traditionally black heterosexual space and transforming it into a space of and for queer desire.

The dynamics of the hip-hop room as a space that lends access to DL positionality is of the utmost interest. Indeed, this space circulates contradictory messages that supersede traditional boundaries of gender and sexuality, where men negotiate their relationship to and their relationship between masculine bravado and black queer culture.

This odd congruence, between hip-hop and queer desire, has "coolness" at its nexus. Here, I wish to discuss coolness as a more general expression, which Marlene Connor understands as a guiding ethic on how to dress, behave, and interact with approval from a largely black and male spectatorship (1995, pp. 1–10). Coolness is a theory in practice—an embodied rubric that regulates and monitors what is and is not acceptable among black men under and outside of white surveillance. While I argue that coolness is not a uniquely black expression, it is a modern descriptor for a historical tactic. Most importantly, coolness acts as a way of survival, a coping stance/pose that black men engage, in order to make do with what they do or do not have (pp. 4–5). Coolness is a performative utterance and action, whereby men define themselves within and against traditional standards. Indeed, like all performances, it changes depending on those involved, the dimensions of space/place, and who is reading and interpreting the scene of action. The Gate's hip-hop room spilled over with coolness.

This dynamic duo, the combination of hip-hop and queer space (or coolness and queerness), are incongruous at surface level, but a deeper examination can explain this coupling. Historically, hip-hop culture and music have gone against the grain of traditional American music and style—often critiquing dominant structures and modifying other musical forms. Likewise, queerness has also disrupted normative tales of sexuality, re-structuring the perceived composition of our society and generally challenging normative socio-sexual rules and regulations. Together, they seem to make a "fabulous" pair. These two world-making apparatuses disrupt norms, interrogate new ground, and encourage exploration outside the domains of normativity. Ultimately, the relationship between hip-hop and black queer expression is, in a sense, a meeting of two queers. Thus, hip-hop music's use as a medium for homoerotic engagements is not odd, but almost anticipatory. Furthermore, The Gate as a predominantly black establishment would naturally welcome black forms of musical and cultural expression—its patrons are young black men and consumers of hip-hop in other contexts.

While the relationship between hip-hop and queerdom presents an enthralling question, of most interest here is how black queer subjects utilize hip-hop in queer space. Particularly, how does hip-hop serve as an interlocutor between discreet performances of sexual identity and explicit engagements of queer desire? How do DL men utilize queer space, navigating their desire for discretion and the pleasure of homoerotic engagement? How do these men literally dance down low, while simultaneously re-mixing the closet? To gain any critical understanding of this process, we must go "in da club."

"In Da Club": Homoerotic Activity in a Heteronormative Playground

It is about 12:45 a.m. on a cold, below-zero, February morning in northwest Chicago. I stand in front of what once was a site of industrialization—a dark brick building with a one-story front and a raised back—now a structure that contains often contradictory architectures of homo and heteronormative performances. The Gate is a parade of contrast. The physical appearances and fashion "looks" are definitely diverse and dynamic. I enter the club, with a huge bouncer behind me yelling, "Have your IDs ready." I scope the never-ending processional, where there are black men and women of all ages, a few whites and Latinos, a couple of drag queens in pumps, and some folks who appear to have got the night "mixed up." I walk into a small corridor, where plastered on the wall still hangs a sign that announces, "Alternative Lifestyle Night." Near this sign is another that reads "After 1:00 AM, the cover is $12.00." Some of those standing in line scream "Hell, no!" and walk away after they read the sign. I, of course, pay the cover, unsure about what is so special about the 1:00 a.m. hour, yet knowing that there is a rich queer world waiting inside.

Bodies of all ages, sizes, shapes, colors, and fragrances fill both the house and hip-hop spaces. First, as I walk past a bar in the house room, I witness bodies divided across the dance floor by wooden beams in a twenty-by-forty-foot space of sensuality and sexuality. Indeed, this house was divided, clearly quartering off one "type" from the "others." There are men over thirty in one quarter, voguers in another, and two quarters contain men and a few women who are under thirty and uninhibited in how they move and groove—who may often be conceived of as the liberal or "queeny" types. As I walk pass the divas on the dance floor, I follow a crowd into another space, located in the back of this warehouse—the hip-hop room.

As I look above me, below me, and beside me, I observe physical and facial expressions that recall childhood experiences of "mackin'" and "hollerin'." These types of poses and approaches were popular when I was a young boy growing up on Chicago's South Side. Men would often stand, in a neutral position, allowing their eyes to do much of the talking. Then, as they approached the person to whom they were attracted, they would quickly perform this "tight" and often "tough guy" posturing. This performance was often accented by a hand on the groin, a smug face almost always absent of any hint of a smile, a cool slouch in the shoulders, and classic concaveness in the chest. A similar aesthetic appreciation is present in The Gate. Interestingly, however, the presence of women in this space is hardly felt. The "mackin'" and "hollerin'" styles of performance are projected onto bodies of the same sex. There is the dancing male butch—femme binary and its ideological counterpart, heterosexual male-female pairing.

As I step down from the passway onto the dance floor, to my surprise I see Shawn. This twenty-two-year-old college student classifies himself as being on the DL, and previously vowed that he would never "be caught dead in one of those sissy clubs." I am even more surprised when Shawn acknowledges me and proceeds to take my hand and place it on his groin. This is the first time he has ever made such a move, but the time and space encourage him to lose many of his inhibitions and insecurities. When I ask Shawn about the incident, particularly the level of comfort he displayed, he insists that it was due to the alcohol and apologetically says, "I guess I'm becomin' a little bit too comfortable." This statement prompts a longer historical explanation:

> I wasn't always that comfortable. For real. I mean, me and my guy—my best friend—the first time we went to the club in D.C., we practically hid. We wore our hats so far down over our faces; the most you probably could see was my smile and his goatee. We wore real big clothes to conceal our identities. . . . Now I don't know who would have known me in D.C., being that I was from the west suburbs of Chicago.

This admission, clearly marking Shawn's evolution from being very discreet to less discreet in his participation in club life, is informative. While it illuminates a certain level of comfort, it could potentially suggest that Shawn has "come into himself." However, this comfort within the space of the club does not speak to his behavior in company outside the club. In fact, I observe that Shawn's anxiety over how his fraternity, friends at school, and family would respond to his presence becomes an almost overwhelming concern. Specifically, he articulates a concern for his reputation amongst his "brotherhood" as the "pretty boy, ladies man"—a title which clearly informs Shawn's general performance of masculinity. The most striking image in this narrative is the costume for concealment, the utilization of hip-hop gear to mask identity. Shawn is astutely aware of the value of clothes in the regulation and monitoring of what is properly masculine. In a sense, Shawn and his friend's clothing is the material mask for their queer desire. His cap is a signifier of hip-hop, while it is also a sign of Shawn's desire to not see and to be seen. All at once, hip-hop is the corroborator and the concealer of queer desire.

Shawn is able not only to be present at The Gate, but also to activate his sexual desires without fear of losing his "masculine" card. My astonishment over Shawn's presence at The Gate, and his behavior therein, is related to his adamant insistence that his identity was "private," a term that connoted a keen sense of discretion. Typically, the men I had encountered previously would not be seen at an announced "gay" or "alternative" night at any club. Since this encounter, I have seen Shawn at one other gay club that offered a hip-hop fix. Later, he told me, "I can't stand house music—hip-hop is where it's at!" It becomes clear that his ability to engage hip-hop texts and perform a hip-hop brand of masculinity was part of the impetus for his participation in this particular "alternative" Friday at The Gate.

Fifty Cent continues:

> *I'm that cat by the bar toasting to the good life You that faggot ass nigga trying to pull me back right?*

The last line invokes audience participation. As I deepen the groove of my sway dance, gay men and women shout "faggot ass nigga." Actually, they shout the whole line, but it is this part of the line that throws me. It seems contradictory for these queers of color to engage in such a chant. I turn to a friend, giving him a look of shock and disheartenment, and he says, "It's just like the way we use nigga by itself." However, why would those who, like myself, have endured being called "faggot," "sissy," and "punk" re-articulate such problematic rhetoric? Why would Shawn, DL men in general, seemingly draw pleasure from this chant of hate and homophobia? As people throw their hands in the air, almost marching to construct a chorus-like concentric circle of "faggot ass nigga," something tells me this is "cool."

This performance of heterosexism seems to work in collaboration with a larger desire to be "cool." The queer subjects who yell "faggot ass nigga" can feel a part of a larger black masculine sphere—one that usually excludes them. In this masculine imaginary, often the way to affirm one's normality is through participation in homophobic or sexist acts. When one takes possession of the "faggot," or the "nigga," it reduces the legitimacy of such ascriptions being made upon the speaker's body. In this way, the utterance of the profane empowers the speaker/chanter, affirming his status as appropriately masculine. This chanting moment is emblematic of the "cooling" of the hip-hop room, while also illuminating the ways in which one type of masculinity seems to pose itself as the cool. In this way, the hip-hop room and its patrons, through so-called performances of heterogender, position the hip-hop space as the greater of the two rooms. It is within the hip-hop room that the "real men" reside. Traditional heteromasculine behavior and codes deem this space "hot." This behavior, though highly problematic, suggests that the "aesthetics of the cool" is always a balancer of the hot (Thompson 1966 85–102). Whereas Thompson is speaking to the literal hotness of bodies, I employ "hot" to align with contemporary black vernacular, where this adjective signifies the place in vogue—"the spot"—the atmosphere that is most enlivened. Indeed, the men in the hip-hop room understand the hip-hop room as such, while the "room of sissies" is the place less desired—really gay, so to speak.

It would be dishonest to ignore the ways in which "faggot ass nigga" is something of an inside joke. All those who participate in the "alternative" night at The Gate are aware of their appetite for those of the same sex. Thus, the utterance of the chant also brings with it a reminder that the space is a queer, or "faggot," terrain. In some ways, the mass chant announces, "We are black faggots, but look who's in possession of these words now?!" In this sense, my friend's comparison of the chanted phrase and the vernacular use of "nigga" is an apt one. Black queer men re-appropriate these terms, turn them on their heads, and thereby reduce the power of the terms in constructing their identities. In addition, the overwhelming presence of homoeroticism present in the oft-cited homophobic space of hip-hop is a running joke. In the popular queer imagining, the hip-hop (hyper) homophobe, in this case Fifty Cent, is often read as indicating a propensity towards, not away from, gayness. However, I suggest that this analysis is less applicable to many men on the DL, as they often disidentify with traditional identifications of sexuality in their everyday lives. Many DL men are like the artists, farthest from "faggots"—they are the embodiment of the properly masculine. Thus, their sexuality is less problematic—deemed legitimate because it is not tainted by femininity or faggotry. While this appears to be internal homophobia run amuck, I caution against this interpretation. For these men, the "faggot" and the "feminine" are classifiers of gender performance, rather than reflective of their views on homoerotic desire or male–male sex.

I spend critical time in this essay discussing this moment of hip-hop heterosexist and homophobic chanting because it exposes what I believe is the true pleasure of this queer zone, for black gay men and DL men alike. In this space, performances of gender and sexuality are in flux—men are able to be queer while also acting straight, or even straight while acting queer. Patrons of The Gate are able to realize the treasure of performance that many of us scholars take as given, whereby performance "is a means by which people reflect on their current conditions, define and/or re-invent themselves and their social world, and either re-enforce, resist, or subvert prevailing social orders" (Drewal 1991, p. 9). The Gate offers an occasion for black queer men to attain pleasure through the stimulation created by the multiple valences within the hip-hop space. In this unique space of queer world-making, these men can "re-enforce, resist, [accept] and subvert" dominant modes of gender and sexuality. While black men can identify and perform their queer desire (resist/subvert), they can still participate in the rituals of patriarchy (re-enforce/accept). At the Gate, or any queer world-making space for that matter, bodies produce paradoxical effects which cannot be understood if one tries to force them into a dichotomy of resistance or submission. At The Gate, a belief in a functional system of resist/re-enforce/subvert would definitely be inappropriate—ignoring the powerful and provocative presence of the both/and operation, an element of constancy within the hip-hop room. This may be the queerest characteristic of this space—where heterogender, hip-hop, and homoeroticism are married through music and dance. In the hip-hop space, all black queer men can participate and feel "normal," almost un-queer, as the culture of the space encourages homoerotic desires for each subject, as he dances in the largely heteronormative playground.

It is DL men's physical presence in the queer club that much of the media has misread, as they stake claim to an "out" DL subject. In actuality, most men at The Gate are not "coming out," but participating in a sort of "comin' in." They have arrived in a queer space that welcomes them, but does not require them to become. The Gate is a black home they can come into, where the relatives understand the fullness of diversity, liberalness, and transgressiveness, and are honest about different forms of desire. The discursive demand that one must be "out" to participate in gay activities ignores the fact that all gay activity does not take place in the public domain; neither does individual participation always guarantee membership. Indeed, DL men are out in the club—in the sense that they are a part of a queer world-making moment. However, outside this club space they live very discreet lives, void of public displays of pleasure and desire for those of the same sex.

The Gate allows DL men to imagine themselves in a sort of utopia (but not quite.) This pleasure, attained through a queer world-making experience, may be the answer to the problematic question: Why are they in a gay club if they are not gay? The answer to this question, I argue here, is all about the structure of the space (its physical frame) and the texture of the space (the ideological frames of gender)—that which I wish to call *architexture*.

The Gate's *architexture* is elastic, but the privileged performance of certain style of masculinity welcomes the presence of DL men. In a sense, The Gate provides a space for DL men to partake in queer desire without having to feel queer (double entendre intended). Most importantly, The

Gate teaches us how DL men not only exercise queer play, but inadvertently challenge the quick assumptions we can often make about queer performance in so-called queer space. This project cautions us always to be attentive to the interplay of race, gender, class, and sexuality—as they are often better arbiters of the meanings of space, Judith Butler's rhetorical questions at the outset of this essay, then, are apropos. Racialized queers often do not desire, and cannot afford, to be "out." Thus, the closet as a threshold apparatus does not fully illustrate the ways in which the patrons of The Gate work through their sexuality. Black queer people have always done queer differently. Symbolically, The Gate, unlike the closet, is not a place of residence, but a place for possibilities to be explored. It is a place where subjects can "come in," while still recognizing the cultural fabrics of heteronormative black life, which they value and experience, as both a part of and separate from their queer experience. The Gate is a heterogeneous playground whose architexture allows its patrons to explore and enjoy temporal pleasure—through the conjoining of oft-thought disparate traditions. As such, the architexture of The Gate accommodates multiple masculinities, speaking for multiple experiences, while still being attentive to the cross-cutting tropes which attract various bodies to specific cultural spaces.

In this essay, I have attempted to highlight one complicated space that exhibits black queers "making do" within a heteronormative society and white cultural tradition. As DL men "come in" The Gate, they redefine the queer world-making experience, as disrupting not only the hetero-norms but also the traditional homonorms of outness as always being predicated upon one's participation in ordained public gay space. This idea of "comin' in" more richly accounts for how it is that many black queer clubs negate and challenge more universal rubrics and force-fitted assertions that queer spaces are always already architextures of outness.

As I sit at my desk, imagining the space of The Gate and the many possibilities within, I am drawn back to Isaac Julien's film *Looking for Langston*. I return to a masterful moment when the film returns to a historic scene, where black men are gathered in a discreet space to party and partake in homoerotic desires. Some stand with drinks, some chat, and some dance with each other—all feeling the pulse of the erotic and the pleasure of this rare opportunity. Dressed in period suits, drinking and tasting the finest of things, these men engage desire on their own terms, in their own way, somewhere "down low" and outside the radar of heteronormative gazes. This moment in film, mirrors so much of what I see at The Gate. Black men and black queer men engage desire and use space, style, and music to guide their performances of sexuality. The Gate is no contemporary coincidence; it is a space that resurrects an older, rich tradition. It is a re-telling of black queer men, cautiously and creatively, dancing desire. It is an illustration of black queer performance happening outside the closet, but still inside The Gate.

DISCUSSION QUESTIONS

1. What does it mean to be "on the down low"? Why might this more likely be for black men than for white men?
2. Who is Shawn? How does he see and enact his sexual orientation?
3. What is counterintuitive about black men who identify, occasionally or entirely, as queer, embracing and enjoying hip-hop music and culture?
4. What does the term *architexture* refer to? How might this term be applied to hook-up culture?

REFERENCES

Betsky, Aaron. 1997. *Queer Space: Architecture and Same-Sex Desire*. New York: Morrow and Company.

Boyd, Todd. 1997. *Am I Black Enough for You*. Bloomington: Indiana University Press.

Buckland, Fiona. 2002. *Impossible Dance: Club Culture and Queer World-Making*. Middletown, CT: Wesleyan University Press.

Butler, Judith. 1993. *Bodies That Matter: On the Discursive Limits of Sex*. New York: Routledge.

Connor, Marlene. 1995. *What Is Cool?: Understanding Black Manhood in America*. New York: Agate.

de Certeau, Michael. 1985. "The Practices of Space." In *On Signs*, edited by Michael Blonsky. Oxford, UK: Blackwell, pp. 122–15.

DeFrantz, Thomas. 2004. "The Black Beat Made Visible." In *Of the Presence of the Body: Essays on Dance and Performance Theory*, edited by Andre Lepecki. Middletown, CT: Wesleyan University Press, pp. 64–81.

Denizet-Lewis, Benoit. 2003. "Double Lives on the Down Low." *New York Times Magazine* (August 3), sec. 6, pp. 28–33, 48, 52–53.

Drewal, Margaret. 1991. "The State of Research on Performance in Africa." *African Studies Review* 34(3):1–64.

Halperin, David. 1995. *Saint Foucault: Towards a Gay Hagiography*. New York: Oxford University Press.

Halperin, David. 2001. "'Quare' Studies or (Almost) Everything I Know about Queer Studies I Learned from My Grandmother." *Text and Performance Quarterly* 20(1):1–25.

King, Jason. 2003. "Remixing the Closet: The Down-Low Way of Knowledge." *Village Voice* (June 25), pp. 38–46.

Lefebvre, Henri. 1991. *The Production of Space*. Trans. Donald Nicholson-Smith. New York: Basil Blackwell.

Reddy, Chandan. 1998. "Home, House, and Nonidentity. Paris Is Burning." In *Burning Down the House: Recycling Domesticity*, edited by Rosemary George. Boulder, CO: Westview Press, pp. 355–79.

Sedgwick, Eve. 1990. *Epistemology of Closet*. Berkeley: University of California Press.

Stockton, Kathryn Bond. 2006. *Beautiful Bottom, Beautiful Shame: Where 'Black' Meets 'Queer'*. Durham, NC: Duke University Press.

Thompson, Robert. 1966. "Dance and Culture, an Aesthetic of the Cool: West African Dance." *African Forum* 2(Fall):85–102.

Venable, Malcolm. 2001. "A Question of Identity." *Vibe* (July):98–108.

Warner, Michael. 1993. *Fear of a Queer Planet Queer Politics and Social Theory*. Minneapolis: University of Minneapolis Press.

NOTES

1. In my forthcoming book manuscript, tentatively titled *Queering the Closet: Black Masculinity and the Politics of Sexual Passing*, I argue that the closet is a traditionally white paradigm, which has little/limited utility for black men who face issues of sexuality under racialized oppression. America's history of racism, and consequent surveillance of black male bodies, makes the closet an inept signifier/descriptor of black masculine performances of discreet sexuality. Rather, I argue that black men, and others within the black community, have found alternative ways of naming and identifying their discreet desire and practice.
2. The DL, in essence, *quares* the closet, in that it introduces a racialized understanding of the world, while also drawing attention to the role of intersecting identities in the production of space and time. Here, I draw on E. Patrick Johnson's instructive theoretical and methodological move to account for different "standpoints" and to recognize how intersectional identities affect gender and sexual performances. The DL, as positionality, signifies a location where space is instantiated with homoerotic codes and meanings, with potentially (non) temporal possibilities. Thus, the DL challenges the popular understanding of the closet as always already a dark place with temporary utility.
3. The name of this club has been modified, to secure confidentiality for the men with whom I speak, as well as the club and its other patrons.

READING 17

Masculine Norms and Infectious Disease

The Case of COVID-19

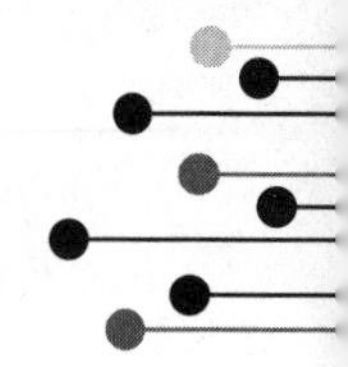

Tyler Reny

How much did you think about what you wore yesterday? If you had a job interview or a first date, you likely gave this a great deal of thought and considered how your different clothing options would be perceived by those you were going to spend time with. But if you had a routine day, odds are you picked your outfit without spending too much time thinking about what each part of your outfit might convey about you—putting on a required uniform for work, stuffing shorts and a t-shirt into a bag for the gym later, or throwing on some comfy pants and a sweatshirt to head to class usually happens without a whole lot of thought as we get on with the business of having a day.

Yet our clothing and accessory choices are full of meaning even when we haven't paid much attention to them. The choices that we make about how to shape our physical appearance reflect the social norms of where and when we are. If you doubt this, ask to see your parents' high school yearbook photo! Each younger generation gleefully teases their elders about their strange haircuts, oddly shaped glasses, and seemingly bizarre fashion choices, all of which were considered just as "cool" at the time as whatever you're wearing right now. Clothing and accessory choices are also shaped by gender norms. In the United States, it is common and unremarkable for women to wear pants, but still unusual for men to wear dresses, reflecting the greater freedom of women to be masculine than there is for men to be feminine. And of course certain professions have particular clothing items and accessories associated with them: white coats and stethoscopes for doctors, polo shirts and an apron for many restaurant servers, hard hats and bright orange vests for construction workers, just to name a few.

Even with this social influence, our choice of clothing and accessories is also a personal choice that we use to symbolically convey information about ourselves. Whether you wear a Taylor Swift t-shirt or a Metallica t-shirt, cutoff jeans or immaculately pressed trousers, bright fluorescent colors or subtle earth

---

Reny, T. (2020). Masculine Norms and Infectious Disease: The Case of COVID-19. *Politics & Gender*, 1–8. Published by Cambridge University Press on behalf of The Women and Politics Research Section of the American Political Science Association.

tones, we often use clothing to convey something about who we are and what we believe.

In the spring of 2020, small, cotton squares of material became a symbolic lightning rod for a whole host of beliefs as the COVID-19 virus spread across the United States and states began either suggesting or mandating wearing a face mask in public. A small but significant number of Americans adamantly opposed being asked or required to do so, even as the scientific evidence mounted that routine mask wearing in public was critical to getting the spread of the virus under control. But unlike the choice of whether to wear jeans or slacks, the choice not to wear a mask has potentially deadly consequences to other individuals and to society. But who is willing to wear a mask and who is not is not just a matter of personality preference that is randomly distributed among those in the United States. In this research, political scientist Tyler Reny shows that mask wearing and not adhering to other protective practices like hand washing and social distancing are much more likely among those with sexist attitudes. And as a result, those with the most sexist attitudes are significantly more likely to contract the COVID-19 virus and become ill themselves, along with passing it to others.

As you read, think about who wears mask and who doesn't, and under what circumstances, as you navigate your day-to-day life. What influence are social norms playing in the decision among those you interact with whether or not to wear mask?

In late May 2020, when the United States had just surpassed 500,000 confirmed COVID-19 cases and nearing 100,000 deaths, President Trump refused to don a mask during a visit to a mask factory in Michigan. The president claimed that he didn't want to give the press the "pleasure of seeing it." He later mocked Democratic presidential candidate Joe Biden for wearing a mask. Trump's refusal to "look weak" highlights how attitudes about masculinity could impede efforts by public health officials to stem the spread of infectious disease.

The vast majority of political science research on the coronavirus pandemic thus far has examined the role of partisan identity. Several researchers have argued that partisanship is among the most significant and consistent factors differentiating health behaviors and policy attitudes (Allcott et al. 2020; Gadarian et al. 2020; Pickup and Stecula 2020). Focus on elites and partisan identity, however, ignores the role that commitments to masculine norms, which cut across predispositions and demographics, can play in shaping health behaviors and preferences.

Building off research in public health and political science, I argue that masculine norms can play understudied but crucial roles in shaping health behaviors and preferences during the coronavirus pandemic, particularly at a time when messages from elites reinforce the link between these perceived attitudes and health behaviors.

Using a large national survey of over 100,000 respondents fielded between March and June 2020 by Democracy Fund and UCLA, I explore the correlates of pandemic-related outcomes. I find that sexism, a component of masculine belief systems, predicts lower levels of concern about the coronavirus, lower levels of engagement in precautionary behaviors, lower levels of support for state and local pandemic policies, and ultimately higher levels of COVID-19 sickness. Sexism is among the strongest correlates of these outcomes, stronger even than partisanship, ideology, gender, and education.

Gendered Personalities and Public Health Behaviors

Public health researchers have long explored how gender shapes public health outcomes. Men have higher levels of negative emotional states, are less likely to seek out physical or mental health services, and are more likely to engage in risky behaviors and exhibit poorer physical and mental health outcomes (see Courtenay 2000 for an overview).

Underlying these gaps is a social construction of gender roles, behaviors, and performance (Kimmel 1995). In many countries, the socially dominant conception of traditional gender norms idealize men as independent, self-reliant, and tough and women as protective and weak (Martin 1995). Belief in these gender norms is reflected in destructive health behaviors like denial of weakness and vulnerability, dismissal of need for help, hiding of disability or illness to avoid seeming feminine or weak (Charmaz 1995; Courtenay 2000; Levant et al. 2009; Yousaf et al. 2015), and support for a variety of related political outcomes (McDermott 2016).[1]

More importantly these health behaviors also serve to sustain and reproduce structures of power (Pyke 1996). As with President Trump's refusal to wear a face mask in public and his criticism of Joe Biden for doing so, health behaviors can demonstrate masculine ideals that serve to reinforce the systematic subordination of women or "weak" men and preserve hierarchies of authority (McDermott 2016).

Importantly, because gendered ideology is socialized, it can be adopted by women and potentially be reflected in women's health behaviors as well. Sloan et al. (2015) find that aspects of masculinity predict worse health behavior for both men and women. As such, this study hypothesizes that gendered ideology, as measured by sexist beliefs that reaffirm men's position in social hierarchies, will be predictive of lower levels of concern about the coronavirus pandemic, less engagement in precautionary behavior, less support for pandemic policies, and finally higher levels of illness regardless of one's gender, race, or partisan identity.

Data and Methods

To test these expectations, this study uses national repeated cross-sectional survey data from Nationscape, an ongoing weekly online survey (n=6,250/week) conducted by Democracy Fund and UCLA. I include all waves that asked questions about COVID-19 (March 19, 2020–June 4, 2020), rendering a total sample of N=100,689. This survey contains multiple questions that tap into COVID-19 concern, behaviors, policy preferences, and self-reported sickness.[2]

The independent variable in my analyses is an additive index measuring sexist attitudes. The scale is comprised of four questions tapping into several components of sexism including a belief in the biological superiority of men over women—old fashioned sexism (Swim et al. 1995)—as well as beliefs that gender hierarchies should be maintained (the measure has been rescaled to range between 0 and 1; mean=0.32, sd=0.18).

The dependent variables are items measuring: (1) coronavirus concern (4=very concerned); (2) self-reported precautionary behaviors (1=yes); (3) attitudes toward pandemic-related policies (4=strongly agree); and (4) contracting COVID-19 (1=yes).

I regress each outcome on the sexism index and control for a host of standard confounders including education (1=college), partisanship (7=strong Republican), ideology (5=very conservative), race (white=1), old-fashioned racism (4=strongly agree), gender (1=female), age, political interest (4=most of the time), household income, population density (logged zipcode population), and employment (1=unemployed). All regressions use survey weights and include fixed effects for survey wave. For additional information on question wording, descriptives, and scales see Appendix B.

Analysis

I begin by using an ordered probit regression to examine whether those high in sexism report being more concerned about the coronavirus than those lower in sexism, all else equal. In Figure 17-1, I plot the predicted probability of reporting being "very concerned" moving from lowest to highest values of sexism and holding all other variables at their means. Those high in sexism are 26 percentage points less likely to report being "very concerned" than those low in sexism. This association is stronger than that of partisanship, ideology, race, education, or gender, and only matched by magnitude of the relationship between age and concern.

Figure 17-1 Sexism and Concern

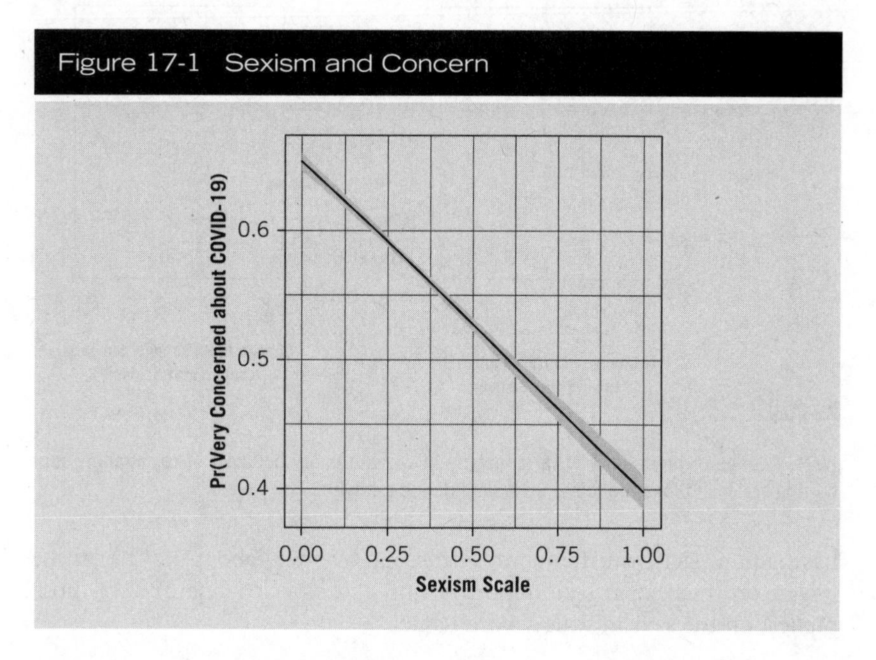

Note: Simulated probability of being "very concerned" about coronavirus. 95% confidence intervals.

Next, we might assume that this lack of concern among those high in sexism would be reflected in both lower levels of precautionary behavior and in lower support for policies targeted at impeding the spread of the coronavirus. In Figure 17-2 Panel A I present the change in the probability of engaging in four different behaviors: (a) stopping visiting family and friends; (b) wearing a mask while outdoors; (c) washing hands more than usual; and (d) self-quarantining at home moving the sexism scale from its observed minimum to maximum holding all other variables at their means. Consistent with expectations, those highest in sexism were between 17 and 23 percentage points less likely to engage in these precautionary behaviors. The same holds for policy support. In Panel B, I show that those highest in sexism are between 21 and 39 percentage points less likely to strongly support these state and local policies than those lowest in sexism, all else equal.

Finally, if those highest in sexism are less likely to be concerned about the coronavirus and less likely to take precautions, it is likely that they would also be more likely to contract COVID-19. In Figure 17-3 I plot the predicted probability that a respondent indicates that they have or may

Figure 17-2 Sexism, Precautions, and Policy Attitudes

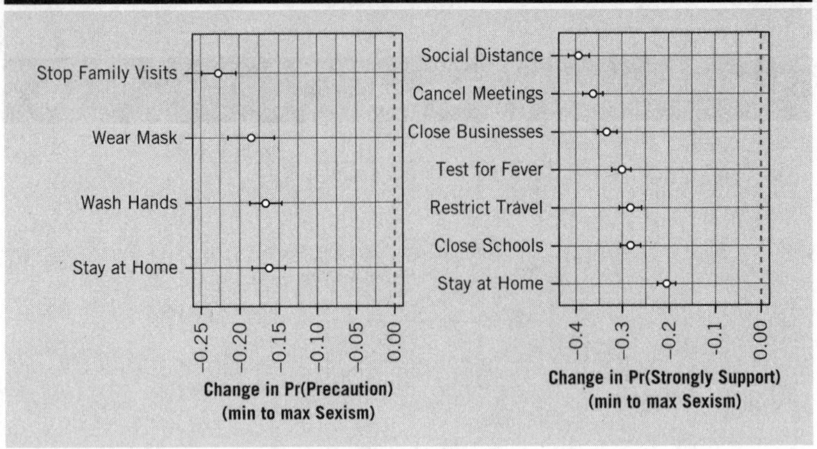

Note: Change in probability of (a) engaging in precautionary behavior or (b) strongly supporting state and local policies. 95% confidence intervals.

have gotten sick with the coronavirus. On average, about 3.2% of those lowest on the sexism scale report having gotten sick while 28% of those highest on the sexism scale say the same.[3]

Figure 17-3 Sexism and Contracting COVID-19

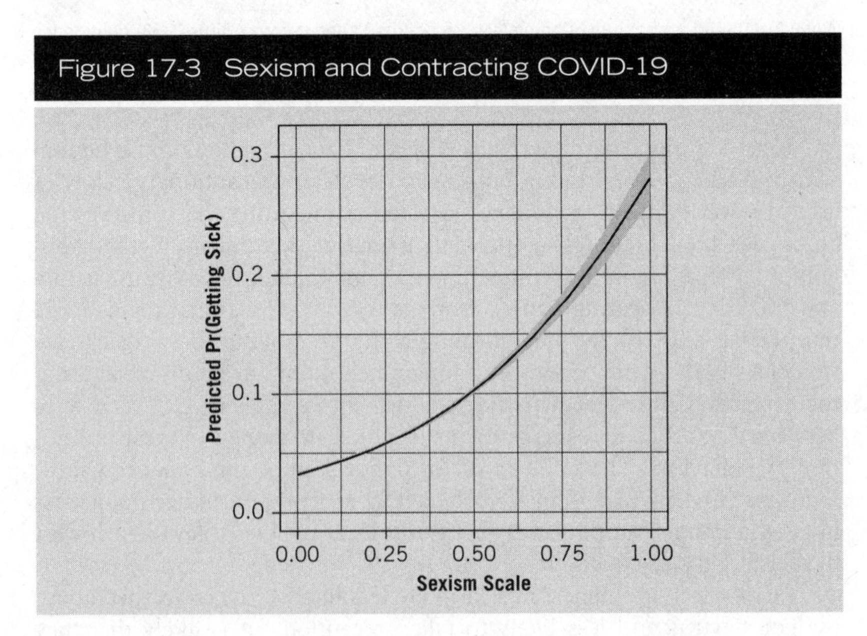

Note: Simulated probability of reporting having contracted COVID-19. 95% confidence intervals.

Conclusion and Discussion

When it comes to public health directives from government officials during an infectious disease pandemic, it's clear that predispositions like partisanship could shape individual responses. Few have yet focused on the role that gender ideology can play in shaping behavior, particularly at a time when the U.S. President openly modeled these norms.

In this research letter I use a large national survey of American adults to estimate the relationship between sexist attitudes and emotional, behavioral, and attitudinal responses to the coronavirus pandemic. I find that sexist individuals are less likely to be worried about the coronavirus, less likely to engage in behaviors to protect themselves and others, less likely to support state and local government policies that aim to stem the spread of the disease, and finally, are more likely to get sick themselves. Together these findings suggest that messaging around public health measures need to overcome barriers around the perceived "masculinity" of behaviors, as Representative Nancy Pelosi recently modeled during an interview with CNBC, when she remarked that "real men wear masks."

While this study finds that sexist attitudes are strongly correlated with coronavirus behaviors and attitudes, it does little to dig into the proposed mechanism underlying this relationship—specifically gendered personality. Future work could use developed measures like the Bern Sex Role Inventory to explore this relationship. Further, future work could leverage survey experiments to assess the role that elite messages or behaviors play in shaping perceptions of health behaviors as masculine or feminine and how those perceptions spill over into mass attitudes and behaviors.

DISCUSSION QUESTIONS

1. Many businesses have signs that say "no shirt, no shoes, no service" that have not been challenged in any meaningful way. What do you think is different about asking people to wear a mask and asking them to wear shoes? Why do you think people object to one but not the other?
2. What other types of health-related behaviors do you think are shaped by someone's attitudes toward gender roles?
3. In other countries, mask wearing in public is commonplace for those who are feeling unwell but must still go about their daily lives. Wearing a mask is seen as a sign of respect for others, and not doing so is seen as rude and inconsiderate in the same way that not wearing pants in public would be

viewed in the United States. What are the different meanings that wearing (or not wearing) a mask have in the United States? Do you think this has changed since the summer of 2020?

4. For men who consider wearing a mask to be a sign of weakness, what kind of public awareness campaign might help persuade them to wear one? Who would you hire as spokespeople? What message would you have them send?

5. The likelihood of someone wearing a mask is shaped by other social characteristics. Look at the results of the Gallup poll "Americans' face mask usage varies greatly by demographics," https://news.gallup.com/poll/315590/americans-face-mask-usage-varies-greatly-demographics.aspx, and find your own social traits in the results. Are you part of a demographic group that is likely to regularly wear a mask? Does your behavior mimic that of others with your social characteristics? Why do you think that is (or is not) the case?

REFERENCES

Allcott, H., L. Boxell, J. Conway, M. Gentzkow, M. Thaler, and D.Y. Yang. 2020. "Polarization and Public Health: Partisan Differences in Social Distancing during the Coronavirus Pandemic". Working Paper No. 26946.

Charmaz, K. 1995. "The Body, Identity, and Self: Adapting to Impairment." *The Sociological Quarterly* 36(4):657–80.

Courtenay, W. H. 2000. "Constructions of Masculinity and Their Influence on Men's Well-Being: A Theory of Gender and Health." *Social Science & Medicine* 50:1385–401.

Gadarian, S. K., S. W. Goodman, and T. B. Pepinsky. 2020. Partisanship, Health Behavior, and Policy Attitudes in the Early Stages of the COVID-19 Pandemic. Available at https://papers.ssrn.com/sol3/papers.cfm?abstract_id=3562796

Kimmel, M. S. 1995. *Manhood in America: A Cultural History*. New York, NY: Free Press.

Levant, R. F., D. J. Wimer, C. M. Williams, S. K. Bryant, and N. Delilah. 2009. "The Relationships between Masculinity Variables, Health Risk Behaviors and Attitudes toward Seeking Psychological Help." *International Journal of Men's Health* 8(1):3–21.

Martin, C. L. 1995. "Stereotypes about Children with Traditional and Nontraditional Gender Roles." *Sex Roles* 33(11/12):727–51.

McDermott, M. 2016. *Masculinity, Femininity, and American Political Behavior*. New York, NY: Oxford University Press.

Pickup, M. and D. Stecula. 2020. "Novel Coronavirus, Old Partisanship: COVID-19 Attitudes and Behaviours in the United States and Canada." *Canadian Journal of Political Science*, 1–8.

Pyke, K. D. 1996. "Class-Based Masculinities: The Interdependence of Gender, Class, and Interpersonal Power." *Gender & Society* 10(5):527–49.

Sloan, C., M. Conner, and B. Gough. 2015. "How Does Masculinity Impact on Health? A Quantitative Study of Masculinity and Health Behavior in a Sample of UK Men and Women." *Psychology of Men and Masculinity* 16(2):206–217.

Swim, J. K., K. J. Aikin, W. S. Hall, and B.A. Hunter. 1995. "Sexism and Racism: Old-Fashioned and Modern Prejudices." *Journal of Personality and Social Psychology* 68(2):199–214.

Yousaf, O., A. Popat, and M. S. Hunter. 2015. "An Investigation of Masculinity Attitudes, Gender, and Attitudes toward Psychological Help-Seeking." *Psychology of Men and Masculinity* 16(2):234–37.

Appendix for "Masculine Norms and Infectious Disease"

The Case of COVID-19

A. Sexism in American Politics

Sexism is uniquely important during the coronavirus pandemic for another reason: President Donald Trump. Scholars have shown that sexism has been playing an increasingly central role in American politics. Sexism conditioned reactions to Donald Trump's campaign attacks on Hillary Clinton (Cassese and Holman 2019; Schaffner et al. 2018), was correlated with support for Trump over Clinton (Schaffner et al. 2018; Sides et al. 2018; Valentino et al. 2018) among both white men and women (Brack et al. 2019; Cassese and Barnes 2019; Frasure-Yokley 2018), and has continued to exert influence in other down ballot elections like the 2018 U.S. midterms (Schaffner 2020). Similarly, gendered personalities are correlated with a variety of political outcomes like identification with and support for the Republican Party, levels of political engagement and interest in politics, and stronger beliefs in traditional gender roles in political and social life (McDermott 2016). It is likely, then, that Trump's brash display of machismo, by going without wearing a mask, taps into an already heightened association among politically aware individuals between masculinity norms, Trump, and the Republican Party.

B. Questions, Descriptive Statistics, and Scale Construction

B.1 Nationscape Data

Nationscape is a large, weekly online survey conducted by Lucid for the Democracy Fund and researchers at UCLA that was designed to collect weekly snapshots of the American electorate throughout the 2019–2020 primary and general elections (Tausanovitch and Vavreck 2020). This cross-section survey is in the field every day of the week and includes weekly collections of N~6,250 responses. While the sample is opt-in, a representativeness assessment of the data finds that the samples are comparable to those collected by well-known pollsters like Pew and YouGov (Tausanovitch et al. 2019). More information on the survey can be found at https://www.voterstudygroup.org/nationscape.

B.2 IV: Sexism Scale

Respondents indicated whether they agreed or disagreed (5-point Likert) with the following statements. The first two are part of an established old-fashioned sexism battery (Swim al. 1995) and the last two, which tap into perceptions of attitudes toward gendered social hierarchies, were created by researchers at Democracy Fund Voter Study Group for their panel study.

- "I would be more comfortable having a man as a boss than a woman" (reversed, mean=2.82)
- "Women are just as capable of thinking logically as men" (mean=1.66)
- "Increased opportunities for women have significantly improved the quality of life in the United States" (mean=2.03)
- "Women who complain about harassment often cause more problems than they solve" (reversed, mean=2.70)

Responses for each range from l=strongly disagree to 5=strongly disagree. While these measures do not directly measure adherence to masculine norms, sexism is a central component of the masculinity belief system and is highly correlated with conforming to masculine norms (Smiler 2006). Questions were added together into a sexism scale (a=0.56) that was re-scaled to range between 0 and 1 (mean=0.32, sd=0.18).

B.3 DV: Behaviors, Attitudes, and Sickness

The dependent variables are a series of items measuring: (1) concern about coronavirus; (2) self-reported precautionary behaviors; (3) attitudes toward pandemic-related state and local policies; and (4) whether the respondent had or has contracted COVID-19. Full question wording below:

Concern

- "How concerned are you about coronavirus here in the United States?" (l=Very concerned; 2=Somewhat concerned; 3=Not very concerned; 4=Not at all concerned; mean=1.57)

Precautionary Behavior

Have you done any of the following things in response to the spread of coronavirus?

- *Wash Hands* "Washed your hands more often than you typically do?" (l=Yes; 0=No; mean=0.92)
- *Wear Mask* "Worn a mask when going out in public?" (l=Yes; 0=No; mean=0.84)
- *Stop Family Visits* "Stopped visiting family or friends?" (l=Yes; 0=No; mean=0.81)
- *Stay Home* "Not left my home for a prolonged period of time?" (l=Yes; 0=No; mean=0.78)

State and Local Policies

"As you may know, some state and local governments have taken certain actions in response to the coronavirus and are considering other actions. Do you support or oppose the following actions?"

- *Cancel Meetings* "Cancel all meetings or gatherings of more than 10 people, like sports events, concerts, conferences, etc." (l=Strongly support; 2=Somewhat support; 3=Somewhat oppose; 4=Strongly oppose; 5=Don't know (recoded as NA); mean=1.65)
- *Close Businesses* "Close certain businesses where larger numbers of people gather, like theaters, bars, restaurants, etc." (l=Strongly support; 2=Somewhat support; 3=Somewhat oppose; 4=Strongly oppose; 5=Don't know (recoded as NA); mean=1.67)
- *Close Schools* "Close schools and universities" (l=Strongly support; 2=Somewhat support; 3=Somewhat oppose; 4=Strongly oppose; 5=Don't know (recoded as NA); mean=1.69)
- *Restrict Travel* "Restrict travel by plane, train, or bus" (l=Strongly support; 2=Somewhat support; 3=Somewhat oppose; 4=Strongly oppose; 5=Don't know (recoded as NA); mean=1.68)
- *Stay at Home* "Restrict all non-essential travel outside the home" (l=Strongly support; 2=Somewhat support; 3=Somewhat oppose; 4=Strongly oppose; 5=Don't know (recoded as NA); mean=1.92)
- *Social Distance* "Encourage people to stay in their homes and avoid socializing with others" (l=Strongly support; 2=Somewhat support; 3=Somewhat oppose; 4=Strongly oppose; 5=Don't know (recoded as NA); mean=1.57)

- *Test for Fever* "Test people for a fever before letting them enter public buildings" (1=Strongly support; 2=Somewhat support; 3=Somewhat oppose; 4=Strongly oppose; 5=Don't know (recoded as NA); mean=1.67)

Sick with COVID-19

Have any of the following people been sick with coronavirus?

- *Sick* "You" (1=Yes/Maybe; 0=No; mean=0.087)

Control Variables

- *College* (1=Bachelor's Degree or greater; mean=0.30)
- *Partisanship* (1=Strong Democrat; 2=Weak Democrat; 3=Lean Democrat; 4=Independent; 5=Lean Republican; 6=Weak Republican; 7=Strong Republicans; mean=3.90)
- *Ideology* (1=Very liberal; 2=Liberal; 3=Moderate/Not Sure; 4=Conservative; 5=Very Conservative; mean=3.04)
- *Gender* (1=Female; 0=Other; mean=0.52)
- *Age* (Continuous; mean=47.46)
- *Race* (1=Non-Hispanic White; 0=Other; mean=0.66)
- *Old-Fashioned Racism* (Additive index of two old-fashioned racism questions below scaled between 0 and 1; mean=0.34)
    - "I prefer that my close relatives marry spouses from their same race" (Strongly agree=5; Somewhat agree=4; Neither agree nor disagree=3; Somewhat disagree=2; Strongly disagree=1)
    - "I think it's alright for blacks and whites to date each other" (Strongly agree=1; Somewhat agree=2; Neither agree nor disagree=3; Somewhat disagree=4; Strongly disagree=5)
- *Interest* (1=Most of the time; 2=Some of the time; 3=Only now and then; 4=Hardly at all; mean=1.83)
- *Household Income* (1=Less than $14,999 to 24=$250,000 and above; mean=12.89)
- *Unemployed* (1=Yes; 0=No; mean=0.10)
- *Logged Population* (mean=12.66)

REFERENCES

Brack, A., M. Israel-Trummel, and A.F. Shortle. 2019. "Is Sexism for White People? Gender Stereotypes, Race, and the 2016 Presidential Election." *Political Behavior* 41(2):281–307.

Cassese, E. C. and M. R. Holman. 2019. "Playing the Woman Card: Ambivalent Sexism in the 2016 U.S. Presidential Race." *Political Psychology* 40(1):55–74.

Cassese, E. C. and T. D. Barnes. 2019. "Reconciling Sexism and Women's Support for Republican Candidates: A Look at Gender, Class, and Whiteness in the 2012 and 2016 Presidential Races." *Political Behavior* 41(3):677–700.

Frasure-Yokley, L. 2018. "Choosing the Velvet Glove: Women Voters, Ambivalent Sexism, and Vote Choice in 2016." *Journal of Race, Ethnicity, and Politics* 3:3–25.

McDermott, M. 2016. *Masculinity, Femininity, and American Political Behavior*. New York, NY: Oxford University Press.

Schaffner, B.F. 2020. "The Heightened Importance of Racism and Sexism in the 2018 U.S. Midterm Elections." *British Journal of Political Science* (Forthcoming).

Schaffner, B., M. MacWilliams, and T. Nteta. 2018. "Understanding White Polarization in the 2016 Vote for President: The Sobering Role of Racism and Sexism." *Political Science Quarterly* 133(1):9–34.

Sides, J., L. Vavreck, and M. Tesler. 2018. *Identity Crisis: The 2016 Presidential Campaign and the Battle for the Meaning of America*. Princeton, NJ: Princeton University Press.

Smiler, A. P. 2006. "Conforming to Masculine Norms: Evidence for Validity among Adult Men and Women." *Sex Roles* 54(11):767–75.

Swim, J. K., K. J. Aikin, W. S. Hall, and B. A. Hunter. 1995. "Sexism and Racism: Old-Fashioned and Modern Prejudices." *Journal of Personality and Social Psychology* 68(2):199–214.

Tausanovitch, C. and L. Vavreck. 2020. Democracy Fund + UCLA Nationscape.

Tausanovitch, C., L. Vavreck, T. Reny, A. R. Hayes, and A. Rudkin. 2019. Democracy Fund + UCLA Nationscape Methodology and Representativeness Assessment.

Valentino, N. A., C. Wayne, and M. Oceno. 2018. "Mobilizing Sexism: The Interaction of Emotion and Gender Attitudes in the 2016 U.S. Presidential Election." *Public Opinion Quarterly* 82:799–821.

NOTES

1. For more on the role of gendered personalities and sexism in American politics, see Appendix A.
2. For more information on the Nationscape Survey, see Appendix B.
3. I show in Appendix C that these findings hold with male/female, white/non-white, and Democratic and Republican split samples as well as controlling for approval of President Trump.

PART

V

Race

The Code of the Streets

Elijah Anderson

In this reading, Elijah Anderson explains the "code of the streets," a set of norms that govern interactions in public spaces in poor, inner-city African American neighborhoods. His insightful analysis sheds light on the social context of the interpersonal violence that is common in many of these neighborhoods. Homicide is the leading cause of death for young African American men, but what is often reported in the news as random or senseless violence often has its basis in the logic of the code of the streets. Anderson points out that the majority of the residents in these neighborhoods are law-abiding citizens with mainstream values, what he and other residents call decent families. *But a small portion of* street families *also live in these neighborhoods. Street families are defined by more extreme poverty, a lack of consideration for others, less involved parenting, and a belief in the values of the code of the streets.*

The main feature of the code of the streets is to display a willingness to use violence to get or maintain respect in interpersonal interactions. Respect is a scarce commodity in communities that lack good job prospects and educational opportunities, so public interactions become an important locale for getting and maintaining respect. Because decent and street families must coexist in the same neighborhood, those from decent families must also adhere to and use the code in order to safely navigate public space. As Anderson insightfully explains, there is much more to the stereotypical image of swaggering, violence-prone, inner-city minorities than there appears on the surface.

Of all the problems besetting the poor inner-city black community, none is more pressing than that of interpersonal violence and aggression. It wreaks havoc daily with the lives of community residents and increasingly spills over into downtown and residential middle-class areas. Muggings, burglaries, carjackings, and drug-related shootings, all of which may leave their victims or innocent bystanders dead, are now common enough to concern all urban and many suburban residents. The inclination to violence springs from the circumstances of life among the ghetto poor—the lack of jobs that

---

Excerpt from "The Code of the Streets" by Elijah Anderson. *The Atlantic* (1994). This essay is further developed in the book, *Code of the Street*, W. W. Norton, 1999. Reprinted with permission from the author.

pay a living wage, the stigma of race, the fallout from rampant drug use and drug trafficking, and the resulting alienation and lack of hope for the future.

Simply living in such an environment places young people at special risk of falling victim to aggressive behavior. Although there are often forces in the community which can counteract the negative influences, by far the most powerful being a strong, loving, "decent" (as inner-city residents put it) family committed to middle-class values, the despair is pervasive enough to have spawned an oppositional culture, that of "the streets," whose norms are often consciously opposed to those of mainstream society. These two orientations—decent and street—socially organize the community, and their coexistence has important consequences for residents, particularly children growing up in the inner city. Above all, this environment means that even youngsters whose home lives reflect mainstream values—and the majority of homes in the community do—must be able to handle themselves in a street-oriented environment.

This is because the street culture has evolved what may be called a code of the streets, which amounts to a set of informal rules governing interpersonal public behavior, including violence. The rules prescribe both a proper comportment and a proper way to respond if challenged. They regulate the use of violence and so allow those who are inclined to aggression to precipitate violent encounters in an approved way. The rules have been established and are enforced mainly by the street-oriented, but on the streets the distinction between street and decent is often irrelevant; everybody knows that if the rules are violated, there are penalties. Knowledge of the code is thus largely defensive; it is literally necessary for operating in public. Therefore, even though families with a decency orientation are usually opposed to the values of the code, they often reluctantly encourage their children's familiarity with it to enable them to negotiate the inner-city environment.

At the heart of the code is the issue of respect—loosely defined as being treated "right," or granted the deference one deserves. However, in the troublesome public environment of the inner city, as people increasingly feel buffeted by forces beyond their control, what one deserves in the way of respect becomes more and more problematic and uncertain. This in turn further opens the issue of respect to sometimes intense interpersonal negotiation. In the street culture, especially among young people, respect is viewed as almost an external entity that is hard-won but easily lost, and so must constantly be guarded. The rules of the code in fact provide a framework for negotiating respect. The person whose very appearance—including his clothing, demeanor, and way of moving—deters transgressions feels that he possesses, and may be considered by others to possess, a measure of respect. With the right amount of respect, for instance, he can avoid "being bothered" in public. If he is bothered, not only may he be in physical danger but he has been disgraced or "dissed" (disrespected). Many of the forms that dissing can take might seem petty to middle-class people (maintaining eye contact for too long, for example), but to those invested in the street code, these actions become serious indications of the other person's intentions. Consequently, such people become very sensitive to advances and slights, which could well serve as warnings of imminent physical confrontation.

This hard reality can be traced to the profound sense of alienation from mainstream society and its institutions felt by many poor inner-city black people, particularly the young. The code of the streets is actually a cultural adaptation to a profound lack of faith in the police and the judicial system. The police are most often seen as representing the dominant white society and not caring to protect inner-city residents. When called, they may not respond, which is one reason many residents feel they must be prepared to take extraordinary measures to defend themselves and their loved ones against those who are inclined to aggression. Lack of police accountability has in fact been incorporated into the status system: the person who is believed capable of "taking care of himself "is accorded a certain deference, which translates into a sense of physical and psychological control. Thus, the street code emerges where the influence of the police ends and personal responsibility for one's safety is felt to begin. Exacerbated by the proliferation of drugs and easy access to guns, this volatile situation results in the ability of the street-oriented minority (or those who effectively "go for bad") to dominate the public spaces.

Decent and Street Families

Although almost everyone in poor inner-city neighborhoods is struggling financially and therefore feels a certain distance from the rest of America, the decent and the street family in a real sense represent two poles of value orientation, two contrasting conceptual categories. The labels "decent" and "street," which the residents themselves use, amount to evaluative judgments that confer status on local residents. The labeling is often the result of a social contest among individuals and families of the neighborhood. Individuals of the two orientations often coexist in the same extended family. Decent residents judge themselves to be so while judging others to be of the street, and street individuals often present themselves as decent, drawing distinctions between themselves and other people. In addition, there is quite a bit of circumstantial behavior—that is, one person may at different times exhibit both decent and street orientations, depending on the circumstances. Although these designations result from so much social jockeying, there do exist concrete features that define each conceptual category.

Generally, so-called decent families tend to accept mainstream values more fully and attempt to instill them in their children. Whether married couples with children or single-parent (usually female) households, they are generally "working poor" and so tend to be better off financially than their street-oriented neighbors. They value hard work and self-reliance and are willing to sacrifice for their children. Because they have a certain amount of faith in mainstream society, they harbor hopes for a better future for their children, if not for themselves. Many of them go to church and take a strong interest in their children's schooling. Rather than dwelling on the real hardships and inequities facing them, many such decent people, particularly the increasing number of grandmothers raising grandchildren, see their difficult situation as a test from God and derive great support from their faith and from the church community.

Extremely aware of the problematic and often dangerous environment in which they reside, decent parents tend to be strict in their child-rearing practices, encouraging children to respect authority and walk a straight moral line. They have an almost obsessive concern about trouble of any kind and remind their children to be on the lookout for people and situations that might lead to it. At the same time, they are themselves polite and considerate of others, and teach their children to be the same way. At home, at work, and in church, they strive hard to maintain a positive mental attitude and a spirit of cooperation.

So-called street parents, in contrast, often show a lack of consideration for other people and have a rather superficial sense of family and community. Though they may love their children, many of them are unable to cope with the physical and emotional demands of parenthood, and find it difficult to reconcile their needs with those of their children. These families, who are more fully invested in the code of the streets than the decent people are, may aggressively socialize their children into it in a normative way. They believe in the code and judge themselves and others according to its values.

In fact the overwhelming majority of families in the inner-city community try to approximate the decent-family model, but there are many others who clearly represent the worst fears of the decent family. Not only are their financial resources extremely limited, but what little they have may easily be misused. The lives of the street-oriented are often marked by disorganization. In the most desperate circumstances people frequently have a limited understanding of priorities and consequences, and so frustrations mount over bills, food, and, at times, drink, cigarettes, and drugs. Some tend toward self-destructive behavior; many street-oriented women are crack-addicted ("on the pipe"), alcoholic, or involved in complicated relationships with men who abuse them. In addition, the seeming intractability of their situation, caused in large part by the lack of well-paying jobs and the persistence of racial discrimination, has engendered deep-seated bitterness and anger in many of the most desperate and poorest blacks, especially young people. The need both to exercise a measure of control and to lash out at somebody is often reflected in the adults' relations with their children. At the least, the frustrations of persistent poverty shorten the fuse in such people—contributing to a lack of patience with anyone, child or adult, who irritates them.

In these circumstances a woman—or a man, although men are less consistently present in children's lives—can be quite aggressive with children, yelling at and striking them for the least little infraction of the rules she has set down. Often little if any serious explanation follows the verbal and physical punishment. This response teaches children a particular lesson. They learn that to solve any kind of interpersonal problem one must quickly resort to hitting or other violent behavior. Actual peace and quiet, and also the appearance of calm, respectful children conveyed to her neighbors and friends, are often what the young mother most desires, but at times she will be very aggressive in trying to get them. Thus, she may be quick to beat her children, especially if they defy her law, not because she hates them but because this is the way she knows to control them. In fact, many street-oriented women love their children dearly. Many mothers in the community subscribe to the notion that there is a "devil in the boy" that must be beaten out of him or that socially "fast girls need to be whupped." Thus, much of what borders on child abuse in the view of social authorities is acceptable parental punishment in the view of these mothers.

Many street-oriented women are sporadic mothers whose children learn to fend for themselves when necessary, foraging for food and money any way they can get it. The children are sometimes employed by drug dealers or become addicted themselves. These children of the street, growing up with little supervision, are said to "come up hard." They often learn to fight at an early age, sometimes using short-tempered adults around them as role models. The street-oriented home may be fraught with anger, verbal disputes, physical aggression, and even mayhem. The children observe these goings-on, learning the lesson that might makes right. They quickly learn to hit those who cross them, and the dog-eat-dog mentality prevails. In order to survive, to protect oneself, it is necessary to marshal inner resources and be ready to deal with adversity in a hands-on way. In these circumstances physical prowess takes on great significance.

In some of the most desperate cases, a street-oriented mother may simply leave her young children alone and unattended while she goes out. The most irresponsible women can be found at local bars and crack houses, getting high and socializing with other adults. Sometimes a troubled woman will leave very young children alone for days at a time. Reports of crack addicts abandoning their children have become common in drug infested inner-city communities. Neighbors or relatives discover the abandoned children, often hungry and distraught over the absence of their mother. After repeated absences, a friend or relative, particularly a grandmother, will often step in to care for the young children, sometimes petitioning the authorities to send her, as guardian of the children, the mother's welfare check, if the mother gets one. By this time, however, the children may well have learned the first lesson of the streets: survival itself, let alone respect, cannot be taken for granted; you have to fight for your place in the world.

Campaigning for Respect

These realities of inner-city life are largely absorbed on the streets. At an early age, often even before they start school, children from street oriented homes gravitate to the streets, where they "hang"—socialize with their peers. Children from these generally permissive homes have a great deal of latitude and are allowed to "rip and run" up and down the street. They often come home from school, put their books down, and go right back out the door. On school nights eight- and nine-year-olds remain out until nine or ten o'clock (and teenagers typically come in whenever they want to). On the streets they play in groups that often become the source of their primary social bonds. Children from decent homes tend to be more carefully supervised and are thus likely to have curfews and to be taught how to stay out of trouble.

When decent and street kids come together, a kind of social shuffle occurs in which children have a chance to go either way. Tension builds as a child comes to realize that he must choose an orientation. The kind of home he comes from influences but does not determine the way he will ultimately turn out—although it is unlikely that a child from a thoroughly street-oriented family will easily absorb decent values on the streets. Youths who emerge from street-oriented families but develop a decency orientation almost always learn those values in another setting—in school, in a youth group, in church. Often it is the result of their involvement with a caring "old head" (adult role model).

In the street, through their play, children pour their individual life experiences into a common knowledge pool, affirming, confirming, and elaborating on what they have observed in the home and matching their skills against those of others. And they learn to fight. Even small children test one another, pushing and shoving, and are ready to hit other children over circumstances not to their liking. In turn, they are readily hit by other children, and the child who is toughest prevails. Thus, the violent resolution of disputes, the hitting and cursing, gains social reinforcement. The child in effect is initiated into a system that is really a way of campaigning for respect.

In addition, younger children witness the disputes of older children, which are often resolved through cursing and abusive talk, if not aggression or outright violence. They see that one child succumbs to the greater physical and mental abilities of the other. They are also alert and attentive witnesses to the verbal and physical fights of adults, after which they compare notes and share their interpretations of the event. In almost every case the victor is the person who physically won the altercation, and this person often enjoys the esteem and respect of onlookers. These experiences reinforce the lessons the children have learned at home: might makes right, and toughness is a virtue, while humility is not. In effect they learn the social meaning of fighting. When it is left virtually unchallenged, this understanding becomes an ever more important part of the child's working conception of the world. Over time the code of the streets becomes refined.

Those street-oriented adults with whom children come in contact—including mothers, fathers, brothers, sisters, boyfriends, cousins, neighbors, and friends—help them along in forming this understanding by verbalizing the messages they are getting through experience: "Watch your back." "Protect yourself." "Don't punk out." "If somebody messes with you, you got to pay them back." "If someone disses you, you got to straighten them out." Many parents actually impose sanctions if a child is not sufficiently aggressive. For example, if a child loses a fight and comes home upset, the parent might respond, "Don't you come in here crying that somebody beat you up; you better get back out there and whup his ass. I didn't raise no punks! Get back out there and whup his ass. If you don't whup his ass, I'll whup your ass when you come home." Thus the child obtains reinforcement for being tough and showing nerve.

While fighting, some children cry as though they are doing something they are ambivalent about. The fight may be against their wishes, yet they may feel constrained to fight or face the consequences—not just from peers but also from caretakers or parents, who may administer another beating if they back down. Some adults recall receiving such lessons from their own parents and justify repeating them to their children as a way to toughen them up. Looking capable of taking care of oneself as a form of self-defense is a dominant theme among both street-oriented and decent adults who worry about the safety of their children. There is thus at times a convergence in their child-rearing practices, although the rationales behind them may differ.

Self-Image Based on "Juice"

By the time they are teenagers, most youths have either internalized the code of the streets or at least learned the need to comport themselves in accordance with its rules, which chiefly have to do with interpersonal communication. The code revolves around the presentation of self. Its basic requirement is the display of a certain predisposition to violence. Accordingly, one's bearing must send the unmistakable if sometimes subtle message to "the next person" in public that one is capable of violence and mayhem when the situation requires it, that one can take care of oneself.

The nature of this communication is largely determined by the demands of the circumstances but can include facial expressions, gait, and verbal expressions—all of which are geared mainly to deterring aggression. Physical appearance, including clothes, jewelry, and grooming, also plays an important part in how a person is viewed; to be respected, it is important to have the right look.

Even so, there are no guarantees against challenges, because there are always people around looking for a fight to increase their share of respect—or "juice," as it is sometimes called on the street. Moreover, if a person is assaulted, it is important, not only in the eyes of his opponent but also in the eyes of his "running buddies," for him to avenge himself. Otherwise he risks being "tried" (challenged) or "moved on" by any number of others. To maintain his honor he must show he is not someone to be "messed with" or "dissed." In general, the person must "keep himself straight" by managing his position of respect among others; this involves in part his self-image, which is shaped by what he thinks others are thinking of him in relation to his peers.

Objects play an important and complicated role in establishing self-image. Jackets, sneakers, and gold jewelry reflect not just a person's taste, which tends to be tightly regulated among adolescents of all social classes, but also a willingness to possess things that may require defending. A boy wearing a fashionable, expensive jacket, for example, is vulnerable to attack by another who covets the jacket and either cannot afford to buy one or wants the added satisfaction of depriving someone else of his. However, if the boy forgoes the desirable jacket and wears one that isn't "hip," he runs the risk of being teased and possibly even assaulted as an unworthy person. To be allowed to hang with certain prestigious crowds, a boy must wear a different set of expensive clothes—sneakers and athletic suit—every day. Not to be able to do so might make him appear socially deficient. The youth comes to covet such items—especially when he sees easy prey wearing them.

In acquiring valued things, therefore, a person shores up his identity—but since it is an identity based on having things, it is highly precarious. This very precariousness gives a heightened sense of urgency to staying even with peers, with whom the person is actually competing. Young men and women who are able to command respect through their presentation of self—by allowing their possessions and their body language to speak for them—may not have to campaign for regard but may, rather, gain it by the force of their manner. Those who are unable to command respect in this way must actively campaign for it—and are thus particularly alive to slights.

One way of campaigning for status is by taking the possessions of others. In this context, seemingly ordinary objects can become trophies imbued with symbolic value that far exceeds their monetary worth. Possession of the trophy can symbolize the ability to violate somebody—to "get in his face," to take something of value from him, to "dis" him, and thus to enhance one's own worth by stealing someone else's. The trophy does not have to be something material. It can be another person's sense of honor, snatched away with a derogatory remark. It can be the outcome of a fight. It can be the imposition of a certain standard, such as a girl's getting herself recognized as the most beautiful. Material things, however, fit easily into the pattern. Sneakers, a pistol, even somebody else's girlfriend can become a trophy. When a person can take something from another and then flaunt it, he gains a certain regard by being the owner, or the controller, of that thing. But this display of ownership can then provoke other people to challenge him. This game of who controls what is thus constantly being played out on inner-city streets, and the trophy—extrinsic or intrinsic, tangible or intangible—identifies the current winner.

An important aspect of this often violent give-and-take is its zero-sum quality. That is, the extent to which one person can raise himself up depends on his ability to put another person down. This underscores the alienation that permeates the inner-city ghetto community. There is a generalized sense that very little respect is to be had, and therefore everyone competes to get what affirmation he can of the little that is available. The craving for respect that results gives people thin skins. Shows of deference by others can be highly soothing, contributing to a sense of security, comfort, self-confidence, and self-respect. Transgressions by others which go unanswered diminish these feelings and are believed to encourage further transgressions. Hence one must be ever vigilant against the transgressions of others or even appearing as if transgressions will be tolerated. Among young people, whose sense of self-esteem is particularly vulnerable, there is an especially heightened concern with being disrespected. Many inner-city young men in particular crave respect to such a degree that they will risk their lives to attain and maintain it.

The issue of respect is thus closely tied to whether a person has an inclination to be violent, even as a victim. In the wider society people may not feel required to retaliate physically after an attack, even though they are aware that they have been degraded or taken advantage of. They may feel a great need to defend themselves during an attack, or to behave in such a way as to deter aggression (middle-class people certainly can and do become victims of street-oriented youths), but they are much more likely than street-oriented people to feel that they can walk away from a possible altercation with their self-esteem intact. Some people may even have the strength of character to flee, without any thought that their self-respect or esteem will be diminished.

In impoverished inner-city black communities, however, particularly among young males and perhaps increasingly among females, such flight would be extremely difficult. To run away would likely leave one's self-esteem in tatters. Hence people often feel constrained not only to stand up and at least attempt to resist during an assault but also to "pay back"—to seek revenge—after a successful assault on their person. This may include going to get a weapon or even getting relatives involved. Their very identity and self-respect, their honor, is often intricately tied up with the way they perform on the streets during and after such encounters. This outlook reflects the circumscribed opportunities of the inner-city poor. Generally people outside the ghetto have other ways of gaining status and regard, and thus do not feel so dependent on such physical displays.

By Trial of Manhood

On the street, among males these concerns about things and identity have come to be expressed in the concept of "manhood." Manhood in the inner city means taking the prerogatives of men with respect to strangers, other men, and women—being distinguished as a man. It implies physicality and a certain ruthlessness. Regard and respect are associated with this concept in large part because of its practical application: if others have little or no regard for a person's manhood, his very life and those of his loved ones could be in jeopardy. But there is a chicken-and-egg aspect to this situation: one's physical safety is more likely to be jeopardized in public because manhood is associated with respect. In other words, an existential link has been created between the idea of manhood and one's self-esteem, so that it has become hard to say which is primary. For many inner-city youths, manhood and respect are flip sides of the same coin; physical and psychological well-being are inseparable, and both require a sense of control, of being in charge.

The operating assumption is that a man, especially a real man, knows what other men know—the code of the streets. And if one is not a real man, one is somehow diminished as a person, and there are certain valued things one simply does not deserve. There is thus believed to be a certain justice to the code, since it is considered that everyone has the opportunity to know it. Implicit in this is that everybody is held responsible for being familiar with the code. If the victim of a mugging, for example, does not know the code and so responds "wrong," the perpetrator may feel justified even in killing him and may feel no remorse. He may think, "Too bad, but it's his fault. He should have known better."

So when a person ventures outside, he must adopt the code—kind of a shield, really—to prevent others from "messing with" him. In these circumstances it is easy for people to think they are being tried or tested by others even when this is not the case. For it is sensed that something extremely valuable is at stake in every interaction, and people are encouraged to rise to the occasion, particularly with strangers. For people who are unfamiliar with the code—generally people who live outside the inner city—the concern with respect in the most ordinary interactions can be frightening and incomprehensible. But for those who are invested in the code, the clear object of their demeanor is to discourage strangers from even thinking about testing their manhood. And the sense of power that attends the ability to deter others can be alluring even to those who know the code without being heavily invested in it—the decent inner-city youths. Thus a boy who has been leading a basically decent life can, in trying circumstances, suddenly resort to deadly force.

Central to the issue of manhood is the widespread belief that one of the most effective ways of gaining respect is to manifest "nerve." Nerve is shown when one takes another person's possessions (the more valuable the better), "messes with" someone's woman, throws the first punch, "gets in someone's face," or pulls a trigger. Its proper display helps on the spot to check others who would violate one's person and also helps to build a reputation that works to prevent future challenges. But since such a show of nerve is a forceful expression of disrespect toward the person on the receiving end, the victim may be greatly offended and seek to retaliate with equal or greater force. A display of nerve, therefore, can easily provoke a life-threatening response, and the background knowledge of that possibility has often been incorporated into the concept of nerve.

True nerve exposes a lack of fear of dying. Many feel that it is acceptable to risk dying over the principle of respect. In fact, among the hard-core street-oriented, the clear risk of violent death may be preferable to being "dissed" by another. The youths who have internalized this attitude and convincingly display it in their public bearing are among the most threatening people of all, for it is commonly assumed that they fear no man. As the people of the community say, "They are the baddest dudes on the street." They often lead an existential life that may acquire meaning only when they are faced with the possibility of imminent death. Not to be afraid to die is by implication to have few compunctions about taking another's life. Not to be afraid to die is the quid pro quo of being able to take somebody else's life—for the right reasons, if the situation demands it. When others believe this is one's position, it gives one a real sense of power on the streets. Such credibility is what many inner-city youths strive to achieve, whether they are decent or street-oriented, both because of its practical defensive value and because of the positive way it makes them feel about themselves. The difference between the decent and the street-oriented youth is often that the decent youth makes a conscious decision to appear tough and manly; in another setting—with teachers, say, or at his part-time job—he can be polite and deferential. The street-oriented youth, on the other hand, has made the concept of manhood a part of his very identity; he has difficulty manipulating it—it often controls him.

Girls and Boys

Increasingly, teenage girls are mimicking the boys and trying to have their own version of "manhood." Their goal is the same—to get respect, to be recognized as capable of setting or maintaining a certain standard. They try to achieve this end in the ways that have been established by the boys, including posturing, abusive language, and the use of violence to resolve disputes, but the issues for the girls are different. Although conflicts over turf and status exist among the girls, the majority of disputes seem rooted in assessments of beauty (which girl in a group is "the cutest"), competition over boyfriends, and attempts to regulate other people's knowledge of and opinions about a girl's behavior or that of someone close to her, especially her mother.

A major cause of conflicts among girls is "he say, she say." This practice begins in the early school years and continues through high school. It occurs when "people," particularly girls, talk about others, thus putting their "business in the streets." Usually one girl will say something negative about another in the group, most often behind the person's back. The remark will then get back to the person talked about. She may retaliate or her friends may feel required to "take up for" her. In essence this is a form of group gossiping in which individuals are negatively assessed and evaluated. As with much gossip, the things said may or may not be true, but the point is that such imputations can cast aspersions on a person's good name. The accused is required to defend herself against the slander, which can result in arguments and fights, often over little of real substance. Here again is the problem of low self-esteem, which encourages youngsters to be highly sensitive to slights and to be vulnerable to feeling easily "dissed." To avenge the dissing, a fight is usually necessary.

Because boys are believed to control violence, girls tend to defer to them in situations of conflict. Often if a girl is attacked or feels slighted, she will get a brother, uncle, or cousin to do her fighting for her. Increasingly, however, girls are doing their own fighting and are even asking their male relatives to teach them how to fight. Some girls form groups that attack other girls or take things from them. A hard-core segment of inner-city girls inclined toward violence seems to be developing. As one thirteen-year-old girl in a detention center for youths who have committed violent acts told me, "To get people to leave you alone, you gotta fight. Talking don't always get you out of stuff." One major difference between girls and boys: girls rarely use guns. Their fights are therefore not life-or-death struggles. Girls are not often willing to put their lives on the line for "manhood." The ultimate form of respect on the male-dominated inner-city street is thus reserved for men.

"Going for Bad"

In the most fearsome youths such a cavalier attitude toward death grows out of a very limited view of life. Many are uncertain about how long they are going to live and believe they could die violently at any time. They accept this fate; they live on the edge. Their manner conveys the message that nothing intimidates them; whatever turn the encounter takes, they maintain their attack—rather like a pit bull, whose spirit many such boys admire. The demonstration of such tenacity "shows heart" and earns their respect.

This fearlessness has implications for law enforcement. Many street oriented boys are much more concerned about the threat of "justice" at the hands of a peer than at the hands of the police. Moreover, many feel not only that they have little to lose by going to prison but that they have something to gain. The toughening-up one experiences in prison can actually enhance one's reputation on the streets. Hence the system loses influence over the hard core who are without jobs, with little perceptible stake in the system. If mainstream society has done nothing for them, they counter by making sure it can do nothing to them.

At the same time, however, a competing view maintains that true nerve consists in backing down, walking away from a fight, and going on with one's business. One fights only in self-defense. This view emerges from the decent philosophy that life is precious, and it is an important part of the socialization process common in decent homes. It discourages violence as the primary means of resolving disputes and encourages youngsters to accept nonviolence and talk as confrontational strategies. But "if the deal goes down," self-defense is greatly encouraged. When there is enough positive support for this orientation, either in the home or among one's peers, then nonviolence has a chance to prevail. But it prevails at the cost of relinquishing a claim to being bad and tough, and therefore sets a young person up as at the very least alienated from street-oriented peers and quite possibly a target of derision or even violence.

Although the nonviolent orientation rarely overcomes the impulse to strike back in an encounter, it does introduce a certain confusion and so can prompt a measure of soul-searching, or even profound ambivalence. Did the person back down with his respect intact or did he back down only to be judged a "punk"—a poison lacking manhood? Should he or she have acted? Should he or she have hit the other person in the mouth? These questions beset many young men and women during public confrontations. What is the "right" thing to do? In the quest for honor, respect, and local status—which few young people are uninterested in—common sense most often prevails, which leads many to opt for the tough approach, enacting their own particular versions of the display of nerve. The presentation of oneself as rough and tough is very often quite acceptable until one is rested. And then that presentation may help the person pass the test, because it will cause fewer questions to be asked about what he did and why. It is hard for a person to explain why he lost the fight or why he backed down. Hence many will strive to appear to "go for bad," while hoping they will never be tested. But when they are tested, the outcome of the situation may quickly be out of their hands, as they become wrapped up in the circumstances of the moment.

An Oppositional Culture

The attitudes of the wider society are deeply implicated in the code of the streets. Most people in inner-city communities are not totally invested in the code, but the significant minority of hard-core street youths who are have to maintain the code in order to establish reputations, because they have—or feel they have—few other ways to assert themselves. For these young people the standards of the street code are the only game in town. The extent to which some children—particularly those who through upbringing have become most alienated and those lacking in strong and conventional social support—experience, feel, and internalize racist rejection and contempt from mainstream society may strongly encourage them to express contempt for the more conventional society in turn. In dealing with this contempt and rejection, some youngsters will consciously invest themselves and their considerable mental resources in what amounts to an oppositional culture to preserve themselves and their self-respect. Once they do, any respect they might be able to garner in the wider system pales in comparison with the respect available in the local system; thus they often lose interest in even attempting to negotiate the mainstream system.

At the same time, many less alienated young blacks have assumed a street-oriented demeanor as a way of expressing their blackness while really embracing a much more moderate way of life; they, too, want a nonviolent setting in which to live and raise a family. These decent people are trying hard to be part of the mainstream culture, but the racism, real and perceived, that they encounter helps to legitimate the oppositional culture. And so on occasion they adopt street behavior. In fact, depending on the demands of the situation, many people in the community slip back and forth between decent and street behavior.

A vicious cycle has thus been formed. The hopelessness and alienation many young inner-city black men and women feel, largely as a result of endemic joblessness and persistent racism, fuels the violence they engage in. This violence serves to confirm the negative feelings many whites and some middle-class blacks harbor toward the ghetto poor, further legitimating the oppositional culture and the code of the streets in the eyes of many poor young blacks. Unless this cycle is broken, attitudes on both sides will become increasingly entrenched, and the violence, which claims victims black and white, poor and affluent, will only escalate.

DISCUSSION QUESTIONS

1. Why does use of the code by those from "decent" families make perfect sense according to Anderson?
2. How does enactment of the code of the streets relate to Goffman's ideas from *The Presentation of Self*?
3. If you had to write a code of the campus for your school, what would the rules be? What are the norms and expectations that govern interactions in public spaces where you go to school?
4. What does the code of the streets have in common with bullying that happens in middle-class, mostly White communities?
5. You can watch Dr. Anderson describe his work while visiting the types of neighborhoods he did his research in at this link: https://uep.yale.edu/videos/street-codes-code-street-elijah-anderson. How are interactions in public similar to or different from what you are accustomed to?

She's Not a Low-Class Dirty Girl

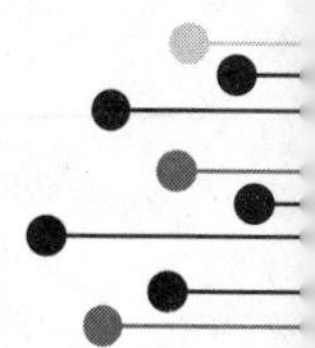

Kimberly Kay Hoang

Images of sex workers in popular culture shape many of our ideas about who has sex for money and why. From the prostitutes in HBO's Westworld to Hulu's Harlots to Julia Roberts in Pretty Woman, women who work for sex are often portrayed as feisty, enjoying their work, and relatively independent. On the other hand, news stories about sex workers and sex trafficking tend to cast all sex workers as helpless victims working in deplorable conditions who require rescuing from their profession.

Both sets of cultural images fail to use sociological imagination to capture the range and nuances of experiences among different sex workers and the complicated interplay between gender, race, class, and geography that shapes the experience of each particular individual. In this reading, Kimberly Kay Hoang describes the experiences of sex workers in Ho Chi Minh City, Vietnam. She identifies three different tiers of workers who cater to different types of clients and offer different services and relationships that hinge on the race, class, and geography of people involved. Some of the women do indeed engage in sex work because it is the best economic option available to them, and they perform perfunctory sexual acts with and for clients directly for cash, what she calls sexual exchanges. But others cater to primarily white tourists who want to take advantage of a "Third World sexscape" by having romantic relationships with local women (see p. 273). These women often try to parlay these temporary relationships into long-term financial support or relationships that would allow them to leave the country. Women in the high-end sector tend to be involved in intimate exchanges that require a particular kind of cultural, economic, and bodily capital. These women are often from upper-class families and have no interest in leaving Vietnam or forming long-term relationships. They carefully select their clients from overseas Vietnamese men (Viet Kieu) and avoid both locals and white tourists.

One of the main differences among the different "tiers" of sex workers in her study is the different types of capital they have at their disposal. She introduces Pierre Bourdieu's concept of cultural capital (the tastes, styles, habits, and

---

Excerpt from "'She's Not a Low- Class Dirty Girl': Sex Work in Ho Chi Minh, Vietnam" by Kimberly Kay Hoang, in *Journal of Contemporary Ethnography* 40 (4): 2011. Reprinted with permission.

dispositions associated with a group) as an important difference among workers and their clients. This compliments the available economic capital (income, assets, and other monetary resources) that each group has. Workers and clients with similar levels of cultural and economic capital tend to wind up together, and these similarities or differences tend to map along racial lines. Interestingly, this is no different than how Western romantic relationships tend to develop—we are most likely to wind up with a romantic partner who is socially, economically, and racially similar to us (recall that this is the idea of endogamy introduced in Reading 6, "Disciplined Preferences"). As you read, think about how romantic relationships without any overt economic transactions in them may in fact be similar to the types of relationships described in the reading.

Introduction

Studies on sex work pay particular attention to the growth of global sex tourism, marked by the production and consumption of sexual services across borders. A recent body of literature uncovers the complexities of stratified sex industries around the world (Bernstein 2007; Zheng 2009). This article extends the literature on the stratification of sex work by comparing three racially and economically diverse sectors of Ho Chi Minh City's (HCMC's) global sex industry: a *low-end* sector that caters to poor local Vietnamese men, a *mid-tier sector* that caters to white backpackers, and a *high-end sector* that caters to overseas Vietnamese (*Viet Kieu*) men.

Sex Work in Ho Chi Minh City's International Economy

Vietnam is an ideal case for the study of sex work because rapid economic restructuring has triggered new inflows of people and capital, creating a segmented sex market. After the fall of Saigon in 1975, Vietnam effectively closed its doors to foreign relations with most of the international community except the Soviet bloc. In 1986, after a decade of full state management of the economy, heavily subsidized production, and postwar infrastructural instability, the Vietnamese government introduced an extensive economic and administrative renovation policy called *Doi Moi* (literally "renovation" or "renewal") that transitioned Vietnam from a socialist to a market economy.

HCMC has a distinctive sex industry with an estimated 200,000 Vietnamese women involved in prostitution (CATW 2005).

The movement of people and capital makes HCMC a critical site where globalization generates new types of inequality, which in turn create new segments of sex work. Unlike studies on sex trafficking that tend to view all women as poor victims in need of rescue, I argue that it is important to examine the social and economic distinctions between sex workers in a stratified economy. Globalization does not create a single market for poor exploited women who cater to wealthy foreigners; rather, I contend that globalization creates diverse markets and new segments that expand already existing inequalities. Structural factors such as women's access to economic, cultural, and bodily resources position them in higher and lower paying sectors of sex work with different relations of intimacy.

Sex Work Through the Lens of Capital and Intimate Relations

In this article, I focus on how structural factors such as exchange of different bodily, cultural, and economic capitals lead to a range of short-term and long-term relationships that emerge through client–worker interactions.

First, I turn to Bourdieu's theories of capital to explain how clients and sex workers draw on different economic, cultural, and bodily resources to enter various sectors of HCMC's sex industry. To develop Bourdieu's theories in the context of sex work, I also draw on Zelizer's (2005) concept of *intimate relations* to illustrate how clients and sex workers mingle sex, money, and intimacy in different ways that correspond to their position in a particular stratum.

Bourdieu defines *economic capital* as the monetary income, assets, or other financial resources that an actor can access (Bourdieu 1986). *Cultural capital* refers to actors' dispositions and embodiment in specific social fields. It is the ability to acquire and manipulate a system of embodied, linguistic, or economic markers that carry cultural meaning, especially within a hierarchical social system of status (Bourdieu 1977). Broadly, the relevant demarcations of cultural capital in the world of HCMC's sex industry are the resources, dispositions, and modes of embodiment that allow individuals to position themselves within the particular social field of sex work in HCMC. More specifically, on the client side, I use the term "cultural capital" to draw attention to *Viet Kieu* clients' understanding of the local culture and their ability to speak Vietnamese when navigating the sex industry in HCMC. For sex workers, I use the term "cultural capital" to refer to the linguistic and discursive abilities needed for communication with clients, and also to the sex workers' level of comfort within particular bars and restaurants. In addition, sex workers' cultural capital encompasses the ability to embody and project to clients an imagined nation: Vietnam as nostalgic "home" for *Viet Kieu* men and, alternatively, Vietnam as foreign and exotic other for Western men (Nguyen-Vo 2008).

I also incorporate Bernstein's (2007) term *body capital*, which she defines as an attractive appearance used to sell sexual services. In this article, I highlight dimensions of body capital such as apparent age, designer clothing, hairstyle, and make-up, as well as strategies to acquire body capital, such as cosmetic surgery. Sex workers' bodies serve as assets that allow them to work as entrepreneurs in bodily capital (Wacquant 1995) to market themselves as attractive and thus more valuable in relation to global men.

Bourdieu (1986) argues that different forms of capital have varied meanings within social fields. A *field*, in Bourdieu's oeuvre, is a terrain of struggle in which agents strategize to preserve or improve their positions (Bourdieu 1984). While men and women use different forms of capital to enter and maneuver within specific sectors of sex work in HCMC, these various forms of capital are only valued through the relations between men and women in this particular field. In this paper I highlight the forms of capital that are relevant and valued in relations between clients and sex workers in HCMC's sex industry.

While Bourdieu's (1984) theories of social fields and capital help us to understand the structure of the HCMC's stratified sex industry and the relations within a particular field, his theories inhibit our examination of the *product of interactions* between clients and sex workers. Zelizer's (2005) concept of intimate relations is more useful because it provides a critical tool for understanding how the exchange of different resources leads to a range of short-term and long-lasting relationships between clients and sex workers.

How does Zelizer (2005) define intimacy and economic activity? Intimacy refers to "the transfer of personal information and wide-ranging, long-term relations which connect and overlap" between people (Zelizer 2005, p. 16). Intimate relations vary over time along a continuum and as people exchange different degrees of physical, informational, and emotional closeness with each other. Economic transactions, in contrast, go beyond the mere use of money. People may use gifts, different forms of compensation, or entitlements as payment, corresponding to the way they define their relationships with one another. They use varied symbols, rituals, practices, and distinguishable forms of money to mark distinct social relations (Zelizer 2004).

Integrating Bourdieu's theories of capital and Zelizer's concept of intimate relations, I argue that sex workers and their clients engage in three types of relationships with varying degrees of intimacy, capital, and duration (see Table 1).

Table 1 Economic, Relational, and Intimate Exchanges			
	Relations	**Capital at Stake**	**Duration**
Low-end	Sexual exchange (only sex and money are exchanged)	Economic capital: poor rural and urban women Body capital: lack of access to plastic surgery Cultural capital: lack of cultural and language skills	Short one-time interaction
Mid-tier	Relational exchange (sex, gifts, and money are exchanged)	Economic capital: poor urban women Body capital: plastic surgery, hair, clothing, etc. Cultural capital: ability to speak English and navigate in foreign spaces	Short-term and long-term remittance relationships that often develop into boy–girlfriend or husband–wife relations
High-end	Intimate exchange (sex, gifts, money, and intimacy are exchanged)	Economic capital: college- or trade-school-educated urban women from wealthy families Body capital: higher-end plastic surgeries, spas, designer clothing Cultural capital: ability to display comfort in navigating high-end hotels, bars, and restaurants	Short-term intimate relationships where marriage and migration are not the end goal

Note: These typologies are ideal types specific to Ho Chi Minh City's sex industry.

Sexual exchanges are swift encounters between clients and sex workers that involve direct sex-for-money exchanges and happen almost entirely in the low-end sector. Although interactions between sex workers and clients are sexually intimate, they are not personal. That is, men and women do not build emotional ties with one another. *Relational exchanges*, which take place primarily in the mid-tier sector, involve a complex set of intimate and economic arrangements, the exchange of bodily and cultural capitals, as well as short-term client–worker interactions that sometimes develop into long-term boyfriend–girlfriend relationships. *Intimate exchanges*, which occur mostly in the high-end sector, also involve a complex set of economic and intimate arrangements and the deployment of economic, cultural, and bodily capitals. However, relations between sex workers and clients in the high-end sector are short-term relationships that last only for the duration of the client's visit and rarely develop into long-term remittance relationships.

Research Methods

I carried out seven months of ethnographic field research in three intervals between June 2006 and August 2007 in HCMC.

I conducted participant observation in local bars, cafes, sex workers' homes, malls, restaurants, and on the streets. All of the sex workers I studied were women over the age of eighteen who *chose* to enter sex work as independent agents. None of my participants were trafficked or forced into prostitution.

I focused on three sectors of HCMC's sex industry: those catering to poor local Vietnamese men, to white backpackers, and to overseas Vietnamese (*Viet Kieu*) men. I chose these sectors because together they represent a large portion of the sex work industry in HCMC and because the relations between clients and sex workers in these sectors are largely public and therefore easier to observe. I later returned to Vietnam for fifteen months between 2009 and 2010 to examine sex work relationships within private spaces and enclosed karaoke bars that cater to wealthy Vietnamese entrepreneurs and Asian businessmen. Here I focus on the sectors that are more publicly visible because I did not have access to enclosed spaces during 2006–2007.

My research began with time spent in local bars and on the streets to meet and develop rapport with various sex workers, clients, and bar owners before asking the women to participate in my project. The second phase of the research process involved intensive participant observation and informal interviews with individual sex workers who agreed to participate in the project. Being an overseas Vietnamese woman helped me gain access to female sex workers because many of them suspected local Vietnamese men who asked them questions of being undercover police. Although all of the women knew that I was a researcher from the United States who would eventually write about their lives, this was not important to them. They cared more about my family history and my life overseas, wanting to situate me in their mental universe.

In my attempt to expand the literature on sex work empirically, I also incorporated male clients into my analysis. All of the clients knew that I was a researcher from the United States. Overseas white backpackers and *Viet Kieu* clients in my study were much more open with me than local Vietnamese men. White backpackers and *Viet Kieu* could converse with me in English and relate to me about the context of their lives overseas and the dynamics of their relations in HCMC. I befriended two local motorbike-taxi drivers who introduced me to the low-end sector that catered to local Vietnamese men. Cuong and Loc taught me how to approach men and women in this sector. They also helped ease me into conversations with local male clients. Their assistance was crucial in my understanding of the spatial and structural differences between the local sector and the sectors that cater to overseas male clients.

The Low-End Sector: "Touching Them Makes Me Want to Throw Up!"

Sex workers who catered to local Vietnamese men generally engaged in sexual exchanges that involved direct sex-for-money transactions. These women worked in brothels disguised as barbershops in HCMC's Districts Ten and Four, the Binh Thanh district, and the area surrounding the Tan Son Nhat Airport.

All twelve women in this sector were single mothers between the ages of twenty-nine and sixty who had no more than a grade school education. They were poor, urban women or rural migrants who once worked in the service or manufacturing sectors before entering sex work. Sex workers in this sector provided men with a variety of *sexual labors* (Boris et al. 2010), offering a quick orgasm within a twenty-minute interaction. Men typically paid three U.S. dollars for this service, and clients and sex workers rarely negotiated these prices. On average, women earned a hundred dollars per month, which was forty to fifty dollars more than they would earn working in local restaurants, legitimate barbershops, or as house cleaners.

I asked Dung, a thirty-four-year-old single mother of two, why she worked for such low pay and why she did not try to find work in District One, the business district, where she could capitalize on the flow of men with overseas money. She said very bluntly:

> I am old. I have a kid. I don't look pretty. I don't speak English or even know how to get to those places [that cater to foreign men]. I don't have the clothes or money to walk around in those kinds of bars so I could never work there. I could never compete with those women. Money is never easy to get from white men.[1]

At the beginning of my research, I naively invited some of these women to have lunch or dinner in District One. I quickly realized that they felt extremely uncomfortable, if not illegitimate, in these spaces. True, for example, said:

> I do not go into those restaurants that mostly foreigners go into because I am so afraid that I will sit down, look at the prices on the menu, and panic because I couldn't even afford the cheapest thing there. If I turned around and walked out everyone would laugh at me.

In sum, sex workers' lack of economic and cultural resources placed them in a sector of sex work where they engaged in relations of subordination with poor local men.

In addition to the lack of economic resources and cultural capital that limited them, the women in the low-end sector did not have the *body capital* to participate in mid-tier or high-end sectors. As Mai, a woman from the Mekong Delta who worked in one of these barbershops, stated, "I am in my mid-thirties, I have a child, and I am not good looking. . . . So I don't have a choice but to do this." While women who catered to foreign men reinvested a significant portion of their earnings into their appearance by purchasing cosmetic surgery, clothing, accessories, and make-up, the women in the low-end sector spent all of their earnings on necessities like housing, food, and schooling for their children. As such, the women in the low-end sector typically wore the same plain house-like clothing in both their homes and work places. They did not dress up for work or wear any clothing that marked them in an explicitly sexual way. In fact, these women's bodies resembled the bodies of poor homemakers, sisters, or mothers. They were women who shared similar class dispositions with poor local men.

Although they were not forced into sex work, many entered and continued to do this work as a means to escape poverty. The women in the low-end sector were among the most vulnerable and the most exploited. These women did not have much choice in terms of which clients they would service. In most cases, they served any client, because they needed the money. Mai said:

> What we do is dirty. Old dirty men come in here and they are rough with my body. They don't care about me because to them I am just a worker. When I first started working, I would throw up after each client, but now I am used to it.

Although some women had a set of regular clients, these clients were purchasing a product—an orgasm—and nothing more. Sex workers and clients engaged in direct sex-for-money exchanges where economic and intimate relationships were not closely intertwined.

Mid-Tier Sector: "She's a Smart Woman Who Is Just Trapped in a Poor Country"

The "backpacker" area in HCMC is well known as the central location for people traveling on a budget. Lining the streets are souvenir shops, mini-hotels, tourist agencies, restaurants, cafes, and bars catering to foreigners. The majority of shopkeepers in this area speak some English. I conducted participant observation in seven of the roughly twenty-five bars located in this area. The clients I met in this sector ranged in age from twenty-two to sixty-five, and all were white Americans, Europeans, or Australians. White men in the mid-tier sector viewed themselves as savvy travelers who were able to take advantage of a Third-World sexscape (Brennan 2004). They tended to stay in a host of mini-hotels, parching for the "authentic" Vietnamese experience.

Sex workers in this sector exploited the transnational sex market by developing relations with overseas men and engaging in what Smith and Guarnizo (1998) refer to as practices of "transnationalism from below." While the women in this sector were certainly involved in direct sex-for-money exchanges, they also made use of their cultural capital to feign love and provide their clients with a variety of other services. The following account illustrates how transnationally savvy sex workers create and sustain intimate relations through their English-language skills and their bodies.

I met Linh in June 2006 and continued to maintain ties with her through August 2007. Linh was working in Pink Star, a bar located in the backpacker area of District One. At 5 foot 6 inches, Linh was taller than most Vietnamese women and had a slender body and long legs. She always wore tight pink and black dresses that accentuated her thin legs. Like many of the women working in this sector, Linh invested more than a thousand dollars in a variety of body modifications: breast implants, eyebrow tattoos, Botox injections in her forehead, and liposuction to flatten her stomach. While nearly all of the women in the low-end sector were rural migrants, women like Linh tended to come from urban families that were poor by city standards, but possessed more economic resources than the families of women in the lower-end sector. They were aware of places that catered to overseas white men looking for an authentic Vietnamese experience, and all of them could speak some English. All of these women worked in local bars disguised as bartenders. However, they did not receive a wage for bartending, instead earning money from tips and from their sexual liaisons with their clients. Many of these women learned English by talking to overseas men in the bars, and the more ambitious ones spent their earnings on formal English-language classes. Investing in her body and in English-language skills enabled Linh to initiate and establish ties with white men with economic resources from developed nations.

On one evening, a client named Jeff, a man in his midfifties from New York, walked in and sat down in Pink Star. Jeff was dressed in khaki shorts, a short-sleeve button-up shirt, and flip-flop sandals. He was sweating, so Linh walked over with a wet towel and wiped down his face, something she frequently did for men to demonstrate her care for them. The two sat and made small talk, despite Linh's limited English skills. They exchanged typical questions including, "Where are you from?" "How long are you here for?" "What do you do?" "How old are you?" "Where does your family live?" After five drinks, Linh moved in, nudged him, and said, "You take me home with you." He smiled and said, "Okay." After which she said, "You pay me hundred dollars?" He laughed and said, "Too much. . . I pay you fifty." They smiled silently at each other for several minutes before she said, "Okay, sixty." They got up and left.

The next morning, Linh called and asked me to go with her and her daughter to a local amusement park. After several hours of walking through the park, we sat down to eat while her daughter took a short nap. During this time, Linh told me that she used her employment at the bar to meet clients from overseas. With clients she knew were in Vietnam for a short period, she was direct and asked if they wanted to go with her for fifty to seventy dollars a night. However, with clients who visited Vietnam for an extended time, she engaged in *relational exchanges* in an attempt to develop long-term relationships that sometimes turned into complicated boyfriend–girlfriend relations. Nearly all of the women in this sector had multiple "boyfriends." When I asked her if she loved any of the men she dated, she said:

> When I first started working, I was young and not so smart. I would fall in love easily and then get hurt when things did not work out. Now, I don't let myself fall in love. I think I can grow to love the man who takes the best care of me in Vietnam or some other country. I want to change my life first and fall in love second.

In both long-term and short-term relations, Linh always attempted to develop remittance relationships after the men left Vietnam. She also dated multiple men as a strategy to migrate abroad: as she reasoned, if one man was unwilling to help her migrate, then she had other men who might take her.

After leaving the amusement park, Linh asked me to translate the first of what turned into more than a hundred e-mails between her and James, a sixty-seven-year-old Australian man who owned a small business before retiring. She met James in December 2005 at Pink Sty while he was on a holiday in Vietnam.

She wanted to build an emotional relationship with James so that he would sympathize with her "struggles" and send her money. James deposited several chunks of money ranging from five hundred to five thousand dollars in her bank account to help her through these crises, in addition to monthly remittances of three hundred dollars a month to pay for English lessons and beauty school. Through these transactions, by August 2006, she received a monthly remittance of about seven hundred dollars from three overseas men, two from Australia and one from the United States. Linh convinced all three men that each was the only man in her life. While Linh did take English lessons, she had several men paying for the same set of classes, which provided her with extra money to pay for plastic surgery or purchase nicer clothing and fancier phones. Women like Linh capitalized on global linkages by creating and maintaining a series of fictitious stories about their lives in HCMC.

I first met James that day through Yahoo Messenger, an Internet chat system. Linh introduced me to him as someone studying transnational relationships. To my surprise, James took an interest in my project, and he and I went on to communicate via e-mail, Internet chat, and postal mail more than sixty times between July 2006 and August 2007. In August 2007, I met James in person at a local cafe in District One. The sixty-seven-year-old Australian decided that he was going to spend the rest of his life traveling as a back-packer on a budget.

In several conversations that I had with James, he repeatedly described Linh in these terms:

> Linh is an honest person; she is a strong woman with a lot of integrity. You know she only went to school through sixth grade, but she can speak English fairly well. We talk about many things. I love Linh a lot and I want what is best for her. She is a smart and intelligent woman who is just living in a poor country where there aren't very many opportunities. I want to help her start her own small business in Vietnam, you know, so that she can be self-sufficient and not have to work in a bar.

In his e-mails to me, James did not speak of a sex-for-money exchange. Instead, he framed his relationship with Linh as one based on true love. James stated that he was in love with Linh, and that he believed she was truly in love with him. He expressed strong convictions that he was going to be the man who would "save" her from her life as a bar girl. The moral characteristics (Lamont 1992) of honesty, hard work, and personal integrity that James attributed to Linh motivated him to send her large sums of money without questioning her stories of need. He sympathized with her because, as he said, "as a first-world man with so much privilege, I felt that it was important to help."

Linh and James began their relationship as worker and client, and while Linh held on to multiple men until she was able to secure her visa to migrate, she eventually fell in love with James. Vietnam's status as a poor country allowed Linh, and other women in the same position, to represent themselves as victims of global poverty, generating sympathy and regular, large remittances from several men like James. Linh's ability to speak English, navigate foreign spaces, act as a personal tour guide, and induce feelings of love and sympathy in her clients made this relationship possible. Her simultaneous involvement with multiple men across transnational social fields also allowed her to choose whom she would serve, and determine the country to which she would eventually emigrate. Likewise, James drew on moral discourses about global inequality to explain why Linh entered sex work. James and other foreign men like him also made use of the expanded sexual and relational possibilities in a developing country like Vietnam, where they knew their money would both buy more sex and go further to support women they deemed deserving. The stories of men and women like Linh and James demonstrate how seemingly powerless women can exploit global and local systems of oppression by capitalizing on transnational linkages and engaging in relational sex with the hope of migrating to a country with better opportunities, and if they are "lucky," maybe even falling in love.

High-End Sector: "She's Not a Low-Class Dirty Girl"

Workers and clients in the high end of HCMC sex work engaged in intimate exchanges, blurring the boundaries between economic and intimate relations even further than those in the middle tier.

Clients in the high-end sector engaged in relationships with sex workers possessed levels of economic and cultural capital similar to them. These men were not looking for poor women whom they could save. Instead, they sought young, desirable women with options. Unlike the women in the mid-tier sector, the women who catered to wealthy *Viet Kieu* (overseas Vietnamese) did not come from poverty. In fact, many of them came from relatively wealthy families who owned small businesses and had the social networks and resources to comfortably navigate some of HCMC's most expensive establishments. Although women in the high-end sector often received money from their clients, sex workers and clients both framed the transfer of money as a *gift*, never as a form of *payment*, and most definitely not as a way to help save women from poverty.

In the next account, I illustrate the various forms of economic, cultural, and bodily resources that women in this sector possess. I met Ngoc, a tall, slender twenty-four-year-old woman, in May 2007 inside Dragonfly, one of HCMC's most expensive bars.

Ngoc's family owned a small electronics store in District One. She just started a job at Star Capital, an investment company whose global headquarters was based in the United States. She made roughly six hundred dollars per month working as an assistant to an account manager. Like Ngoc, most of the women that I studied in this sector had a college or university degree. Along with a well-respected job, and a salary that was relatively high by HCMC standards, Ngoc's parents supplemented her income.

Ngoc always dressed in trendy clothing, owned several different designer handbags, and owned multiple cell phones. While spending a day in a local spa together, Ngoc described to me the various surgeries that she underwent to enhance her body. She showed me her breast implants, saying [in Vietnamese]:

> Don't these look good to you? I got them done in Thailand by a doctor who specializes in breast implants for transsexuals: you know, men who want to be women. The doctor told me to stay with a C [size] cup because they would look more natural and my nipples would look better. You don't want to get those cheap implants like a lot of girls in Vietnam get [because] they look fake.

In addition to the breast implants, at the age of twenty-four Ngoc had nose surgery to create a nose bridge, double eye-lid surgery, liposuction from her thighs and stomach, and Botox injections in her forehead. With the exception of the Botox, she completed all of these procedures in Thailand—a mark of distinction that differentiated her from local women who could only afford surgery in Vietnam. These cosmetic alterations cost her more than twelve thousand dollars in total. Ngoc also had regular appointments at a local spa, where she got a massage and a facial once a week. She spent several hours in local beauty salons getting her hair and make-up done prior to going out at night. For Ngoc, having plastic surgery, wearing designer clothing, spending days in spas, and getting her hair and nails done at beauty salons distinguished her from poorer Vietnamese women who catered to white men.

Ngoc and I also spent several nights out in cafes, restaurants, and bars where she introduced me to many of her friends, who were local bar and restaurant owners. These men and women often referred clients to Ngoc. On our outings together, rich local men would often proposition Ngoc. She always declined because, as she said, "They would automatically know that I was working, and if something bad happened, everyone would know I was working." I asked her, "What about Western guys?" She said, "Those are for the village girls who want to migrate. If I go with a white guy, everyone will know I'm a working girl." In addition to the rich local Vietnamese clients and white businessmen, she also turned down several *Viet Kieu* men. When I asked why she turned down so many clients when she had not been with anyone for nearly two weeks, she explained:

> You have to know how to pick out men. Many *Viet Kieu* men come to Vietnam and they show off, but they are actually poor men. You can tell the difference between rich and poor men by the kind of clothes they wear, their watches, and the kinds of places where they hang out. Poorer *Viet Kieu* men will eat at places that don't cost much, but men with money, know about good restaurants.

While overseas *Viet Kieu* men certainly leverage the power of the dollar to consume more in Vietnam than they could in the United States, Ngoc used the consumption patterns of male clients to distinguish richer *Viet Kieu* men from working-class *Viet Kieu* men. Women like Ngoc avoided men whom they thought were "working-class *Viet Kieu*" because these women had no desire to develop relationships that would result in marriage and migration. As Ngoc said:

> I love Vietnam and I am comfortable here. I don't want to live anywhere else. In Vietnam, when you have money, you can afford everything. I have aunts and uncles in America, and you know in America people have to clean their own houses, buy their own food, and cook it themselves. I speak English, but I know that I could never get a job overseas that will pay me enough to live like this. Life here is just so much easier if you have money. If my family was poor, I think I would want to marry someone who will take me to the U.S., so that I could live a better life. I am not poor. Why would I give up this life?

Ngoc's ability to live a high-end lifestyle year-round kept her in short term, noncommittal relationships with several *Viet Kieu* men, who spent large sums of money on her while they were in Vietnam. She was aware that immigrants from Vietnam to first-world countries rarely find coveted jobs in the primary labor market, often ending up with low-status, low-paying jobs instead (Thai 2008). She had no desire to marry and migrate abroad, because the possibility of downward mobility was too great. On another occasion, I asked Ngoc, "If you have the money already, and you don't want to live in the U.S., why do you spend your time with these men?" She responded [in English]:

> I am twenty-six years old and I don't want to settle down yet. Marriage here is not easy. I see so many husbands cheat on their wives with younger, more attractive women and I want to have fun for as long as I can. It's temporary: these men will eventually go back home, and it is nice to be spoiled with nice gifts and extra money. I have fun doing it. I'm young, so why not, right? I can't do this when I'm in my thirties, so that's when I'll get married.

Ngoc's social, cultural, economic, and physical advantages allowed her to move with ease in spaces where high-end *Viet Kieu* men spent their time and money. Her body capital, economic resources, and ability to convey a high-class image enabled her to exert power over her clients.

In June 2007, Ngoc introduced me to Tuan, a *Viet Kieu* from France who had worked as an orthodontist for fifteen years in France before returning to Vietnam to open a practice. During one of four informal interviews with Tuan over coffee, he remarked:

> I am thirty-nine, almost forty years old, and I am not ready to settle down with anyone, but I don't want to spend my days alone either. This is a fun city to go out in at night. I don't want to be tied down, so I spend my time with girls who are sort of working. I mean, I know that I have to buy her things and spend money on her. Otherwise, she won't waste her time with me. I can't be with just any girl, either. I need to be with someone who is young and beautiful. When you go out in Vietnam, people see you. If you have money, you can't have a cheap girl.

Viet Kieu men looked for intimate relationships with local women that involved more than just sex. These men purchased the services of women whose skills and looks distinguished them from the lower-class sex workers who accompanied white men. Men like Tuan wanted to be around women who helped them display their masculinity in very public places (Allison 1994). High-end sex workers were better than women in other tiers at disguising the nature of their relationships as boyfriend–girlfriend relations rather than client–worker relations, because they did not work as disguised bartenders. Instead, they could afford to pay for drinks and services in the high-end bars and cafes that cater to foreigners.

Moreover, while relations of intimacy certainly involved sex in private spaces, the relationships took place in very public places like local bars, cafes, restaurants, hotels, and on the streets. The multiple sites of intimate labors went hand in hand with the multiple forms of compensation. These clients often spent large sums of money on expensive cellular phones, motorbikes, and designer handbags and clothing for the sex workers, all of which served as markers of distinction. The clients were often willing to spend liberally on gifts for their women because—as Thanh, a computer technician from Paris, explained—"I don't go to those low-class dirty girls, you know? These girls are young and pretty, and other men want them. You know they are smart, they speak English, and they come from good families." In short, the purchase of intimacy from high-end sex workers involved the deployment of economic, cultural, and bodily capital. In return, high-end clients compensated women with expensive gifts and cash. However, the cash was always framed as a gift and not, as in the middle and lower sectors, a way of fulfilling a need.

Viet Kieu men also sought relations with local women who embodied their ideals of Vietnamese femininity. When I asked Tuan why he preferred local Vietnamese women to *Viet Kieu* women, he said:

> The women whom I dated back in France all had careers. One was a lawyer. [She] loved me a lot, but she was too independent, and as a man, I just wanted to feel like I could protect her. I didn't feel that way. I didn't feel like a man who could take care of her, because she was just too independent.

As Tuan stated, Vietnamese women could make men like him feel good because, unlike women in the West, they knew how to foreground their dependence on men and shunt their autonomy into the background in a way that made men feel important.

Viet Kieu men, unlike white men, had the linguistic and cultural resources to participate in the high-end sector. Whereas in the low-end and mid-tier sectors clients and sex workers talked more directly and explicitly about forms of payment, relations between men and women in the high-end sector often involved more indirect and discreet exchanges. In fact, because so many of the high-end sex workers disguised their labor so skillfully, many of the white men in my study could not figure out how to engage in relations with high-end women. In contrast, *Viet Kieu* men were comfortable participating in the oblique, elaborate *pas de deux* that high-end sex workers expected. This was most evident in moments of rupture, when relationships between clients and sex workers in the high-end sector grew precarious. Clients understood that they needed to compensate the women in some way; otherwise, their relationships would dissolve.

In my conversations with high-end sex workers and clients, the physical act of sex served both as a way for sex workers to distinguish themselves as upscale women and to make clients feel more intimately involved. These women often withheld sex from their clients, projecting the image that they were not "easy" girls who would go with just anyone.

Economic and intimate relations in this sector were closely intertwined, as both clients and sex workers went to great lengths to distinguish themselves as high-end. The consumption practices of high-end women enabled men like Tuan to distinguish themselves from the white men who participated in the mid-tier market. While some white men spent just as much money in their relations with mid-tier sex workers, they justified their consumption practices in different ways. White men engaged in relations with women who "needed" help, while *Viet Kieu* men engaged in relations with women who helped them assert a particular class status in public. This cultural logic of desire (Constable 2003) is embedded not only in a client's ability to engage in relations with high-end women but also in the sex worker's ability to distinguish herself from mid-tier and low-end sex workers who do not have her bodily, cultural, social, and symbolic capital. Women like Ngoc are among the most sophisticated workers because they have the money, skill, and looks to mask their work. Clients in the high-end sector pay for intimate relationships characterized by a hidden set of intimate labors that are intertwined with a complex set of economic arrangements. While low-end women provide their clients mainly with sexual services, women in the high-end sector provide their clients with short-term physical, sexual, and emotionally intimate encounters.

DISCUSSION QUESTIONS

1. What role did race and ethnicity play in the sexual marketplace in Ho Chi Minh City? What other factors intersected with race and ethnicity to shape the types of clients that the women had as clients?
2. What are the different types of capital discussed in the article? In what aspect of your own life do these types of capital play a role?
3. Are there any similarities between the three different tiers of sexual markets in Ho Chi Minh City and the different types of sexual experiences that college students have?
4. What role does globalization play in shaping the sex industry in Vietnam? How might globalization play a role in your choice of romantic partner?

REFERENCES

Allison, Anne. 1994. *Nightwork: Sexuality, Pleasure, and Corporate Masculinity in a Tokyo Hostess Club*. Chicago: University of Chicago Press.

Bernstein, Elizabeth. 2007. *Temporarily Yours: Intimacy, Authenticity, and the Commerce of Sex*. Chicago: University of Chicago Press.

Boris, Eileen, Stephanie Gilmore, and Rhacel Parrenas. 2010. "Sexual Labors: Interdisciplinary Perspectives toward Sex as Work." *Sexualities* 23:131–37.

Bourdieu, Pierre. 1977. *Outline of a Theory of Practice*. Cambridge: Cambridge University Press.

Bourdieu, Pierre. 1984. *Distinction: A Social Critique of the Judgment of Taste*. Cambridge, MA: Harvard University Press.

Bourdieu, Pierre. 1986. "The Forms of Capital." In *Handbook of Theory and Research for the Sociology of Education*, edited by J. Richardson. New York: Greenwood.

Bourdieu, Pierre and Loic Wacquant. 1992. *An Invitation to Reflexive Sociology*. Chicago: University of Chicago Press.

Brennan, Denise. 2004. *What's Love Got to Do with It? Transnational Desires and Sex Tourism in the Dominican Republic*. Durham: Duke University Press.

Cabezas, Amalia. 2009. *Economies of Desire: Sex and Tourism in Cuba and the Dominican Republic*. Philadelphia: Temple University Press.

Coalition against Trafficking in Women (CATW). 2005. Trafficking and prostitution in Asia and the Pacific, http://www.catw-ap.org/programs/research-documentation-publications/facts-and-statistics/.

Constable, Nicole. 2003. *Romance on a Global Stage: Pen Pals, Virtual Ethnography, and "Mail-Order" Marriages*. Berkeley: University of California Press.

Hayton, Bill. 2010. *Vietnam: Rising Dragon*. New Haven: Yale University Press.

Hoang, Kimberly Kay. 2010. "Economies of Emotion, Familiarity Fantasy and Desire: Emotional Labor in Ho Chi Minh City's Sex Industry." *Sexualities* 13:255–72.

Hoogvelt, Ankie. 1997. *Globalization and the Postcolonial World: The New Political Economy of Development*. Hampshire: Macmillan.

Lamont, Michele. 1992. *Money, Morals and Manners: The Culture of the French and the American Upper-Middle Class*. Chicago: University of Chicago Press.

MacKinnon, Catharine. 1982. "Feminism, Marxism, Method, and the State: An Agenda for Theory." *Signs* 7:515–44.

Nguyen-Vo, Thu-Huong. 2008. *The Ironies of Freedom Sex, Culture, and Neoliberal Governance in Vietnam*. Seattle: University of Washington Press.

Pateman, Carole. 1988. *The Sexual Contract*. Stanford: Stanford University Press.

Pham, Chi Do. 2003. *The Vietnamese Economy: Awakening the Dormant Dragon*. New York: Routledge.

Rosen, Eva and Sudhir Venkatesh. 2008. "A 'Perversion' of Choice: Sex Work Offers Just Enough in Chicago's Urban Ghetto." *Journal of Contemporary Ethnography* 37:417–41.

Sassen, Saskia. 2001. *The Global City: New York, London, Tokyo*. Princeton: Princeton University Press.

Sassen, Saskia. 2002. "Global Cities and Survival Circuits." In *Global Woman: Nannies, Maids, and Sex Workers in the New Economy*, edited by B. Ehrenreich and A. Hochschild. New York: Metropolitan Books.

Smith, Michael Peter and Luis Eduardo Guarnizo. 1998. *Transnationalism From Below*. New Brunswick: Transaction Publishers.

Thai, Hung. 2008. *For Better or for Worse: Vietnamese International Marriages in the New Global Economy*. New York: Rutgers University Press.

Truong, Thanh-Dan. 1990. *Sex, Money and Morality: Prostitution and Tourism in Southeast Asia*. London: Zed Books.

Wacquant, Loic. 1995. "Pugs at Work: Bodily Capital and Bodily Labour among Professional Boxers." *Body & Society* 1:65–93.

Weitzer, Ronald. 2010. "The Ethnography of Prostitution: New International Perspectives." *Contemporary Sociology* 39:262–69.

Wonders, Nancy and Raymond Michalowski. 2001. "Bodies, Borders and Sex Tourism in a Globalized World: A Tale of Two Cities—Amsterdam and Havana." *Social Problems* 48:545–71.

WTO. 2006. *General council approves Vietnam's membership*. WTO: 2006 Press Releases, vol. Press/455.

Zelizer, Viviana. 2004. *The Social Meaning of Money*. New York: Basic Books.

Zelizer, Viviana. 2005. *The Purchase of Intimacy*. Princeton: Princeton University Press.

Zheng, Tiantian. 2009. *Red Lights: The Lives of Sex Workers in Postsocialist China*. Minneapolis: University of Minnesota Press.

NOTE

1. All of the conversations that I had with the women in the low-end sector took place in Vietnamese. The quotations are my English translations.

America for Americans

A History of Xenophobia

Erika Lee

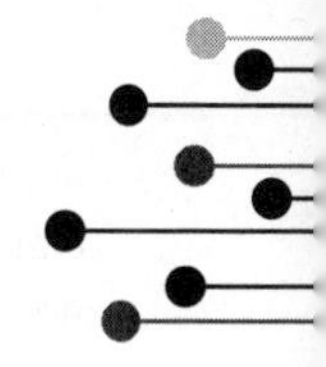

Fourth of July celebrations highlight cultural beliefs about American history, culture, and identity. With fireworks, concerts, and parades across the country and many images of the American flag and Statue of Liberty abounding in the media, the nation's birthday provides a feel-good party to celebrate the American Dream and the idea that America is the land of opportunity. But America's actual history, culture, and identity are much more complicated than the stories and sentiments celebrated around barbeques and concerts in the middle of summer. America is at the same time a nation that celebrates and welcomes immigrants and the immigrants of the past while also being deeply racist and xenophobic, erasing or disregarding the experiences of many nonwhite immigrants and using fears of "illegal" immigration to only thinly hide overtly racist sentiments.

In this reading, historian Erika Lee traces the history of xenophobia in the United States. She notes the strange juxtaposition of a trip to Ellis Island where immigration is loudly and proudly celebrated with Donald Trump's 2016 election to the presidency, which was based in large part on an overtly racist immigration platform. She provides useful historical context for understanding how the apparatus of immigration enforcement was built by various xenophobic laws over the past 150 years, starting with the Chinese Exclusion Act of 1882 and ending with Trump's ban on refugees and immigrants from Muslim countries in 2017. Although she is a historian, her work is sociological in its tracing of the social forces that shaped the treatment of different racial and ethnic groups in relation to immigration. She shows how economic changes often spur racist changes to immigration policies and how politicians use the specter of dangerous immigrants (a danger that is unsupported by research or reality) to maintain power for those who are members of the most privileged social group—white Christians.

This excerpt covers the Chinese Exclusion Act of 1882, the mass deportation of citizens of Mexican descent during the great depression, and the Islamophobia that followed the September 11, 2001, attacks and Donald Trump's election as president. Language plays an important role in each of these instances, with the more recent emphasis on the "illegal" status of immigrants

---

acting as thin cover for racism against Latinos and Middle Easterners. Social class also plays a role in who is allowed into America and who is not. As in 1882 when the United States passed the Chinese Exclusion Act, being wealthy and having a high-status job provided a way around immigration laws and some protection from immigration enforcement.

As you read, think about the parallels between the rhetoric she describes that was used in 1882, during the Great Depression, and after September 11th, and the language used by politicians today. How do the words we use to describe a problem (or try to convince others there is a problem) shape the assumptions that people make about an issue?

It's a beautiful midsummer day in Jersey City, New Jersey, and I am on a boat heading to the Statue of Liberty and the Ellis Island National Museum of Immigration. My shipmates reflect America's diversity. There are South Asian grandmothers wearing saris and baseball caps, and Chinese women holding umbrellas to shield themselves from the hot sun. A white father explains to his squirming children how their great-great-grandfather came to the United States a century ago from Austria. The mood is cheerful. An African American family records a video. "Everyone excited to see the Statue of Liberty?" the mother asks. The kids all yell, "Yes!"

A soothing woman's voice welcomes us on board and begins a brief history lesson. She informs us that we're heading to Ellis Island, the "main gateway into America." Our journey, we're told, "recalls the voyages" of approximately twelve million immigrants who "passed through these waters on their way to Ellis Island—and a new life."

I am trying to share in this patriotic celebration of Ellis Island, a place that serves as a symbol of America's welcome to immigrants, but I keep thinking about another message I've heard that day. The 2016 Republican National Convention has just ended, and the GOP platform, put forward by Donald Trump, was one of pure xenophobia. Ever since launching his presidential campaign, Trump had pledged to beef up border security, ban Muslim immigrants, deport eleven million undocumented people living in the United States, and build a massive wall along the country's southern border with Mexico. And now that he was the official Republican presidential nominee, his extreme views were being repeated by a growing number of voters and politicians.

Riffing on the convention's opening theme—"Make America Safe Again"—speaker after speaker painted a terrifying portrait of America under siege by immigrant criminals, terrorists, and gang members. Former New York City mayor Rudy Giuliani claimed, for example, that Democratic presidential nominee Hillary Clinton supported "open borders" that would admit Syrian refugees posing as "operatives who are terrorists," who were "going to come to Western Europe and here and kill us." US senator Jeff Sessions from Alabama falsely claimed that 350,000 people succeeded in "crossing our borders illegally each year." He also blamed immigrants for taking away jobs from Americans.

Most of the statements made by Trump and other convention speakers were either patently false or grossly misleading, but none of that seemed to matter. The number of undocumented immigrants cited by convention speakers was much too high, and these claims ignored the larger trend of an overall decline in undocumented immigration. Studies also reported that immigrants, including those who were undocumented, were less likely to commit crimes than people born in the United States. Yet the crowd inside the Quicken Loans Arena went crazy for Trump's message. During his seventy-five-minute speech, in which he identified immigration as one of the greatest threats to the United States and promised to restore America's "immigration security," he was repeatedly interrupted by cheers, applause, and chants of "Build the wall!"

I can't forget the angry tones and raised fists as I alight on Ellis Island and walk through the museum exhibits. We learn about earlier chapters in our anti-immigrant history, but we are meant to understand them as just that: history that is over and done with. By the time visitors get to the museum gift shop, we are encouraged to banish this ugly past from our minds and celebrate our immigrant roots instead. In true American fashion, we do this by buying something. Team Italy or Team Poland T-shirts, snow globes of the Statue of Liberty or the Leaning Tower of Pisa. The Ellis Café, however, takes different inspiration, offering menu items like the All-American Angus Cheeseburger and the Freedom Burger. Between the gift shop and the café, it seems that we can buy both immigrant and all-American identities that happily coexist. But I know that it is not that simple.

I am struggling to figure out how these two Americas fit together.

There is the United States that is known as a nation of immigrants. Three-fifths of all the world's immigrants settled in the United States from the beginning of the nineteenth century to the beginning of the twentieth; over the course of the twentieth century, the United States remained the world's largest immigrant-receiving country, and into the start of the twenty-first century, it still admitted more immigrants than any other country—over a million per year. More than eighty million have arrived in the last two hundred years alone. The United States has also historically led the world in resettling refugees, bringing in three million since 1980. Americans celebrate this United States by referring to their "nation of immigrants," a country that values immigrants and offers a haven for refugees. Even as this story has obscured a violent history of invasion, native dispossession, and slavery, defining the United States as a nation of immigrants continues to be a popular way of reaffirming America's acceptance of racial and ethnic diversity. This is the America that my grandparents—immigrants from China—knew and loved. They braved long transpacific journeys and worked long hours as domestic servants, in Chinese restaurants and in laundries, so that their children and grandchildren could have a chance to claim the promised American dream.

But the United States is also a nation of xenophobia. Even as it has welcomed millions from around the world, it has also deported more immigrants than any other nation—over fifty-five million since 1882. Americans have been wary of almost every group of foreigners that has come to the United States: German immigrants in the eighteenth century; Irish and Chinese in the nineteenth century; Italians, Jews, Japanese, and Mexicans in the twentieth century; and Muslims today. Americans have labeled immigrants threatening because they were poor, practiced a different faith, were nonwhite. They have argued that immigrants were too numerous, were not assimilating, were taking jobs away from deserving Americans, were bringing crime and disease into the country, had dangerous political ideals, were un-American, or even hated America. The United States has passed discriminatory immigration laws and detained, incarcerated, and expelled immigrants. It has exploited and segregated the foreign-born, allowing them to be in America but not accepted as fully American.

History shows that xenophobia has been a constant and defining feature of American life. It is deeply embedded in our society, economy, and politics. It thrives best in certain contexts, such as periods of rapid economic and demographic change, but it has also been actively promoted by special interests in the pursuit of political power. It has influenced elections and dictated policies. It has shaped American foreign relations and justified American imperialism. It has played a central role in America's changing definitions of race, citizenship, and what it means to be "American." It has endured because it has been an indelible part of American racism, white supremacy, and nationalism, and because it has been supported by American capitalism and democracy.

As a form of racial discrimination, xenophobia has not distinguished between immigrants who have entered with authorization and those who have not, or between immigrants and US citizens. Instead, it has ensnared entire populations, regardless of immigration or citizenship status, and the strain and violence of xenophobia has had generational consequences. Take, for example, the 1882 Chinese Exclusion Act, initially passed as a temporary measure to bar Chinese laborers; it made it harder for all Chinese, including American citizens of Chinese descent, to enter and reenter the country for generations, until the law was repealed in 1943. Or consider the mass deportation of Mexicans during the Great Depression. Initially designed to target those in the country without authorization, the xenophobic campaign ultimately involved the removal of legal residents and US-born Mexican American citizens. Such episodes continued: during

World War II, two-thirds of the Japanese Americans who were forced out of their homes and into incarceration camps were US citizens. And today, many of the people impacted by the United States' growing deportation regime are US citizens in mixed-status families, typically undocumented immigrant parents and their citizen children.

Xenophobia is not only about immigration; it is about who has the power to define what it means to be American, who gets to enjoy the privileges of American citizenship, and who does not. The nation's founding documents outlined the basic rights to be bestowed on Americans (equality; the fundamental rights to life, liberty, and the pursuit of happiness; and the right of the people to govern themselves democratically). But the question of who actually counts as an American has been a source of constant debate. Xenophobia has been instrumental in creating the terms of permission. Immigrants who were deemed capable and worthy of American citizenship were admitted and allowed to become naturalized citizens; those who were not were increasingly restricted, excluded, barred from naturalized citizenship, or expelled. Race has always been the determining factor in distinguishing "good" immigrants and future Americans from "bad" ones.

The Chinese Are No More

On February 28, 1882, Senator John F. Miller of California introduced a bill in the US Congress to exclude Chinese immigrant laborers from the country. The California Republican spelled out the imminent danger that Chinese immigration posed. There were too many in the country, not to mention the untold millions who could take a boat to American shores, like a naval invasion—they were a "degraded and inferior race" and a threat to national security. With their "machine-like" ways and their "muscles of iron," they stole jobs from white workers in every field of industry: the farm, the shoe bench, and the factory. Miller proclaimed that a vote for Chinese exclusion was thus a vote both for labor and for the "public good" of the country.

A few members of Congress opposed the bill. Former Radical Republicans, such as Massachusetts senator George Frisbie Hoar, called the discriminatory Chinese Exclusion Act "old race prejudice," a crime committed against the Declaration of Independence. But on the whole, politicians in both the Senate and House, from both political parties, and from across the United States, quickly agreed with Senator Miller. "The gate . . . must be closed," Representative Edward Valentine of Nebraska implored.

The Chinese Exclusion Act marked one of the most important turning points in America's long history of xenophobia. First, it established the United States' sovereign right to regulate foreigners into and within the nation and legalized the restriction, exclusion, and deportation of immigrants considered to be threats to the United States. In 1889, the US Supreme Court upheld the constitutionality of the Chinese Exclusion Act, and more broadly, the right of the United States to exclude foreign immigrants, stating that the power to exclude foreigners was one of the sovereign rights of the US government as delegated by the Constitution. This right also included barring returning American residents of Chinese descent who had previously been legally admitted in order to protect US "peace and security." In doing so, Chinese exclusion set in motion the transformation of the United States into a "gatekeeping nation," one that began using federal immigration laws to exclude, restrict, and control allegedly dangerous foreigners, often on the basis of race, national origin, ethnicity, class, and sexuality. In the 1880s, the United States was the first gatekeeping nation. Today, of course, every nation is.

The Chinese Exclusion Act also justified immigration restriction in the name of national security, a rationale that would later be used to close the gate to more immigrants, especially in times of war. The first lines of the law specifically stated that it was the "opinion of the Government of the United States [that] the coming of Chinese laborers to this country endangers the good order of certain localities within the territory thereof."

And the act also established Chinese immigrants—categorized by their race, class, and gender relations as the ultimate example of the dangerous, degraded alien—as the yardstick by which to measure the desirability (and "whiteness") of other immigrant groups. No other group had been officially singled out for immigration exclusion or banned from naturalized citizenship based on their race and national origin before. Moreover, the only other immigrants to be similarly banned from the country in 1882 were convicts, lunatics, idiots, or any people considered to be public charges. Because it specifically barred Chinese laborers, the Exclusion Act also discriminated on the basis of class. Laborers were barred for a period of ten years, but certain professional and elite classes were exempt from exclusion: students, teachers, travelers, merchants, and diplomats. These migrants benefited cross-national interests, maintaining friendly and profitable economic, diplomatic, cultural, and educational ties between the United States and China. By creating a two-tiered system of exclusion (laborers) and entry (elites) among Chinese immigrants, the Exclusion Act thus also created a hierarchy and paradigm of "good" versus "bad" immigrants that would shape both xenophobia and immigration policy in later decades.

The Chinese Exclusion Act also transformed how immigration restrictions were enforced in the United States. Written into the act itself were several major changes. All would become standard means of inspecting, processing, admitting, tracking, punishing, and deporting immigrants in the United States. First, the Exclusion Act laid the foundation for the establishment of the country's first federal immigrant inspectors. Although the Bureau of Immigration was not established until 1894 and did not gain jurisdiction over the Chinese exclusion laws until 1903, the inspectors for Chinese immigrants (under the auspices of the US Customs Service) were the first to be authorized to act as immigration officials on behalf of the federal government under the terms of the Exclusion Act.

Second, the enforcement of the Chinese exclusion laws set in motion the federal government's first attempts to establish a system of surveillance and control over a specific immigrant population in the United States. Because the Chinese were considered such a threat, a population that required massive amounts of regulation, US officials painstakingly identified and recorded all of the movements, occupations, and familial relationships of Chinese immigrants, returning residents, and US-born citizens of Chinese descent. Government officials on both sides of the Pacific Ocean achieved this through registration documents, records of entry and reentry, certificates of identity, and voluminous interviews with individuals and their families. Section 4 of the Exclusion Act, for example, required that all departing Chinese laborers apply for and possess "certificates of registration" that contained their name, age, occupation, last place of residence, and personal description. This information was recorded in Chinese registry books kept in the customs house. The certificate entitled the holder to "return and reenter the United States upon producing and delivering the [document] to the collector of customs." This laborer's return certificate was the first reentry document issued to an immigrant group by the federal government, and it served as an equivalent passport facilitating reentry into the country. The Chinese remained the only immigrant group required to hold such reentry permits (or passports) until 1924, when the new Immigration Act of that year issued—but did not require—reentry permits for other aliens.

In 1893, all Chinese people in the United States were also required to register with the federal government to obtain "certificates of residence" and "certificates of identity" that served as proof of their legal entry and lawful right to remain in the country. These documents contained the name, age, local residence, and occupation of the applicant (or "Chinaman," as the law noted), as well as a photograph. Any Chinese laborer found within the jurisdiction of the United States without a certificate of residence was to be "deemed and adjudged to be unlawfully in the United States" and vulnerable to arrest and deportation. No other immigrants were required to hold documents proving their lawful residence or be subjected to what would later be called "show me your papers" practices, until 1928, when immigrant identification cards were first issued to new immigrants arriving for permanent residence. These were eventually replaced by "alien registration receipt cards" (i.e., green cards) after 1940.

The Chinese Exclusion Act set another precedent by defining "illegal immigration" as a crime. With no federal restrictions on immigration prior to the Chinese Exclusion Act, there were no "illegal immigrants"; after the law, there were. Chinese immigrants became the first to be classified as illegal and the first to be charged with the new crime of illegal immigration. The act declared that any person who secured certificates of identity fraudulently or through impersonation to be guilty of a misdemeanor, fined them $1,000, and imprisoned them for up to five years. Any person who knowingly aided and abetted the landing of "any Chinese person not lawfully entitled to enter the United States" could also be charged with a misdemeanor, fined, and imprisoned for up to one year. Defining and punishing undocumented immigration directly led to the establishment of the country's first federal deportation system, and one of the final sections of the act declared that "any Chinese person found unlawfully within the United States shall be caused to be removed therefrom to the country from whence he came." These initial forays into federal immigration regulation would be further codified for all immigrants in the Immigration Act of 1891, helping to turn the United States into a "deportation nation."

"Getting Rid of the Mexicans"

Several hundred people, mostly men, were enjoying the afternoon sun in Los Angeles's La Placita Olvera on February 26, 1931, when federal agents and local police suddenly swept into the park and launched a massive immigration raid. Over two dozen plainclothes Los Angeles policemen blocked the exits while a half dozen federal immigration agents ordered everyone in the plaza to sit down. Panic swept through the crowd as the officers interrogated everyone and demanded identification papers, documents, or passports. After an hour, seventeen men—including eleven Mexicans, five Chinese, and one Japanese—were taken into custody.

Moisés González was one of them. He had just joined a crowd of spectators at the plaza when officials demanded his documentation. He was able to produce the papers given to him when he had entered the country at El Paso in 1923. But the immigration agents confiscated his documents and detained him in the city jail anyway. He was released only after his brother, an official with the local Federation of Mexican Societies, vouched for him. Mexican vice consul Ricardo Hill was also stopped by immigration officials near the plaza. Only after he produced his consular credentials was he let go. Across the country, dozens of raids followed as part of the federal government's new mass deportation campaign targeting Mexicans during the Great Depression.

Once heavily recruited by many US employers, Mexicans had become America's latest "immigration problem" by the 1930s. The charges made against them were numerous and familiar: they were too many; they were an inferior race; they were cheap laborers who took jobs away from deserving American citizens; they were poor and taxed local welfare offices; they were criminals. And they flooded the country in defiance of increasingly stringent immigration policies and procedures at the border. This made them not only undesirable but a new kind of immigrant: "illegal."

During the Depression, Mexicans were targeted for mass deportation like no other group. Violence and what one local government official called scareheading, using a campaign of fear to drive immigrants out of the country, were specifically deployed against them as more and more Americans called on their government to "get rid of the Mexicans." From 1929 to 1935, the federal government deported 82,400 Mexicans—46 percent of all deportees, even though they made up less than 1 percent of the total US population.

Federal deportation drives were also accompanied by local efforts to remove destitute Mexican American families. Social workers and local relief officials pressured, coerced, and deceived thirty thousand to forty thousand Mexican and Mexican American families to go to Mexico and never return. Although officials used the term *repatriation* to convey a voluntary movement, coerced emigration more appropriately described the involuntary—and in many cases, permanent—relocation of Mexicans and American citizens of Mexican descent to Mexico. Some Mexicans did voluntarily return to Mexico, but local and federal policies that one government commission labeled "unconstitutional, tyrannic, and oppressive" also drove this movement. Because these efforts did not distinguish between longtime residents, undocumented immigrants, and American citizens of Mexican descent, this was not just a xenophobic campaign to get rid of foreigners—it was a race-based expulsion of Mexicans. Altogether, nearly 20 percent of the entire Mexican and Mexican American population in the United States was pushed out of the country. Sixty percent were American citizens by birth. For most, expulsion was final.

The mass deportation and repatriation of Mexicans and Mexican Americans revealed how racism, nativism, and xenophobia became more intertwined during the Great Depression. Anti-Mexican racism that classified Mexicans as an inferior and hybrid (Spanish, indigenous, and black) race had long been part of US imperialism and expansion into the Southwest—it had specifically been used to justify the Mexican-American War. Now, under new economic pressures during the 1930s, it worked with xenophobia and nativism to categorize Mexicans as both a racially inferior and, crucially, a foreign population. The anti-Mexican campaign was built on earlier efforts. Laws like the 1882 Chinese Exclusion Act and the 1924 Immigration Act had already given the federal government much greater power to regulate immigration, and during the Great Depression, deportation and repatriation became the government's weapons of choice. The United States was turned into a "deportation nation."

The 1965 Immigration Act

The 1965 Immigration Act was an indelible part of the broader civil rights movement that sought to ensure equality and to eliminate race as a factor in public policy. However, it was imperfect in its design and in its execution. The Immigration Act and the new system of preference categories and ceilings was simultaneously less restrictive and more restrictive than the system it abolished. It ended formal racial discrimination and abolished the national origins quota system. But it allowed other forms of discrimination to persist, both overtly and covertly. Most noticeably, it prohibited people from receiving visas and gaining admission to the United States on the basis of sexual orientation. The immigration act also maintained restrictions based on nationality in its provisions pertaining to refugees—only people who came from "Communist or communist-dominated countr[ies]" or "the general area of the Middle East" qualified for refugee status.

Despite its intent to treat all immigrant groups fairly and equally, the 1965 Immigration Act also ended up reinforcing inclusion for some and exclusion for others. In removing discriminatory national origins quotas that disadvantaged southern and eastern European immigrants, for example, the 1965 act extended both the civil rights rhetoric and the legal principle of nondiscrimination to all European immigrants—and signaled the total integration of all European Americans into America, including groups the Immigration Restriction League had been so hostile toward in the early twentieth century. This act of inclusion mirrored and helped energize European Americans' growing efforts to preserve and celebrate their ethnic heritage while also emphasizing their assimilation into American life and their bootstrap upward mobility. This white ethnic revival of the 1970s and 1980s rhetorically moved the site of the nation's roots away from Plymouth Rock and toward Ellis Island. In a dramatic turnaround in American thought and popular culture, the once "inferior races of Europe" had been rehabilitated as archetypal Americans by the 1980s. What one historian has called "Ellis Island whiteness," which emphasized overcoming hardship through struggle and hard work (and the denial of white privilege), became a dominant form of white identity in the United States and was celebrated and spread through films such as *Fiddler on the Roof* (1971) and the *Rocky* movies as well as the 1986 Statue of Liberty Centennial and the Ellis Island restoration project. The United States as a "nation of [European] immigrants" became entrenched as one of America's cherished myths and effectively obscured America's history of xenophobia.

The 1965 Immigration Act and its consequences led to a new and divisive immigration debate focused on immigrants from Latin America, particularly from Mexico. This debate would reach a new climax in the 1990s, when states like California would begin to address the "illegal immigration problem" with new punitive measures. Color-blind xenophobia would continue to evolve as well. At a time when explicit racism was still taboo, xenophobes increasingly denounced immigrants' undocumented or "illegal" status rather than their race or national origin. But race and the specter of America's changing demographics was always lurking. Advocating for a "war on illegal immigration" became a primary way of channeling the racial anxiety and hostility that was consuming many white Americans. Over time, the war on "illegals" translated into a war that would impact all Mexican people in the United States.

Save Our State

A new debate over immigration surfaced in the 1980s and 1990s. As in decades past, immigration became a flash point for culture wars and other social, economic, and political anxieties. In the last two decades of the twentieth century, these included a rapidly changing and deindustrializing economy that was displacing millions of blue-collar workers; new (and more radical) campaigns for social justice that challenged systemic racism, sexism, and homophobia; rapid demographic change brought on by increasing racial diversity; and the formal end of the Cold War, which raised new questions about the role of American leadership in the world.

The epicenter of the debate was California, the entry point of many of the new immigrants and where citizen activists, politicians, and other leaders—many of them from conservative circles—resurrected the specter of an immigrant invasion, a border "out of control," and emphasized the suffering of (white) Americans. They particularly identified undocumented Mexican immigration as a source of societal and economic woes. But instead of proposing policy solutions that addressed the root causes of immigration, including undocumented immigration, xenophobes relied on both explicit racism and fearmongering, as well as the newfound weapon of color-blind xenophobia, to convince voters that an immigration "crisis" threatened their well-being. Many hard-line immigration activists and politicians, for example, denounced immigrants' "illegal" status rather than their race or national origin. They claimed that their campaign against "illegal immigration" promoted public safety and fiscal responsibility.

But as in the past, race unmistakably and decisively fueled late-twentieth-century xenophobia. The so-called war redeployed deep-rooted stereotypes linking Mexicans to crime, poverty, and welfare dependency. "Illegal aliens" were clearly understood to be Mexican, and the so-called war on illegal immigration obscured a larger racial campaign that considered all Mexican immigration as a reconquest of the United States by Mexican-descended peoples. It was also undeniably part of a larger (white) backlash to the "browning of America," the demographic shift of the US population to a majority-minority society, and the perceived corresponding decline in white political and economic power. Accompanying the anti-Mexican discourse, for example, was a powerful nativist message of white victimization and white displacement that was already a central part of conservative political discourse on race.

Like earlier anti-immigrant campaigns, xenophobes turned to state and federal laws to limit immigration and curb the rights of immigrants already in the country. In 1994, Californians passed Proposition 187, a voter-led ballot initiative informally known as "Save Our State." Its goal was to make the act of entering the country without authorization grounds for denying all public benefits, education, and health services to undocumented immigrants and to require all public employees to report anyone suspected of being in the United States without proper documentation to federal authorities.

Although the courts eventually ruled that most of Proposition 187's provisions were unconstitutional, much of the campaign's xenophobic ideology was later amplified by popular conservative writers and politicians and embraced by both major political parties. It also significantly influenced the overhaul of federal welfare and immigration policies later in the decade. Mass deportation and detention and the militarization of the US-Mexico border followed, while Mexican and Latinx-origin communities were subjected to widespread racial profiling and discrimination. By the early twenty-first century, the xenophobic message that Mexican immigration was endangering America had become so normalized that it helped propel Donald Trump to the White House in 2016.

In the wake of the terrorist attacks of September 11, 2001, the US government's ability to keep track of, arrest, detain, and deport immigrants grew exponentially. Congress established the Department of Homeland Security (DHS) and folded what had been the INS, under the Justice Department, and the US Customs Service, part of the Treasury Department, into three new agencies that enjoyed increased powers and funding: Immigration and Customs Enforcement (ICE), US Citizenship and Immigration Services, and US Customs and Border Protection. In addition, the Bush administration's counterterrorism efforts (which included mandatory registration of certain groups, centralized data sharing capabilities, and increased capacity of local law enforcement officers to enforce federal immigration laws) netted more deportable aliens than ever before. In particular, the Criminal Alien Program and its "jail status check" programs deported growing numbers of immigrants, many of whom were never convicted of crimes. Formal deportations increased accordingly. From 1975 to 1995, there were an average 29,000 removals per year. In 2000, the United States formally deported 188,000 individuals. In 2012, that figure was 410,000. To put these figures in historical perspective, the number of people formally deported from the United States in the first decade of the twenty-first century was greater than the total number removed in the last 110 years. As in the past, formal deportation (and the criminalization of immigration) had a disparate impact on certain immigrant communities. By 2013, black and Hispanic immigrants, mostly men, from Latin America, made up 92 percent of all immigrants imprisoned for unlawful entry and reentry, causing some experts to label current deportation practices a "gendered racial removal program."

Islamophobia

On January 20, 2017, Hameed Khalid Darweesh was granted a special immigrant visa to come to the United States. An Iraqi citizen and electrical engineer, Darweesh had worked for the US military and government as an interpreter, engineer, and contractor for ten years beginning in 2003. He helped the American forces protect Iraqis from al-Qaeda terrorists; provide water and electricity; train local police; and rebuild roads, bridges, schools, and hospitals. It was work that Darweesh was proud to do. But it was also work that placed him at constant risk of being targeted by anti-American militias and insurgents. In 2005, two of his Iraqi colleagues were tracked down and killed in Baghdad. Darweesh was ambushed but he escaped. From that day, he lived in constant fear. After his attackers tracked him down again, Darweesh, his wife, and his three children fled Baghdad and relocated to the city of Kirkuk.

They were safe for a year and a half before they were found again. Once more, Darweesh and his family packed up their belongings and fled to Erbil in another region of the country. But they knew that they would never be safe in Iraq; they would have to seek refuge in the United States. With the help of the International Refugee Assistance Project, Darweesh applied for a special immigrant visa for people who worked with the US Armed Forces in Iraq or Afghanistan. It took three years, but the visas were finally granted to Darweesh and his family on January 20, 2017. Halfway across the world on the same day, Donald Trump was taking the oath of office to become the forty-fifth president of the United States.

Trump's xenophobia and his worldview that immigration—seemingly all immigration—threatened the United States had propelled him to the White House. Alongside his demonization of Mexican immigrants as rapists and criminals and his campaign pledge to build a wall along the entirety of the US-Mexico border was a powerful Islamophobia that functioned as a companion to the fear of "illegal" immigration. In October 2015, he used panic about the millions of refugees seeking entry into Europe to justify his anti-Muslim rhetoric and characterized Syrian refugees as members of ISIS. He claimed that letting any into the United States could be "the greatest Trojan horse." The next month he falsely proclaimed that "thousands of Muslims" in New Jersey had been "cheering as the World Trade Center came down" on September 11, 2001. Just days after a Muslim American couple carried out a deadly shooting attack in San Bernardino, California, Trump called for a "complete and total shutdown of Muslims entering the United States" on December 7, 2015. Trump's proposal drew strong condemnation from not only immigrants, Muslim Americans, civil rights groups, and Democrats, but also from corporate America and other Republicans. Even Indiana governor Mike Pence, who would later become Trump's running mate and vice president, called the ban "unconstitutional" on Twitter when it was first announced.

Trump's anti-Muslim sentiment drew from both the long history of xenophobia in the United States and a new political climate that allowed Islamophobia to flourish. Part of the new immigration transforming the United States after 1965, recent Arab and Muslim immigrants and refugees became targets of the growing backlash to immigration in the twentieth century. But they were also identified as national security threats as well, and America's ongoing war on terror following the terrorist attacks of September 11, 2001, were used to justify rising levels of violence, surveillance, and discrimination aimed at Muslims everywhere, similar to the treatment of Japanese Americans during World War II. Going to war "over there" after 9/11 and excluding and tracking immigrants "over here" worked in tandem to justify continued US intervention overseas and an expanded immigration enforcement regime at home. Cloaked in the language of national security, increased levels of Islamophobic hatemongering became a standard form of religious bigotry and racism in America. First promoted by a fringe network of individuals allied with extreme conservative and religious right organizations after 9/11, Islamophobia eventually became part of the Republican Party and then mainstream media discourse. All of these factors conspired to make Trump's election possible.

Once in office, Trump made good on his promise to ban Muslims. At the end of his first full week in office, he traveled to the Pentagon on Friday, January 27, 2017, to sign Executive Order 13769, "Protecting the Nation from Foreign Terrorist Entry into the United States." As he signed the order, the president announced that it would keep "radical Islamic terrorists out of the United States of America." The order, which took effect immediately, prohibited the entry of all aliens from Iran, Iraq, Libya, Sudan, Somalia, Syria, and Yemen for ninety days on the grounds that such entries were "detrimental to the interests of the United States." It suspended the Refugee

Admissions Program for 120 days and imposed an indefinite ban on Syrian refugees. It also stated that no more than 50,000 refugees were to be admitted in 2017—a significant decrease from the 110,000 that President Obama had set for the year before—and that preference would be given to refugee claims based on "religious-based persecution, provided that the religion of the individual is a minority religion" in the country.

As chaos swirled around the news of the order, Hameed Khalid Darweesh, his wife, and his three children arrived in the United States at John F. Kennedy International Airport that evening at 5:45 p.m. The family waited for an hour to be processed by US Customs and Border Protection. Then Darweesh was moved into "secondary screening." He would ultimately be handcuffed and held in detention for eighteen hours, along with at least ten others, and was denied all requests to speak to his attorney.

Darweesh was crushed. "Over the course of those 18 hours, I had grown more and more disappointed," he later wrote. "They let me down by treating me as a criminal and putting handcuffs on me. . . . This was not the America I knew." Outside the airport, thousands of supporters were spontaneously gathering to protest the order. Darweesh's legal team rushed to file a lawsuit challenging the ban, and he was finally let go. As his lawyers escorted him from the airport, a crowd rushed in to celebrate the temporary legal victory and to welcome the family into the United States. For Darweesh, the moment was a vindication that his faith in the United States had not been misplaced after all. "I felt the greatness of America. Yes, this is the United States of America—this is the America I knew from my work in Iraq." Darweesh's journey to the United States had concluded, but the legal challenges to what many called the Muslim ban would continue well into the next year. The Trump immigration era had begun.

In many ways, Trump's xenophobia was both extreme and normal. In fact, the Trump administration's immigration policies were a logical evolution of America's xenophobic tradition. Beginning in the 1990s, American xenophobia, fueled by the "war on illegal immigration," had created a well-funded and highly resourced immigration enforcement regime that was supported and expanded by politicians in both major parties. Once xenophobia proved to be a viable political issue that mobilized voters and elected politicians, it remained a central aspect of American politics and media coverage. Presidents Bill Clinton, George W. Bush, and Barack Obama all built walls and fortified the US-Mexico border. They increased both the number of Border Patrol agents stationed along the southern border and the number of immigrants deported from the United States.

These federal policies did not always match the reality of changing immigration patterns on the ground. Long after undocumented immigration had stabilized and even dropped, for example, politicians and special interests continued to use xenophobia to mobilize voters, pass more anti-immigrant laws, and support a growing business of for-profit detention facilities. Each presidential administration was pressured into and willingly participated in expanding the government's immigration enforcement regime. By the end of the twentieth century, the idea that undocumented immigrants (and all Latinx people) constituted a clear and present danger to the nation was pervasive. Neither major political party challenged the increasingly alarmist and racist rhetoric; instead, many came to accept it as a truism. By the end of the twentieth century, the United States was well on its way to creating the largest "deportation machine" in American history. Then, on September 11, 2001, terrorists attacked the United States, and Muslims became the latest targets of American xenophobia.

On September 11, 2001, Adam Soltani was just weeks into his freshman year at the University of Central Oklahoma. He proudly served as the president of the campus Muslim Student Association and though non-Muslims considered his faith with curiosity, he "didn't sense any fear in being Muslim at all." That morning, however, would transform Soltani's life and the lives of millions of Muslims in the United States. Terrorist followers of al-Qaida leader Osama bin Laden commandeered four passenger planes. Two were flown into the twin towers of Manhattan's World Trade Center. The third hit the Pentagon. The fourth crashed in Pennsylvania after passengers stormed the cockpit and redirected the plane. Altogether, almost three thousand people died.

Soltani's parents urged him to stay home from school once the news hit. But he brushed off their suggestion and decided to attend the weekly prayer service at the local mosque. Normally, the weekday service would be packed with 150 people. That day, no more than twenty showed up. Weeks after 9/11, Soltani and some Muslim friends were walking to the mosque after a university football game when a truck full of teenagers pulled up and yelled "Go back home, you sand-niggers." Soltani recalled this incident as the first time in his life that he had come face-to-face with an Islamophobic racial slur. "That's when I realized that things weren't the same or as safe as they used to be." Soltani was not alone. Many American Muslims have identified 9/11 as a turning point in their lives in the United States.

Writer Shawna Ayoub Ainslie started keeping a list of the ways that 9/11 changed her life as an American Muslim. She stopped making eye contact with strangers in case she caught the attention of the large numbers of FBI agents and police officers she saw everywhere in the days and weeks after 9/11. A helicopter hovered above her apartment. The FBI was at her mosque for several months. She stopped wearing a headscarf. She stopped reading the Qur'an between classes. She stopped going to mosque. She hid all physical evidence that she was Arab or Muslim. In short, she "learned how to be invisible." Nevertheless, she also came to realize that she was still seen as a "Brown and Muslim or Other" and that Islamophobia would continue to shape her life no matter how hard she tried to hide her Muslim faith.

Islamophobia's identification of Arab and Muslim Americans as a threat because of their religion, their "race," and their foreignness has made it particularly powerful and enduring. But Islamophobia has also treated and impacted men and women differently. Although Arab and Muslim American men, particularly working-class men, have been stereotyped as violent terrorists who threaten national security, women have been viewed as more of a cultural threat. Stereotyped as oppressed and lacking in personal freedom, Arab and Muslim women have come to symbolize backwardness and inassimilability. Women, especially those wearing hijabs or burkas, have been particularly vulnerable to racial violence. Muslim American women in the southwestern suburbs of Chicago, for example, reported experiencing hate acts at a rate more than double that of men—especially when wearing a hijab. These private acts of violence have accompanied post-9/11 government programs singling out Arab and Muslim Americans for surveillance, detention, deportation, and exclusion.

Conclusion

History has shown that xenophobia is not a contradiction to the United States' identity as a "nation of immigrants" or its tradition of immigration. It is not a matter of the United States being either a "nation of immigrants" or a "nation of xenophobia." It is also not a matter of the United States being a "nation of immigrants" during certain moments of its history and a "nation of xenophobia" during others. Rather, just as racial progress and racist progress can happen at the same time, Americans' embrace of immigrants and their fear and hatred of them have coexisted as equally strong forces shaping the United States.

Xenophobia identifies and dehumanizes "bad immigrants" as those who come without authorization, take away jobs from Americans, do not assimilate, rely on welfare, and hate America. Meanwhile, the "nation of immigrants" identifies and disciplines "good immigrants" as those who come in the right way, behave, conform to American needs and desires, assimilate, and accept the status quo unquestioningly. There exists a fine line between the nation of immigrants and the nation of xenophobia, however, whereby the nation of immigrants has easily become a tool of xenophobia itself. This is because xenophobia includes, as it excludes. By celebrating the "good immigrant," the United States has more easily excluded the "bad" one; by demonizing one group, another has been protected. This involves trade-offs and transformations. Previously demonized communities (Germans, Irish, Italians, Chinese) have been remade into "good" immigrants while others have remained or become "bad" (Mexicans and Muslims).

As xenophobia has become increasingly embedded in American politics and life, we must fully understand its costs.

Xenophobia threatens American democracy. It allows the will of a vocal and mobilized minority to dictate policy for the majority. Public opinion polls consistently showed that most Americans rejected Donald Trump's divisive rhetoric and opposed his xenophobic policies before and after the 2016 presidential election and into the first year of the Trump presidency, for example. Americans were less concerned about immigrants' impact on the workforce than they were a decade before. A majority supported legal status for immigrants brought to the United States without documentation as children as well as an increase in legal immigration. What they did not support was a bigger border wall.

American democratic processes and institutions have also been used to support, legalize, and facilitate xenophobia. Politicians have routinely scapegoated immigrants to mobilize voters for political gain or power. Xenophobic laws have granted the US government sweeping power over foreigners, sometimes resulting in practices that violate American laws, democratic principles, and human rights. But perhaps most damaging of all, attacks on immigrants have consistently threatened the core civil and political rights on which American democracy is built. The First Amendment to the US Constitution, for example, states that everyone in the United States has the right to practice their own religion, or no religion at all. But over the centuries, our attacks on Catholics, Jews, and Muslims and their houses of worship have threatened their freedom to practice their faith without harassment. The Fifth Amendment guarantees that "no person" shall be deprived of life, liberty, or property without due process of law. And the Fourteenth Amendment guarantees equal protection of the laws to "any person." Nevertheless, immigrants and refugees have consistently been treated unequally and denied due process and equal protection under the law. One of the most egregious examples includes the violent expulsions of Chinese immigrants in the nineteenth century, often while government officials passively looked on, or even participated. These policies have unfortunately continued. Since the US government began implementing the policy known as expedited removal in 1996, which allows for a sped-up deportation of some non-US citizens, for example, it has done so without extending the due process protections (such as legal counsel or an immigration court hearing) granted to other residents in the United States.

Xenophobia ensnares and de-Americanizes long-term residents and US citizens by stigmatizing them as perpetual foreigners in—or even threats to—the United States, irrespective of their immigration or citizenship status. Mexican Americans who were prevented from voting in the US Southwest, for example, were de-Americanized. Japanese Americans were forcibly relocated and incarcerated during World War II in perhaps the best-known example of de-Americanization. But the process continues today. Since 9/11, Arab and Muslim Americans have been subjected to mass arrests, detention without charges, special registration, wiretapping, and spying without pretext. And as the United States has expanded its immigration enforcement into the interior of the country to target undocumented immigrants, deportation has resulted in the de facto deportation of US citizens as well as undocumented immigrants. These cases typically involve US-born citizen children in so-called mixed-status families who accompany a noncitizen parent deported back to their homeland. Described as "collateral victims" of a cruel deportation machine in the United States, these American citizens have become part of a growing deportation diaspora who have been effectively de-Americanized.

Xenophobia threatens national unity. It allows white supremacy and white nationalism to come to the forefront of American politics and culture. It embraces only some as Americans, while others remain outsiders. It fosters a violent citizenship of exclusion, encouraging citizens to differentiate themselves from and pit themselves against the foreign-born.

In both the past and present, xenophobes have argued that immigrants are threats. But it is xenophobia, not immigration, that is our gravest threat today. It is time to reset the terms of the debate.

DISCUSSION QUESTIONS

1. What is your family's history of immigration? Is there a point in American history where you or any of your relatives would not have been allowed to legally enter the country?
2. Why was the Chinese Exclusion Act so consequential in how it changed America's treatment of immigrants?
3. What were the arguments made for deporting Mexican immigrants (and U.S. Citizens) during the Great Depression? How similar or different are these from arguments made today about immigrants from Mexico and those of Mexican descent?
4. What were some of the consequences of the changes to immigration laws and enforcement after the September 11th attacks for non-Muslim immigrants in the United States?
5. What purpose does emphasizing the (purported) problematic nature of *illegal* immigrants serve for politicians?
6. Watch author Erika Lee (https://www.youtube.com/watch?v=lfLeUx5jWl4) discuss more about her family's immigration history and the experiences of Asian Americans and immigration. How does this compare with your own family history?

The Political Bind of Oil vs. Tribes

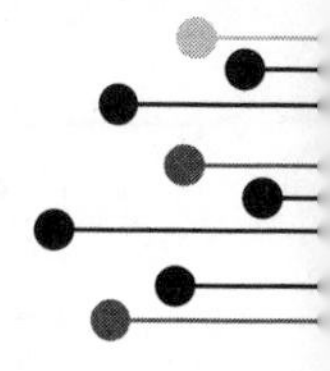

Yvonne P. Sherwood

Standing Rock is a Native American Indian reservation that spans North and South Dakota. In 2016, the planned route for the Dakota Access Pipeline (DAPL) was rerouted to just outside the boundary of the Standing Rock reservation. The oil pipeline was originally supposed to run near the mostly white city of Bismarck, North Dakota, but its route was changed to pass just outside the Standing Rock reservation because of concerns that it would endanger the Bismarck water supply. However, the new route also threatened the water supply of the Standing Rock reservation, as it would pass underneath the Missouri River, the main water source for the reservation. Throughout 2016, local Indigenous people were eventually joined by thousands of others from across the country to protest the building of the pipeline.

News coverage of the protests highlighted the unsettling and disproportionate use of force by police and private security against protestors, and the indigenous protestors were eventually joined by military veterans who pledged to form a human shield to protect protestors from police.

This reading about the protests at Standing Rock, written by sociologist Yvonne Sherwood, is in essay rather than research article form, but it is a challenging read in both its style and the ideas presented. In this reading, Sherwood shows how the concepts of white supremacy and settler colonialism are linked to locations and gender. Using then–North Dakota senator Heidi Heitkamp's statement that she "supports oil and supports women" as a focal point of her analysis, Sherwood shows how the structures and systems of white supremacy and settler colonialism resulted in a "double bind" whereby the Indigenous women protesting the pipeline were considered irrelevant and disposable by the state of North Dakota, at the same time that the state purported to value and protect them.

As you read, pay attention to how you react to Sherwood's description of white supremacy and settler colonialism. Whether it makes you feel solidarity and understanding or defensive and angry, take some time to consider how her

---

Excerpt from "The Political Bind of Oil vs. Tribes" by Yvonne P. Sherwood. *Open Rivers: Rethinking Water, Place & Community* (2019), 13, pp. 48–68. Reprinted with permission.

ideas can be helpful in understanding not just what happened to protestors at Standing Rock but how the lives of millions of nonwhite citizens are affected by the issues she raises every day.

In late 2018, while researching the connections between environmental justice and Indigenous womxn's activism[1], I was invited to story about how *water* might respond to environmental injustice and racism. In preparation, I thought about how the lands and peoples to which I belong struggle against "slow violence" brought on by the toxic effects of uranium contamination and nuclear pollution (Dillon 2015: 1; Nixon 2011). I also reflected on the ways that activists across the hemisphere have pointed out the connections between the struggle in Standing Rock and their own local, ongoing battles against state extraction. In these sorts of cases, I wondered, what would the water say? It was an exciting and inspiring proposition to think with. Yet as an Indigenous womxn familiar with the romanticization of Indigenous peoples' abilities to act as mediums between the environment and humans, the call to imagine what water might say sat uncomfortably with me[2]. I thought I'd better leave the medium work to someone more qualified and instead explore the state's stories to ask, "What stories does the state tell and how does it tell them?" So I dove in and began to unweave how political actors—in this case Senator Heidi Heitkamp in her re-election bid—told stories about their responsibility to the nation, Native Americans, and the environment. What tensions were proposed to be undone by her story? What binds might remain? To ground this incursion, after the introduction of key terms, I begin with the story of Senator Heidi Heitkamp and how she proposed to support both women and big oil. I then briefly explore Indigenous womxn activists' reassertion of their relations to land and water through the expression: "We are Water! We are Sacred!"

Working from the premise that both racialization and settler colonialism are always gendered processes, I reflect throughout this story on the way that white supremacy—the valuing and ordering of racial hierarchies—and settler colonialism—the occupation of Indigenous lands through erasure of the Indigenous peoples—are underlying structural conditions that are performed and reproduced through the ways that political dilemmas and legislation are articulated. Furthermore, I suggest that these structures are the problem and that they create untenable sets of options that place energy extraction and humans, pipelines and Indigenous womxn at odds. Yet, as the story will reveal, these tensions are falsely constructed sets of options and conditions that are dependent on the very structures that promise to get us out of these sorts of binds[3]. We must, then, reassert our relations otherwise.

White Supremacy and Settler Colonialism

White supremacy is a structure of power that is the foundation of white privilege (Bonds and Inwood 2016). It is different from, but related to, the concept white privilege, which focuses our attention to the benefits of whiteness. White privilege, in order to operate, needs white supremacy, the ideological and material domination by white subjects over people of color. White supremacy, as Leonardo (2004: 139) explains, "does not form out of random acts of hatred, although these are condemnable, but rather out of patterned and enduring treatment of social groups. Ultimately, it is secured through a series of actions, the ontological meaning of which is not always transparent to its subjects and objects." In other words, white supremacy is secured through historical and ongoing acts of racial domination, even when these acts are not recognized as securing power over people of color, particularly through anti-black beliefs, laws, and actions.

White supremacy is also spatial. To understand the spatiality of racism, Pulido (2000) asks her readers to imagine the comparison between industrial zones versus suburbs and who lives in which. White supremacy, then, is a process of domination that shapes landscapes and bodies in particular ways. Whiteness, as a relational category, has its origins in the ways that Black and Native peoples were and continue to be differently racialized in relation to property. Natives were massacred for property and Blacks made enslaveable to work that property; arguably these sorts of practices continue (Harris 1993).

Anti-blackness is made possible through its confluence with settler colonialism. Settler colonialism is a specific colonial formation that includes the ongoing attempt to permanently settle a territory through Indigenous erasure, assimilation, or the outright murder of Indigenous peoples (Tuck and Yang 2012; Veracini 2010; Wolfe 2006). Further, it influences the way we think about and react to race and gender, for example by privileging whiteness and discriminating against women and queer family structures (Simpson 2014; Smith 2005, 2012). The goal of settler colonialism is furthered by imagining certain bodies and lands as disposable, as sacrifice zones. These logics—white supremacy and settler colonialism—enmesh to form a network of power that make them inseparable.

On the Front Line of Environmental Contamination

That is worth repeating: people of color and low income communities often bear the largest burdens of environmental contamination and within those communities, women's and children's bodies are particularly susceptible

(Bullard 2000, Mohai et al. 2009). The Environmental Protection Agency reports that tribal communities live in close proximity to the nation's most polluted sites and "environmental mitigation for these communities lags significantly behind that for nontribal communities" (Hoover 2017: 8). Infant mortality, a basic measure for public health across the world, decreased for all racialized groups in the U.S. from 2005–2014 *except for Natives* (Mathews and Driscoll 2017). As Johnston's (1994) research makes clear, the price for consumption and environmental degradation is not paid equally.

Indigenous lands are more likely to be "sacrificed" and as such, Native women's bodies are more likely to experience the embodiment of environmental toxins. This is what is meant by saying these logics *literally* form our bodies, human and non, in particular ways. It was a conscious and strategic choice to reroute the Dakota Access Pipeline (DAPL) away from its first permitted water crossing north of Bismarck, North Dakota, to just upstream of the Standing Rock Sioux tribal reservation. It is also true that Indigenous women experience gender-motivated violence more often than any other racialized group and environmental ruin has been correlated to violence against women[4]. Like rape as an outcome of militarization, intense sites of development can similarly manifest violence against women (Falcón 2001). Paraphrasing Bea Hanson, former Principal Deputy Director of the U.S. Department of Justice Office on Violence against Women (OVW), the OVW *2014 Tribal Consultation Report to Congress* informed readers that the "rapid development for oil production in the Bakken region has brought a massive influx of itinerant workers and a sharp increase in crime and law enforcement issues, including sex and human trafficking" (Department of Justice 2014: 3). Furthermore, the *2014–2015 Violence Against Women Act Conferrals with Stakeholders* reported to congress that funding was increased to Native communities in the Bakken region because of the increase in violent crimes associated with the population boom tied to gas and oil exploration (Department of Justice 2017). The response by the OVW reported in these documents, however, goes only as far as to provide services to affected communities and does not address the underlying issues of settler colonialism and white supremacy.

Picking Sides

Senator Heitkamp, considered an ally to both Native women and big oil, was pressured to pick sides. With the DAPL protest supposedly behind us, the press and the public discussed Senator's Heitkamp's second-term run for Senate as being stuck in a bind between North Dakota's tribal vote and pipeline supporters[5]. Associated Press member James MacPherson (2018) quoted Dave Archambault saying:

> Former Standing Rock Tribal Chairman Dave Archambault, who was the face and voice of the fight against the Dakota Access oil pipeline, said he met with Heitkamp when the pipeline was first proposed and long before the protests "to let her know this was going to be an issue for us."
>
> "I think she was caught in the middle. But when her hand was forced, she chose the pipeline," Archambault said.
>
> "She always said she supported Indian Country, but when all of Indian Country from across the nation was at Standing Rock—she didn't show up . . . . She didn't truly listen to what Indian Country was saying," Archambault said. "Now she's in a bind."

My highlighting of Heitkamp's bind is not an attempt to undermine the Democratic Party in general or Heitkamp in particular nor to diminish her contributions; after all, many other government leaders across the two-party system have far less progressive records and there are substantive differences across the parties[6]. Though she lost her re-election bid to senate, her self-positioning in relation to oil and gendered violence remain important to consider. Furthermore, I focus on Heitkamp as an agent of the state more than personally because I believe her to be sincere in her concern for women in general and Native women and children in particular.

Heitkamp, in fact, and here is the rub, said she supported oil pipelines and supported women. Yet for the senator to overcome the bind, Native womxn find themselves in the double-bind of being protected while simultaneously being threatened. The point that the state cannot protect Indigenous people broadly, and Indigenous womxn particularly, from threat of its presence makes obvious that decolonization is not about sincerity and commitments to democracy (see Tuck and Yang 2012). When any of us commit to turning to the state to redistribute resources we are limited to particular strategies that cannot be truly transformative of the settler state and thus cannot undo the inherent and interconnected oppressive logics of settler colonialism and white supremacy.

Intersections of Power Create Place

Heitkamp's bind, as described above, highlights intersections of power that literally inform the construction of land and water in particular ways. As a set of ongoing material practices, white supremacy and settler colonialism are not things of the past nor some rare extreme position (Bonds and Inwood 2016). Rather, these ongoing ideologies and practices lay the foundation for differently constructed land and bodies. As Harris (1993) writes, race and property are deeply interrelated concepts. She explains that whiteness, initially constructed as a form of racial identity, evolved into a form of property historically and presently acknowledged and protected in American law. The state, as distributor of resources and enforcer of laws that are based on hierarchies of race, is itself a racial project. Citing Pulido (2006), Bonds and Inwood (2016: 728–729) make the point that movements challenging unfettered accumulation and racism must recognize settler colonialism as a material condition that was foundational for "differentially racialized geographies" to occur in the first place. That is to say that the material conditions of settler colonialism inform the way that land, including the people that live on it, are both imagined and produced.

As such, white supremacy is not a problem to be solved outside of our selves, but rather a socially and politically productive force that must be countered (Bonds and Inwood 2016). The actions of our allies and leaders, then, speak louder than words; quite simply, what you do to our lands you do to our bodies.

Reasserting Relations to Land

So, I was asked, "What story does *water* tell?" I want to say that I don't know. That we are all related? Perhaps. It is a powerful assertion but one that is often appropriated into mainstream environmental activism to assert belonging while forgetting what it means to be a good relative. Despite co-optation, Indigenous teachings and counterimagery continue both because of and in spite of settler colonialism (see LeFevre 2013). Importantly, Water is Life, an aphorism that became increasingly popularized during the Standing Rock campaign, continues to be accompanied by related expressions: We are Water and Womxn are Sacred.

Gathering Native and non-native womxn into a teepee at Standing Rock and surrounded by onlookers including myself and my seven-month-old, Melaine Stoneman (Sicangu Lakota) explained the long-theorized relation between these expressions by asserting:

> People ask me how they can help. I tell them your first responsibility is to reconnect with the water. Water is Life. Your presence here is of no help if you do not first connect to water. And remember that women are Water Carriers, we give life. We hold life for nine months in water, and *through water each of you* entered this world. See that little one there [she points to my child intonating in my lap], we do not "shush" him; we recognize him; we acknowledge him; he is sacred. *Mni Wiconi* is not just a phrase to shout across camp. It . . . is a prayer.

At Standing Rock, where thousands from across many different Nations gathered, where protest and prayer came together, womxn activists highlighted the sanctity of life and the important relationships we hold with water and, even if just by extension, with our children and with each other.

Well aware of feminist scholarship that refuses to frame women as sacred and critical postmodern feminism that questions the very category of women, I want to make my reasoning clear here of why I hold up the importance of the statement made by Indigenous womxn activists that water, womxn, and children are sacred. The point is to assist in the work that moves beyond any one category of innocence and instead to reassert our relation to land, self, and other. Water is Life was not shared as a new rallying cry to produce a flat, colorless, disembodied reality, but rather was transmitted as an embodied practice that asserts our connections to land, water, and others within a context that separates our existence.

The Land Speaks Through Our Bodies

When we and the land are more than property and the state is inherently white supremacist and settler, it can be problematic when anti-violence movements depend on the state to solve the problems of injustice. As important as the focus is on providing multicultural services to survivors of violence, it is limited. Therefore, providing "culturally appropriate" services for tribal communities to address gendered violence evades the foundational issues in which this arrangement, called nation-state development, is unlivable for *all* of us. As youth from the *Native Youth Sexual Health Network* put it: we need to talk about and work from these connections because the land speaks through our bodies.

And so I close by turning toward a young Native womxn who organizes with other youth against suicide in their community. Jasilyn Charger (2016) was asked to comment on the fight against the Black Snake, understood as both DAPL and as a greed that feeds into our communities, and why she ran over 2,000 miles with others from North Dakota to the U.S. Army Corps of Engineers in Washington, D.C., to draw attention to the violent threat posed by the DAPL pipeline against the Missouri River. She explained:

> *We wanted to run for our lives.* We connected the past and the future and we put them together. Because the past is what we're leaving behind for our youth, and the future is us. What better voice for the past, than the future . . . because we are the

> embodiment of both. We carry our past and our future with us. And that's what we have to pass down to our children as a legacy. . . . It's our lives that are on the line. . . . We need to make way for our future.

For Jasilyn, this future is a very real embodiment of both her ancestors and the children to come.

Conclusion

To overcome the bind of energy development versus Indian tribes, Heitkamp said she supported both big oil *and* protecting Native women. Given the fact that increases in sexual violence and assault have been shown to increase where energy development is enacted, the double bind, a declaration of conflicted statements, exposes itself in the proposition that we, Indigenous peoples, are both superfluous to the nation-state project and protected by it. More particularly, what the story of Heitkamp's choices demonstrates is how liberal attempts to overcome supposed binds ultimately fail to get at the foundations of the gendered structures and processes of white supremacy and settle colonialism. As such, water politics and activists' strategies must be understood against the background of these logics if we are to ultimately undermine environmental ruin and put back into order our sacred relations.

I started this story by explaining my hesitancy to story what water might say or do in response to environmental injustices. In reflection, I realize I cannot escape storying water or my responsibility as a medium. In fact, we all share this responsibility. As this article has demonstrated, in more ways than one, the land and water speak through our bodies. We are water.

DISCUSSION QUESTIONS

1. In what other contexts have you heard the term *white supremacy*? How is the author's definition of the concept different from that? How is it similar?
2. What does Sherwood mean when she says that white supremacy is also spatial?

3. What is settler colonialism? What are some examples from American history of this? Are there other groups other than Indigenous people whose bodies and land are considered disposable sacrifice zones?

4. What is the relationship she proposes between land, women, and water?

5. Look up news reports of the treatment of protestors at Standing Rock. How is this similar to how Black Lives Matter protestors were treated in places like Portland, Oregon, in July of 2020? Think especially about the veterans who joined the protests at Standing Rock to form a human shield and the "wall of moms" in Portland. Whose bodies are seen as worth of respect and restraining by authorities? Whose are not?

6. Open the link https://time.com/4548566/dakota-access-pipeline-standing-rock-sioux/ to the *Time* magazine news story "What to know about the Dakota Access Pipeline Protest (article and series of videos)." Watch the first four videos that play (at the top of the story) to see footage from the protests, interviews, and updates on what happened at Standing Rock after 2016. Does seeing images and hearing from the people there change your reaction at all to what happened?

NOTES

1. *Womxn* is a term used to highlight and push back against the power dynamics that are expressed through languages, cultures, and institutions that situate women as an extension of men and men as the natural category of human. The term also acknowledges in our communities our transgender womxn and womxn of color.

2. For discussion of the Fourth World that conceptualizes Indigeneity as informed by the settler colonial context but not contained, please see Manuel and Posluns's 1974 *The Fourth World: An Indian Reality* published by Collier-Macmillan Canada, Ltd; for a discussion on the term *Indigenous* in international legal framework, see Anaya's 2003 *Indigenous Peoples in International Law* published by Oxford University Press; toward an Original Nation approach in international law, see Fukurai's 2019 "Original Nation Approaches to 'Inter-National' Law (ONAIL): Decoupling of the Nation and the State and the Search for New Legal Orders," *Indiana Journal of Global Legal Studies* 26 (1): 199–262; and for a discussion on the capitalized versus noncapitalized form of Indigenous, please see Veracini's 2017 "Decolonizing Settler Colonialism: Kill the Settler in Him and Save the Man" in *American Indian Culture and Research Journal* 41 (1): 1–18.

3. Thank you to reviewers and editors for helping me draw out the arguments and lines of this story.

4. Here I am pointing out the racialized experience of violence. We cannot forget, however, that race is both sexed and gendered, and must keep in mind that the violence affecting the LGBTQ2 community is grossly underreported.
5. The resistance to DAPL is an extension of a long and ongoing struggle against settler colonialism, as Nick Estes (2016) points out. While the official line is that DAPL contestation is resolved, the reality is more complicated and the fight continues.
6. For information on rates of sexual violence particular to Native women, a critique of what the government chooses to privilege, and how the Trump administration restricted the U.S. DOJ's definition of domestic abuse and sexual assault, please see Christine Nobiss 2019.

PART VI

Social Class

READING 22

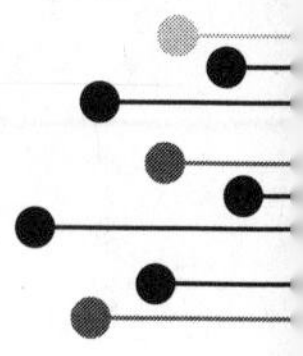

Unequal Childhoods

Class, Race, and Family Life

Annette Lareau

Much attention has been paid to how experiences in childhood shape us as adults. A great deal of this research focuses on how formative experiences affect our personalities and the types of relationships we have as adults. While it is well established that the social class of your parents is an excellent predictor of your future social class, exactly how this happens isn't as straightforward as it seems. Certainly, the amount of wealth a family has contributes to things like quality of education (via neighborhood), social contacts, and formative experiences (attending sailing camp as opposed to playing in the neighborhood vacant lot, for example). But there are even more subtle ways that social class influences our life chances.

In this reading, Annette Lareau uses a sociological approach to examine how social class is reproduced through different parenting styles. The results of her careful ethnographic study reveal general differences in the approach and philosophy of parenting by working-class versus middle-class parents, what she terms the natural growth approach and the concerted cultivation approach. Each has clear benefits and drawbacks for kids, but it is the concerted cultivation approach that middle-class parents use that implicitly teaches children how to negotiate and navigate in social interactions in a way that opens more doors of opportunity and leads to greater rewards.

As you read, think about your own childhood experience. Which approach most closely describes your experience? How do you think you would have benefited if you had grown up in a family that used the other approach?

Laughing and yelling, a white fourth-grader named Garrett Tallinger splashes around in the swimming pool in the backyard of his four-bedroom home in the suburbs on a late spring afternoon. As on most evenings, after a quick dinner his father drives him to soccer practice. This is only one of Garrett's many activities. His brother has a baseball game at a different location. There are evenings when the boys' parents relax, sipping a glass of wine. Tonight is not one of them. As they rush to change out of their work clothes and get the children ready for practice, Mr. and Mrs. Tallinger are harried.

Only ten minutes away, a Black fourth-grader, Alexander Williams, is riding home from a school open house.[1] His mother is driving their beige, leather-upholstered Lexus. It is 9:00 P.M. on a Wednesday evening. Ms. Williams is tired from work and has a long Thursday ahead of her. She will get up at 4:45 A.M. to go out of town on business and will not return before 9:00 P.M. On Saturday morning, she will chauffeur Alexander to a private piano lesson at 8:15 A.M., which will be followed by a choir rehearsal and then a soccer game. As they ride in the dark, Alexander's mother, in a quiet voice, talks with her son, asking him questions and eliciting his opinions. In interactions with professionals, the Williamses, like some other middle-class parents in the study, seem relaxed and communicative. They want Alex to feel this way too, so they teach him how to be an informed, assertive client. On one hot summer afternoon, Ms. Williams uses a doctor visit as an opportunity for this kind of instruction. During the drive to the doctor's office, the field-worker listens as Ms. Williams prepares Alexander to be assertive during his regular checkup: As we enter Park Lane, [Christina] says quietly to Alex, "Alexander you should be thinking of questions you might want to ask the doctor. You can ask him anything you want. Don't be shy. You can ask anything." Alex thinks for a minute, then says, "I have some bumps under my arms from my deodorant." Christina: "Really? You mean from your new deodorant?" Alex: "Yes." Christina: "Well, you should ask the doctor."

Alex's mother is teaching him that he has the right to speak up (e.g., "don't be shy"; "you can ask anything"). Most important, she is role modeling the idea that he should prepare for an encounter with a person in a position of authority by gathering his thoughts ahead of time.

Discussions between parents and children are a hallmark of middle-class child rearing. Like many middle-class parents, Ms. Williams and her husband see themselves as "developing" Alexander to cultivate his talents in a concerted fashion. Organized activities, established and controlled by mothers and fathers, dominate the lives of middle-class children such as Garrett and Alexander. By making certain their children have these and other experiences, middle-class parents engage in a process of *concerted cultivation.* From this, a robust sense of entitlement takes root in the children: This sense of entitlement plays an especially important role in institutional settings, where middle-class children learn to question adults and address them as relative equals.

Only twenty minutes away, in blue-collar neighborhoods, and slightly farther away, in public housing projects, childhood looks different. Mr. Yaneleli, a white working-class father, picks up his son Little Billy, a fourth-grader, from an after-school program. They come home and Mr. Yanelli drinks a beer while Little Billy first watches television, then rides his bike and plays in the street. Other nights, he and his Dad sit on the sidewalk outside their house and play cards. At about 5:30 P.M. Billy's mother gets home from her job as a house cleaner. She fixes dinner and the entire family sits down to eat together. Extended family are a prominent part of their lives. Ms. Yanelli touches base with her "entire family every day" by phone. Many nights Little Billy's uncle stops by, sometimes bringing Little Billy's youngest cousin. In the spring, Little Billy plays baseball on a local team. Unlike for Garrett and Alexander, who have at least four activities a week, for Little Billy, baseball is his only organized activity outside of school during the entire year. Down the road, a white working-class girl, Wendy Driver, also spends the evening with her girl cousins, as they watch a video and eat popcorn, crowded together on the living room floor.

Farther away, a Black fourth-grade boy, Harold McAllister, plays outside on a summer evening in the public housing project in which he lives. His two male cousins are there that night, as they often are. After an afternoon spent unsuccessfully searching for a ball so they could play basketball, the boys had resorted to watching sports on television. Now they head outdoors for a twilight water balloon fight. Harold tries to get his neighbor, Miss Latifa, wet. People sit in white plastic lawn chairs outside the row of apartments. Music and television sounds waft through the open windows and doors.

The adults in the lives of Billy, Wendy, and Harold want the best for them. Formidable economic constraints make it a major life task for these parents to put food on the table, arrange for housing, negotiate unsafe neighborhoods, take children to the doctor (often waiting for city buses that do not come), clean children's clothes, and get children to bed and have them ready for school the next morning. But unlike middle-class parents, these adults do not consider the concerted development of children, particularly through organized leisure activities, an essential aspect of good parenting. Unlike the Tallingers and Williamses, these mothers and fathers do not focus on concerted cultivation. For them, the crucial responsibilities of parenthood do not lie in eliciting their children's feelings, opinions, and thoughts. Rather, they see a clear boundary between adults and children. Parents tend to use directives: they tell their children what to do rather than persuading them with reasoning. Unlike their middle-class counterparts, who have a steady diet of adult organized activities, the working-class and poor children have more control over the character of their leisure activities. Most children are free to go out and play with friends and relatives who typically live close by. Their parents and guardians facilitate the *accomplishment of natural growth.*[2] Yet these children and their parents interact with central institutions in the society, such as schools, which firmly and decisively promote strategies of concerted cultivation in child rearing. For working-class and poor families, the cultural logic of child rearing at home is out of synch with the standards of institutions. As a result, while children whose parents adopt strategies of concerted cultivation appear to gain a sense of entitlement, children such as Billy Yanelli, Wendy Driver, and Harold McAllister appear to gain an emerging sense of distance, distrust, and constraint in their institutional experiences.

Table 1 Typology of Differences in Child Rearing

	Child-Rearing Approach	
	Concerted Cultivation	*Accomplishment of Natural Growth*
Key Elements	Parent actively fosters and assesses child's talents opinions, and skills	Parent cares for child and allows child to grow
Organization of Daily Life	Multiple child leisure activities orchestrated by adults	"Hanging out," particularly with kin, by child
Language Use	Reasoning/directives; child contestation of adult statements; extended negotiations between parents and child	Directives; rare questioning or challenging of adults by child; general acceptance by child of directives
Interventions in Institutions	Criticisms and interventions on behalf of child; training of child to take on this role	Dependence on institutions; sense of powerlessness and frustration; conflict between child-rearing practices at home and at school
Consequences	Emerging sense of entitlement on the part of the child	Emerging sense of constraint on the part of the child

What is the outcome of these different philosophies and approaches to child rearing? Quite simply, they appear to lead to the transmission of differential advantages to children. In this study, there was quite a bit more talking in middle-class homes than in working-class and poor homes, leading to the development of greater verbal agility, larger vocabularies, more comfort with authority figures, and more familiarity with abstract concepts. Importantly, children also developed skill differences in interacting with authority figures in institutions and at home. Middle-class children such as Garrett Tallinger and Alexander Williams learn, as young boys, to shake the hands of adults and look them in the eye. In studies of job interviews, investigators have found that potential employees have less than one minute to make a good impression. Researchers stress the importance of eye contact, firm handshakes, and displaying comfort with bosses during the interview. In poor families like Harold McAllister's, however, family members usually do not look each other in the eye when conversing. In addition, as Elijah Anderson points out, they live in neighborhoods where it can be dangerous to look people in the eye too long.[3] The types of social competence transmitted in the McAllister family are valuable, but they are potentially less valuable (in employment interviews, for example) than those learned by Garrett Tallinger and Alexander Williams.

The white and Black middle-class children in this study also exhibited an emergent version of the sense of entitlement characteristic of the middle-class. They acted as though they had a right to pursue their own individual preferences and to actively manage interactions in institutional settings. They appeared comfortable in these settings; they were open to sharing information and asking for attention. Although some children were more outgoing than others, it was common practice among middle-class children to shift interactions to suit their preferences. Alexander Williams knew how to get the doctor to listen to his concerns (about the bumps under his arm from his new deodorant). His mother explicitly trained and encouraged him to speak up with the doctor. Similarly, a Black middle-class girl, Stacey Marshall, was taught by her mother to expect the gymnastics teacher to accommodate her individual learning style. Thus, middle-class children were trained in "the rules of the game" that govern interactions with institutional representatives. They were not conversant in other important social skills, however, such as organizing their time for hours on end during weekends and summers, spending long periods of time away from adults, or hanging out with adults in a nonobtrusive, subordinate fashion. Middle-class children also learned (by imitation and by direct training) how to make the rules work in their favor. Here, the enormous stress on reasoning and negotiation in the home also has a potential advantage for future institutional negotiations. Additionally, those in authority responded positively to such interactions. Even in fourth grade, middle-class children appeared to be acting on their own behalf to gain advantages. They made special requests of teachers and doctors to adjust procedures to accommodate their desires.

The working-class and poor children, by contrast, showed an emerging sense of constraint in their interactions in institutional settings. They were less likely to try to customize interactions to suit their own preferences. Like their parents, the children accepted the actions of persons in authority (although at times they also covertly resisted them). Working-class and poor parents sometimes were not as aware of their children's school situation (as when their children were not doing homework). Other times, they dismissed the school rules as unreasonable. For example, Wendy Driver's mother told her to "punch" a boy who was pestering her in class; Billy Yanelli's parents were proud of him when he "beat up" another boy on the playground, even though Billy was then suspended from school. Parents also had trouble getting "the school" to respond to their concerns. When Ms. Yanelli complained that she "hates" the school, she gave her son a lesson in powerlessness and frustration in the face of an important institution. Middle-class children such as Stacey Marshall learned to make demands on professionals, and when they succeeded in making the rules work in their favor they augmented their "cultural capital" (i.e., skills individuals inherit that can then be translated into different forms of value as they move through various institutions) for the future.[4] When working-class and poor children confronted institutions, however, they generally were unable to make the rules work in their favor nor did they obtain capital for adulthood. Because of these patterns of legitimization, children raised according to the logic of concerted cultivation can gain advantages, in the form of an emerging sense of entitlement, while children raised according to the logic of natural growth tend to develop an emerging sense of constraint.[5]

How Does It Matter?

Both concerted cultivation and the accomplishment of natural growth offer intrinsic benefits (and burdens) for parents and their children. Nevertheless, these practices are accorded different social values by important social institutions. There are signs that some family cultural practices, notably those associated with concerted cultivation, give children advantages that other cultural practices do not.

In terms of the rhythms of daily life, both concerted cultivation and the accomplishment of natural growth have advantages and disadvantages. Middle-class children learn to develop and value an individualized sense of self. Middle-class children are allowed to participate in a variety of coveted activities: gymnastics, soccer, summer camps, and so on. These activities improve their skills and teach them, as Mr. Tallinger noted, to be better athletes than their parents were at comparable ages. They learn to handle moments of humiliation on the field as well as moments of glory. Middle-class children learn, as Mr. Williams noted, the difference between baroque and classical music. They learn to perform. They learn to present themselves. But this cultivation has a cost. Family schedules are disrupted. Dinner hours are very hard to arrange. Siblings such as Spencer and Sam Tallinger spend dreary hours waiting at athletic fields and riding in the car going from one event to another. Family life, despite quiet interludes, is frequently frenetic. Parents, especially mothers, must reconcile conflicting priorities, juggling events whose deadlines are much tighter than the deadlines connected to serving meals or getting children ready for bed. The domination of children's activities can take a toll on families. At times, everyone in the middle-class families—including ten-year-old children—seemed exhausted. Thus, there are formidable costs, as well as benefits to this child-rearing approach.

Working-class and poor children also had advantages, as well as costs, from the cultural logic of child rearing they experienced. Working-class and poor children learned to entertain themselves. They played outside, creating their own games, as Tyrec Taylor did with his friends. They did not complain of being bored. Working-class and poor children also appeared to have boundless energy. They did not have the exhaustion that we saw in middle-class children the same age. Some working-class and poor children longed to be in organized activities—Katie Brindle wanted to take ballet and Harold McAllister wanted to play football. When finances, a lack of transportation, and limited availability of programs conspired to prevent or limit their participation, they were disappointed. Many were also deeply aware of the economic constraints and the limited consumption permitted by their family's budget. Living spaces were small, and often there was not much privacy. The television was almost always on and, like many middle-class children growing up in the 1950s, working-class and poor children watched unrestricted amounts of television. As a result, family members spent more time together in shared space than occurred in middle-class homes. Indeed, family ties were very strong, particularly among siblings. Working-class and poor children also developed very close ties with their cousins and other extended family members.

Within the home, these two approaches to child rearing each have identifiable strengths and weaknesses. When we turn to examining institutional dynamics outside the home, however, the unequal benefits of middle-class children's lives compared to working-class and poor children's lives become clearer. In crucial ways, middle-class family members appeared reasonably comfortable and entitled, while working-class and poor family members appeared uncomfortable and constrained. For example, neither Harold nor his mother seemed as comfortable as Alexander and his mother had been as they interacted with their physician. Alexander was used to extensive conversation at home; with the doctor, he was at ease initiating questions. Harold, who was used to responding to directives at home, primarily answered questions from the doctor, rather than posing his own. Unlike Ms. Williams, Ms. McAllister did not see the enthusiastic efforts of her daughter Alexis to share information about her birthmark as appropriate behavior. Ms. Williams not only permitted Alexander to hop up and down on the stool to express his enthusiasm; she explicitly trained him to be assertive and well prepared for his encounter with the doctor. Harold was reserved. He did not show an emerging sense of entitlement, as Alexander and other middle-class children did. Absorbing his mother's apparent need to conceal the truth about the range of foods in his diet, Harold appeared cautious, displaying an emerging sense of constraint.

This pattern occurred in school interactions, as well. Some working-class and poor parents had warm and friendly relations with educators. Overall, however, working-class and poor parents in this study had much more distance or separation from the school than did middle-class mothers. At home, Ms. McAllister could be quite assertive, but at school she was subdued. The parent–teacher conference yielded Ms. McAllister few insights into her son's educational experience.[6]

Other working-class and poor parents also appeared baffled, intimidated, and subdued in parent–teacher conferences. Ms. Driver, frantically worried because Wendy, a fourth-grader, was not yet able to read, resisted intervening, saying, "I don't want to jump into anything and find it is the wrong thing." When working-class and poor parents did try to intervene in their children's educational experiences, they often felt ineffectual. Billy Yanelli's mother appeared relaxed and chatty when she interacted with service personnel, such as the person who sold her lottery tickets on Saturday morning. With "the school," however, she was very apprehensive. She distrusted school personnel. She felt bullied and powerless.

There were also moments in which parents encouraged children to outwardly comply with school officials but, at the same time, urged them to resist school authority. Although well aware of school rules prohibiting fighting, the Yanellis directly trained their son to "beat up" a boy who was bothering him. Similarly, when Wendy Driver complained about a boy who pestered her and pulled her ponytail, and the teacher did not respond, her mother advised her to "punch him." Ms. Driver's boyfriend added, "Hit him when the teacher isn't looking."[7]

The unequal level of trust, as well as differences in the amount and quality of information divulged, can yield unequal profits during a historical period such as ours, when professionals applaud assertiveness and reject passivity as an inappropriate parenting strategy.[8] Middle-class children and parents often (but not always) accrued advantages or profits from their efforts. Alexander Williams succeeded in having the doctor take his medical concerns seriously. The Marshall children ended up in the gifted program, even though they did not qualify.

Overall, the routine rituals of family life are not equally legitimized in the broader society. Parents' efforts to reason with children (even two-year-olds) are seen as more educationally valuable than parents' use of directives. Spending time playing soccer or baseball is deemed by professionals as more valuable than time spent watching television. Moreover, differences in the cultural logic of child rearing are attached to unequal currency in the broader society. The middle-class strategy of concerted cultivation appears to have greater promise of being capitalized into social profits than does the strategy of the accomplishment of natural growth found in working-class and poor homes. Alexander Williams's vocabulary grew at home, in the evenings, as he bantered with his parents about plagiarism and copyright as well as about the X-Men. Harold McAllister, Billy Yanelli, and Wendy Driver learned how to manage their own time, play without the direction of adults, and occupy themselves for long periods of time without being bored. Although these are important life skills, they do not have the same payoff on standardized achievement tests as the experiences of Alexander Williams.

These potential benefits for middle-class children, and costs for working-class and poor children, are necessarily speculative, since at the end of the study, the children were still in elementary school. Still, there are important signs of hidden advantages being sown at early ages. The middle-class children have extensive experience with adults in their lives with whom they have a relatively contained, bureaucratically regulated, and somewhat superficial relationship. As children spend eight weeks playing soccer, baseball, basketball, and other activities, they meet and interact with adults acting as coaches, assistant coaches, car pool drivers, and so on. This contact with relative strangers, although of a different quality than contact with cousins, aunts, and uncles, provides work-related skills. For instance, as Garrett shakes the hand of a stranger and looks him or her in the eye, he is being groomed, in an effortless fashion, for job interviews he will have as an adult (employment experts stress the importance of good eye contact). In the McAllister home, family members have great affection and warmth toward one another, but they do not generally look each other in the eye when they speak; this training is likely to be a liability in job interviews. In settings as varied as health care and gymnastics, middle-class children learn at a young age to be assertive and demanding. They expect, as did Stacey Marshall, for institutions to be responsive to them and to accommodate their individual needs. By contrast, when Wendy Driver is told to hit the boy who is pestering her (when the teacher isn't looking) or Billy Yanelli is told to physically defend himself, despite school rules, they are not learning how to make bureaucratic institutions work to their advantage. Instead, they are being given a lesson in frustration and powerlessness.

DISCUSSION QUESTIONS

1. Which of these styles was closest to your own childhood experience? Do you think there is perhaps a third or fourth model of parenting that should be examined?
2. How does concerted cultivation prepare middle-class and upper-class children for success later in life?

3. What are the advantages of the natural growth approach? What are the downsides of concerted cultivation?
4. In recent years, the "helicopter parent" phenomenon has gotten a fair bit of attention. Which parenting style is this associated with? What do you think motivates parents to engage in this behavior?
5. How can parents try to balance both of these approaches to child rearing to maximize the benefits of each? What about the way our social institutions are set up would have to change in order to accommodate parents who wish to use both approaches?

NOTES

1. Choosing words to describe social groups also becomes a source of worry, especially over the possibility of reinforcing negative stereotypes. I found the available terms to describe members of racial and ethnic groups to be problematic in one way or another. The families I visited uniformly described themselves as "Black." Recognizing that some readers have strong views that Black should be capitalized, I have followed that convention, despite the lack of symmetry with the term white. In sum, this book alternates among the terms "Black," "Black American," "African American," and "white," with the understanding that "white" here refers to the subgroup of non-Hispanic whites.
2. Some readers have expressed concern that this phrase, "the accomplishment of natural growth," underemphasizes all the labor that mothers and fathers do to take care of children. They correctly note that working-class and poor parents themselves would be unlikely to use such a term to describe the process of caring for children. These concerns are important. As I stress in the text (especially in the chapter on Katie Brindle, Chapter 5) it does take an enormous amount of work for parents, especially mothers, of all classes to take care of children. But poor and working-class mothers have fewer resources with which to negotiate these demands. Those whose lives the research assistants and I studied approached the task somewhat differently than did middle-class parents. They did not seem to view children's leisure time as their responsibility; nor did they see themselves as responsible for assertively intervening in their children's school experiences. Rather, the working-class and poor parents carried out their chores, drew boundaries and restrictions around their children, and then, within these limits, allowed their children to carry out their lives. It is in this sense that I use the term "the accomplishment of natural growth."
3. Elijah Anderson, *Code of the Street;* see especially Chapter 2.
4. For a more extensive discussion of the work of Pierre Bourdieu, see the theoretical appendix; see also David Swartz's excellent book *Culture and Power.*
5. I did not study the full range of families in American society, including elite families of tremendous wealth, nor, at the other end of the spectrum, homeless families. In addition, I have a purposively drawn sample. Thus, I cannot state

whether there are other forms of child rearing corresponding to other cultural logics. Still, data from quantitative studies based on nationally representative data support the patterns I observed. For differences by parents' social class position and children's time use, see especially Sandra Hofferth and John Sandberg, "Changes in American Children's Time, 1981–1997." Patterns of language use with children are harder to capture in national surveys, but the work of Melvin Kohn and Carmi Schooler, especially *Work and Personality,* shows differences in parents' child-rearing values. Duane Alwin's studies of parents' desires are generally consistent with the results reported here. See Duane Alwin, "Trends in Parental Socialization Values." For differences in interventions in institutions, there is extensive work showing social class differences in parent involvement in education. See the U.S. Department of Education, *The Condition of Education, 2001,* p.175.

6. Of course, some middle-class parents also appeared slightly anxious during parent–teacher meetings. But overall, middle-class parents spoke more, and they asked educators more questions, including more critical and penetrating ones, than did working-class and poor parents.

7. Working-class and poor children often resisted and tested school rules, but they did not seem to be engaged in the same process of seeking an accommodation by educators to their own *individual* preferences that I witnessed among middle-class children. Working-class and poor children tended to react to adults' offers or, at times, plead with educators to repeat previous experiences, such as reading a particular story, watching a movie, or going to the computer room. In these interactions, the boundaries between adults and children were firmer and clearer than those with middle-class children.

8. Carol Heimer and Lisa Staffen, *For the Sake of the Children.*

Social Class Differences in College Student Participation in Peace Corps, Teach for America, and Other Service Programs

Alanna Gillis

A college education is seen by many who attend as a ticket to a career with stable, robust earning prospects. In general, statistics comparing the average earnings of college graduates to those without college degrees bears this thinking out. Those with a four-year college degree earn on average about $18,000 more annually than those with only an associate degree, and about $23,000 more than those with only a high school diploma. But for others, college is also seen as a place for identity exploration—trying new things both academically and socially to find the answer to the perpetual question asked of young people: "What (or who) do you want to be when you grow up?"

Previous sociological research has shown that how much of college is experienced as practical preparation for a career versus a time for exploration and experimentation is closely tied to social class, with wealthier students being more likely to select majors based on interest and those with fewer financial resources more likely to be focused on majors that will lead to stable employment. In this reading, Alanna Gillis looks at the role of social class in how students think about their plans to participate in short-term service programs for college graduates such as Teach for America and the Peace Corp, which have grown immensely in popularity in recent years. The service programs she looks at are short-term commitments, usually one to two years, and have either

---

Excerpt from "Identity Exploration or Labor Market Reaction: Social Class Differences in College Student Participation in Peace Corps, Teach for America, and Other Service Programs" by Alanna Gillis. *Qualitative Sociology* (2019), 42, pp. 615–638. DOI: 10.1007/s11133-019-09433-z.

relatively low pay or require fundraising by the student in order to participate. As she notes, the assumption among researchers had been that these programs were a response to emerging adulthood, the idea that there is a life stage between adolescence and young adulthood that is characterized by identity exploration—a focus on the self, and uncertainty. She challenges assumption by pointing out that little research has looked at the role that social class might play in students' decisions to participate in these types of programs. She uses the concepts of work values—whether a potential job is wanted for intrinsic reasons (interest, self-expression, or creativity) or extrinsic reasons (prestige and pay) and students' perception of how likely they are to be able to start the career they want immediately after college (labor market conditions) to explore the role of social class in decisions to participate in these programs. She develops a typology of four different orientations toward these short-term service programs among the students she interviewed: Backup Planners, Delayed Careerists, Enthusiasts, and Professionals.

For each of these groups, social class, work values, and labor market conditions interact with each other in different ways, which results in each type of student having a distinctly different rationale for participating in service programs, despite the common link that they all were about to graduate from an elite university. This is another example of heterogeneity, highlighted in Reading 3 about W. E. B. Du Bois. Not only is there considerable variation between colleges and their graduates, even the graduates of elite colleges see and experience the world in quite different ways based on variations in their social traits.

As you read, think about whether you have or would consider a service program after graduation. Which category that she describes do you think you would fit into? If you would not consider a service program, what social traits are shaping that preference?

Service programs, such as Teach for America (TFA) and the Peace Corps, have gained popularity in recent years. In the decade since the economic recession from December 2007 to June 2009, applications hit record numbers for TFA (Teach for America 2018a) and near record numbers for Peace Corps (Butterfield 2015). The scope of service programs has massively increased as well, and there has been large growth in nonprofit secular and religious programs using either AmeriCorps or private donation funding (Stiffman 2017). The rise of these programs fits within the broader trends documented in sociological and psychological research of young adults taking a longer time to transition into stable, long-term careers than they did in the past (Settersten and Ray 2010).

Service programs are short-term programs with specific time limits, usually one or two years, that are oriented toward a social problem or mission and generally require a college degree. For instance, TFA is an AmeriCorps-funded program that seeks high-achieving recent college graduates for two-year placements in low-income schools (Teach for America 2018b), and the Peace Corps is an international government program that places participants for two-year commitments in countries around the world to help with different social projects (Peace Corps 2018). There are also a wide number of smaller scale programs that do not have the same level of name recognition or prestige, such as small evangelical religious programs. Service programs are by definition low paying though vary in amount received: TFA participants receive the typical first year teacher salary, Peace Corps participants receive a cost-of-living-based stipend for their placement country, while smaller programs often require their participants to fundraise their own stipends. Within this study, the fundraising obligations ranged from $15,000 for a one-year program to more than $75,000 for a three-year program. Certainly, some young adults are blocked from participating due to the financial costs. Nevertheless, this study shows that within an elite college, students from a variety of class backgrounds aspire to participate.

College students considering service programs, regardless of class background, are all on the cusp of entry into the middle class (if they are not there already) thanks to the credential they are about to receive (Dale and Krueger 2002; Hout 2012). However, students' socioeconomic backgrounds may influence how they perceive service programs among their choice set after graduation. This study seeks to understand whether students from disparate backgrounds have different orientations toward participating in service programs after graduation.

Currently, the dominant explanation for the rise of short-term work experiences of people in their early twenties is emerging adulthood (Arnett 2004). This theory argues that emerging adults seek short-term work experiences to explore their identity prior to settling down into adulthood and careers. Previous sociological research demonstrates that emerging adulthood is not an adequate explanation for the work patterns of young adults who do not attend college (Benson and Furstenberg 2006; Furstenberg 2016; Nelson and Padilla-Walker 2013). However, fewer studies have critically examined whether emerging adulthood sufficiently explains the short-term work behaviors of recent college graduates. In this study, I ask the following research question: Are soon-to-be college graduates aspiring to participate in a service program in order to engage in identity exploration or, by analyzing differences by social class, do we see various other forces at play? If social class differences do result in varied orientations, I examine two possible alternative explanations for service program aspirations: work values and labor market constraints.

In order to answer this question, I conducted 30 in-depth interviews with college juniors and seniors at an elite public university in the Southeast. I inductively created a typology of the orientations students have toward participation in service programs. I find that social class background, current financial security, and work orientations for the short- and long term shape the orientation each student has for aspiring to participate in a service program.

Dominant Explanation: Emerging Adulthood

Compared to past decades, the transition to adulthood has been delayed, as many youth postpone full-time employment, marriage, and children until after they complete their education, especially if they are enrolled full time in college (Oesterle et al. 2010; Eliason et al. 2015; Ryberg 2018; Shanahan 2000). In response to this delayed transition to adulthood, developmental psychologist Jeffrey Arnett (2004) proposed that a new life course stage exists between adolescence and young adulthood, a stage he calls emerging adulthood, for ages 18 to 25. He characterized this stage of life as being concerned with identity exploration, instability, self-focus, feeling in-between, and feeling it is the age of possibilities.

[Some] sociologists have challenged the concept of emerging adulthood and the twenties as a time of identity exploration. First, sociologists reject that this is a universal developmental stage for all youth, as youth from poor backgrounds who do not attend college tend to move rapidly into adult transitions of full-time work, cohabitation, and childbearing (Côté 2014; Deluca et al. 2016; Edin and Kefalas 2005; Furstenberg 2016). Youth from more economically disadvantaged backgrounds feel like adults sooner and are treated as such by their parents and family members (Benson and Furstenberg 2006; Lareau 2011). Second, even youth who attend college do not necessarily have the financial resources to explore their identities or seek fun jobs. Students are graduating with record levels of student loan debt (Houle 2014), which may influence their job selection (Rothstein and Rouse 2011). A number of other college students must become financially self-supporting during college or upon graduation (Armstrong and Hamilton 2013; Tevington et al. 2017). While institutional and other social factors may shape the extent to which college students are focused on identity exploration (Fosse and Toyokawa 2016; Nelson and Padilla-Walker 2013), the evidence suggests that social class significantly shapes the experience of the transition to adulthood and challenges the universal nature of emerging adulthood (Furstenberg 2016; Ryberg 2018).

This study offers the opportunity to directly examine whether the universal claim about identity exploration is true when social class differences are considered. Service programs are an ideal case study to examine this question because they have many of the structural components that seem best aligned with the identity exploration framework: they are short-term commitments, there is no expectation that participants will stay in the job after the program is completed, and they are built to provide young adults with the opportunity to help social causes they see as important while traveling or living somewhere new.

Social Class Differences through Work Values and Labor Market

If students are not engaging in service programs in order to explore their identities, but instead social class differences reveal differing orientations, what sociological explanations may exist to explain the differences? One way that social class may shape differing orientations is through work values. An extensive literature investigates different work values and orientations (Johnson and Mortimer 2011; Kalleberg 1977; Kohn 1969). While authors vary in the number of values they study, these values are generally divided between intrinsic values—seeking work that allows for creativity and self-expression—and extrinsic values—job rewards such as salary and prestige (Johnson and Mortimer 2011). Other dimensions of work that people might value are influence, social rewards, altruism, and leisure (Johnson 2002). While some people may see intrinsic and extrinsic values as competing factors in deciding jobs, these are not opposites along one single continuum; instead they are different values that people have on varying levels: it is possible to be high on both intrinsic and extrinsic values, be low on both, or be higher on one than the other (Johnson and Mortimer 2011).

Research consistently finds that these work orientations are closely related to social class: parents from higher social class backgrounds teach their children to value intrinsic rewards more than parents from lower social class backgrounds, while parents from lower social class backgrounds tend to primarily emphasize extrinsic rewards (Johnson and Mortimer 2011; Kohn 1969). Current social class (e.g., represented by financial security), in addition to class origins, may influence work values. Even among college graduates, youth have different levels of financial security, which will impact what they see as their biggest challenges in the transition out of college (Aronson et al. 2015). Youth who graduate with much higher debt or who are no longer receiving financial support from their families may feel compelled to adjust their work values to their current situation and lower their intrinsic values (Johnson 2002), especially during the period of recovery from an economic recession (Koen et al. 2012). Based on this past research, we might expect that college students from lower social class backgrounds would pursue service programs for extrinsic reasons, while youth from higher social class backgrounds would pursue them for intrinsic reasons. Likewise, despite being socialized with middle-class intrinsic work values, youth from middle-class families who have less financial security during the transition out of college (i.e., more debt and no continued parental financial assistance) may be pushed toward extrinsic values in their job searches more than those with greater current financial security.

Looking specifically at the transition to adulthood, many scholars are interested in explaining stability or change during this period. In other words, do young adults consistently have the same work values or do they vary at different stages, such as temporarily prioritizing intrinsic work while later planning for more extrinsic work? Traditionally it was assumed that work values remained relatively stable after adolescence. However, research in the last few decades has found a few ways in which they change: work values narrow with age (Johnson and Monserud 2012), youth adjust to realistic expectations about work (Johnson 2002), and young adults adjust their work values based on the jobs they find themselves doing (Johnson et al. 2012).

While this strand of research suggests that work-value changes occur in a linear fashion, life course literature suggests that people value different characteristics at different stages, so that work values during the transition to adulthood may intentionally diverge from those in adulthood (Arnett 2004). For instance, a high school student's first job may be chosen with different values than their full-time career after completing their education. The period after college could be another unique life course stage, especially given that young adults do not feel compelled to settle down as quickly into adult roles of career and family as they did in previous generations (Arnett 2004). Some young adults may look for different values in their work for the first few years out of college than they would for later careers. Thus, instead of work values during the transition to adulthood always developing in a linear way, it could be that some youth value different things in work for different stages of their life. Given the temporary nature of service programs, some youth may see this as a gap year for pursuing intrinsic values before pursuing different values for long-term careers (Arnett 2004; King 2011; Settersten and Ray 2010). For instance, previous research on service program participants assumes participation is an example of civically engaged students who are passionate about the work (Finlay et al. 2011; McAdam and Brandt 2009). In other words, if service program participation is not primarily about identity development as emerging adulthood would suggest, social class differences could emerge due to work values: students from working-class backgrounds may be participating because they see the programs as providing extrinsic rewards and students from middle-class backgrounds may be participating because they see the programs as providing intrinsic rewards.

A second way that social class could influence different orientations for participation in service programs is through labor market conditions. Specifically, as college degrees have become more common, the risk that college graduates will be underemployed has increased (Horowitz 2018). Recent college graduates may be forced into jobs that do not require a college degree and those most at risk are students from disadvantaged class backgrounds. Therefore, facing this risk of being unable to enter their desired careers, working-class students may turn to service programs as a way to build their human capital and try to improve their chance of being able to enter a stable middle-class career in the future.

Data, Methods, and Analytical Strategy

In order to answer why students seek to participate in service programs—and whether this is consistent with the identity exploration explanation given by emerging adulthood theory—I conducted semi-structured in-depth interviews with 30 juniors and seniors at a highly selective public university, who were considering participating in a service program after college graduation. The students were asked questions about their pre-college and college experiences, as well as their immediate and long-term goals after college in order to better understand the mechanisms that led to their service program interest and their aspirations for the future. I conducted in-depth interviews because they are the most effective method to analyze accounts of motivations, interpret meaning, and attempt to find common understandings or frameworks. The interviews lasted an average of one hour and 40 minutes. Data collection occurred between March 2015 and April 2016. During this period the economy had mostly recovered from the 2007–2009 Great Recession, but the students still believed there were limited opportunities—and the recession quickened the process of reducing the availability of good middle-class jobs (Horowitz 2018).

The university at which this study occurred is a highly selective, four-year, residential, public research university in the Southeast. It was selected for two primary reasons. First, its students have high rates of participation in TFA, Peace Corps, and other service programs after graduation, enabling me to sample a greater diversity of students who aspired to participate in service programs. Second, given the claims that elite universities are the ideal setting for emerging adulthood and identity exploration (Arnett

2016a), this study design would allow me to test the theory in the setting in which it is most likely to be supported. If it is not supported in its ideal setting, then I would have strong evidence that emerging adulthood is not a satisfactory explanation for the rise of these types of jobs.

Findings

Four orientations toward participation in service programs emerged from the interviews: Backup Planners who participate for extrinsic reasons, Delayed Careerists who participate as a short-term exciting opportunity at the right stage of their unsettled life course, Enthusiasts who participate because they have developed identity projects around social or religious issues, and Professionals who participate as an easy way to enter their chosen career field at an unusual time.

Backup Planners: Primary Orientation

Backup Planners are students who would prefer to be entering long-term careers immediately after college but are willing to engage in short-term, temporary work through a service program for strategic benefits. For instance, Michelle, a working-class exercise and sports science major, was nervous that her 3.3 GPA might keep her out of any of the five graduate programs she applied to in occupational therapy (OT). She applied to City Year, a service program, so that "I can use it as a backup if I don't get into OT school." Likewise, Mathilde, a working-class global studies major, explained that Peace Corps is her backup plan if graduate school doesn't work out immediately after college, based on advice from a teaching assistant.

> She talked about her experience, and it just seemed really interesting to me. And I thought, "Well, if I don't get into grad school or anything like that, why not? Use that time to do something beneficial like Peace Corps." Yeah. And there's a lot of things about Peace Corps after you come back that are also really beneficial. Like, . . . they give you readjustment help and they help you get into grad schools.

Both students have concrete career plans they hope to pursue through graduate school, but they recognize that they need a backup plan in case they are not accepted and see a service program as the best opportunity.

Students considering graduate educations as diverse as medical school, law school, an MA in occupational therapy, and a PhD in archeology all argued that their service programs could be a "résumé builder" that facilitates future acceptances.

Unlike some other students in the sample, Backup Planners know what they want to do for their long-term careers and would prefer to be immediately entering those careers after college. For instance, Erica, a lower-middle-class journalism and global studies major, began her nonprofit job search hoping to immediately start her career, not wanting short-term work. Discussing the roughly 80 applications she considered submitting, she explained:

> Some were actual jobs. I applied to some internships too that were short-term, but I was really focusing my efforts on long-term stuff or organizations that I could have progressed in. Like, started as one position and then moved up, moved up the totem pole.

However, Erica realized that almost all positions she was interested in required, she explained, "two or three years of experience, which I don't have—full-time experience. I have part-time experience." Realizing it was unlikely for her to successfully get offered a job that could kick start a long-term career, she decided to pursue a service program through an international nonprofit that would give her a year of full-time experience but requires her to fundraise $15,000 to participate and has no room for advancement. She now sees the benefits, as she explains, of an "international experience to be somewhere between a year and two years, just to kind of re-solidify Spanish, get me some really good experience, and then I could come back and look for something here"—before she pursues her long-term career in the U.S., but this was not her original goal when she began her job search during her senior year. She would have preferred to immediately begin a position that could be part of a long-term career instead of a one-year program that required massive fundraising. Nevertheless, she sees this as an acceptable backup plan because she can use the service program to add experience to her résumé so that she may become qualified for the long-term career she hopes to pursue in the very competitive labor market. Thus, Backup Planners tend to seek service programs for extrinsic reasons if they are unable or fear being unable to immediately enter their long-term careers. While most Backup Planners do make a point of saying that they appreciate that service programs will enable them to address a social need or help others, this is not their primary orientation to participation.

Backup Planners: Social Class Background and Financial Security

Backup Planners generally come from more disadvantaged social class backgrounds—either working-class or lower-middle-class—and many must make their post-college decisions at least partly dependent on finances. For instance, the two students who said that service programs could be backup plans to their graduate school aspirations are both financially constrained and cannot afford to not take money into account. Due to a difficult family situation, Michelle knew that "I just needed something to do after graduation" if she was not accepted to OT school because "I don't have an option to go back home," after her father made it clear she was not welcome to live with him during college breaks or after graduation. Mathilde has been financially supporting her family throughout her four years in college, generally working 35–40 hours per week while being a full-time student (despite having a full need-based scholarship that covers all of her tuition and living expenses). Neither woman can risk not having a job to pay the bills after graduation and so they must be proactive in forming backup plans. Neither has the opportunity to redshirt, or stay out of the labor market while they await the perfect job or graduate program (Carr and Kefalas 2018), because they do not have families who can or will economically support them.

Backup Planners can be best understood as students from disadvantaged class backgrounds or those who are more economically insecure at graduation, who feel forced to seek work for primarily extrinsic reasons. They seek jobs that can serve as the first steps on the ladder toward long-term careers, but they discover or worry that they are not sufficiently prepared for the increasingly competitive labor market that in recent years is leaving many recent college graduates underemployed (Horowitz 2018; Kalleberg 2018). As a reaction to this structural barrier, and lacking the kinds of networks and connections that could help privileged students in their situation (Armstrong and Hamilton 2013; Carr and Kefalas 2018), Backup Planners turn to service programs as skill-building opportunities: the programs require a college degree, even if they do not immediately facilitate career entry, and thus are better than being underemployed in fields such as retail (Carr and Kefalas 2018). Despite previous accounts, Backup Planners do not necessarily need service programs because they underachieved in college (Armstrong and Hamilton 2013), or because they seek to explore their identities (Arnett 2004). Instead, their backup plans are a reaction to the labor market having more college graduates than full-time career positions requiring college degrees. Backup Planners have high ambitions for middle-class or professional careers and want to be realistic about their mobility pathway aspirations, as they may not get accepted the first time they apply to graduate school or full-time work. Pursuing a service program as a backup is a rational plan that will allow them to build up work experience and financially support themselves—even if the low-paid position will make it difficult to cover all their expenses.

Delayed Careerists: Primary Orientation

A second orientation to service programs are Delayed Careerists. These students prioritize participating in a service program in the short term after college to take advantage of this perceived unsettled stage of life before they start different long-term careers in the future. Unlike any of the other students in this study, Delayed Careerists have explicitly different work orientations for short- and long-term work. In the short term, they prioritize work that they find meaningful, fits with their identity, and will be an exciting opportunity. In the long term, they prioritize careers that will be stable and well-paid, allowing for conventionally settled careers. For example, Hope, a lower-middle-class linguistics major, is certain that she wants a career in federal law enforcement because she "ha[s] a lot of family in law enforcement." However, based on her new interest in international service work during college, she may want to participate in the Peace Corps before she starts her law enforcement career: "Things get messy when you start a career, and it feels like you can't really get out of that. So before I start a career, if I want to do the Peace Corps, that's the time to do it." Thus, Hope explains that she sees the time before starting career as unsettled, and that trying to participate in a program like Peace Corps once she already started her career would be too hard because of her obligations at that stage of her life course. She sees immediately after graduation as the right timing to participate in a program like this.

Delayed Careerists want their programs to be short-term because they anticipate transitioning to stable, long-term, and extrinsically motivated jobs later. For example, Jackson, an upper-middle-class business major, intends to work in the financial industry where he expects to work his way up the ladder in positions he does not find rewarding:

> I do want to do some kind of economic development in the Middle East, and the best way to do that, from what I understand . . . is to get a big name on your résumé basically, and get that sort of experience with a large company. So that's what I'm hoping to do with [big financial company]. . . . So, learn the intricacies and sort of develop my skills, and then hopefully transfer to a branch in the Middle East or work for a company doing that kind of work in the Middle East.

Delayed Careerists: Social Class Background and Financial Security

Delayed Careerists tend to not be as concerned about money as Backup Planners because they see it as a short-term program before beginning their careers as full adults. For instance, despite Hope—the student aspiring to participate in the Peace Corps before a law enforcement career—paying for college herself through attending community college and then transferring to the four-year college to minimize costs, she is not worried about participating in a low-paid program because it is only two years long and is worth the experience:

> Remember, are you living to work or working to live? And it's like, I always saved all my money, and that's a really good habit to have, but what are you saving it for anyway? Like, save it and use it to live and have experiences. . . . And I do want to always be financially secure, but every now and then to spend that money for experience. I think that's worth it.

Viewing the program as a meaningful, temporary detour before well-planned out careers enables the students to not feel nervous about the fact that service programs are low-paid. Delayed Careerists come from a mix of class backgrounds, but all have medium to high current financial security. Unlike Backup Planners who feel financially compelled to try to enter careers immediately, this moderate level of financial security allows Delayed Careerists to feel capable of temporarily pursuing a meaningful opportunity and prevents them from feeling fully adult. This orientation in some ways fits with emerging adulthood theory (Arnett 2004) in that they see the period immediately after college as a distinct time in their life course to do something different and more meaningful before they transition into fully adult roles for career, though they are not exploring their identity so much as they are following their already strong identities. I discuss this distinction and how it challenges emerging adulthood theory in the discussion.

Enthusiasts: Primary Orientation

Enthusiasts prioritize participating in a service program immediately after college as an end in itself, hoping it will be a meaningful experience and clarify their long-term career aspirations that are currently unknown or vague. Enthusiasts participate in service programs because they seek to engage in meaningful work that fits with their identities—but unlike Delayed Careerists, they also hope to pursue long-term careers that are highly intrinsically rewarding based on their passions. For instance, Riley, an upper-middle-class environmental studies major, is unsure what she wants to do for her career, but she hopes that participating in a service program will help clarify her aspirations:

> Hopefully out of my time doing the [small service] program and/or Peace Corps, I would find—specifically, either a job would come out of that, and I would just do that job and be able to progress from that job, like, my career or whatever, or I would find something to go to graduate school for. But I'm hoping to find specifically what I want to focus on, because right now it's just like, animals, wildlife, environment, apex predators, things like that, but there's not really a specific focus because I just want to do everything. So I'm hoping out of my time doing this, I either figure out, like, no, I don't wanna be doing this, or yes, I do want to be doing this. So I hope not only to get research, and experience, and once-in-a lifetime opportunities travel wise, but actually have a more concrete idea of what I want to do in my career, in my professional life.

Riley explains that she is passionate about the work she will do with either of the service programs and hopes that it will help her figure out how to follow those passions into a long-term career.

Enthusiasts also sought to use their service program participation to enact constructed identities and passions during college. For instance, Emily, an upper-class environmental studies major, entered college participating in a varsity sport that took up much of her time. However, after being forced to medically retire, she constructed an identity of being passionate about agriculture. She plans to participate in a Peace Corp agricultural position to pursue this passion while she figures out her vague career aspirations somehow involving organic farming. See Gillis and Krull (2019) for more information about this accidental conversion process.

> I like meeting people, new people, and interacting with them. And I knew I wanted to help people [laughs]. I didn't know what I wanted to do [long-term]. Um, but that's one of the reasons that I got so into agriculture, is because I can be outside, doing things that I love doing while helping people towards good, better food, a cleaner future, whatever it may be. But that's one of the reasons why I loved [agricultural volunteering] was because I got to interact with people and I got to do what I loved.

Enthusiasts: Social Class Background and Financial Security

Enthusiasts generally, though not exclusively, come from privileged backgrounds and do not see the low pay of the programs as a particularly negative aspect of participation, as they tend to have the highest current financial security of all groups in the study. For instance, Mark, an upper-middle-class history and political science major, explained that his family paid for all his college expenses and will continue helping him financially after college: "I'm extremely lucky that I'm graduating without any debt and that my parents will be willing to subsidize me for a few years if I need their help." Many of the Enthusiasts never discussed the pay of the programs until explicitly asked about it and they generally assumed that the program would provide enough for them to live on because they have few to no adult expenses yet. For instance, Emma, an upper-middle-class economics and public policy major, explained, "What I'm told about the Peace Corps is they give you a stipend that you can live to the same standards as the people in the community you're serving," and so she is not concerned about money. Some Enthusiasts were so financially secure and came from class backgrounds with such extensive resources that they were able to participate in programs that required massive amounts of fundraising. For example, one woman had to fundraise $25,000 for her one-year program even though only $15,000 of it would be paid back as her salary for the year. Another man had to fundraise $40,000 to participate in his one-year program and a third student had to fundraise $75,000 for her three-year program (all of which had to be pledged before she could begin the position a few months after college graduation). This level of fundraising is only possible for students who come from social backgrounds of extensive privilege whereby not only their parents, but also their parents' friends, church members, and neighbors are willing and able to donate to support them during their service programs.

The few Enthusiasts from lower-class backgrounds did have to consider finances before deciding to participate, but they came from families with low enough incomes that they qualified for the university's generous need-based financial aid, which allowed them to graduate debt-free and thus be more financially secure than other disadvantaged students in the study. As long as the program provided enough to live on during that one- or two-year commitment, they felt financially secure enough to sacrifice making more money to pursue their passions.

Professionals: Primary Orientation

The final orientation toward service program participation are students I call Professionals. They prioritize participating in a service program immediately after college as an easy way to enter careers that they decided on too late to pursue as vocational degrees during college. For instance, Jayla, a lower-middle-class psychology and sociology major, explains that she realized she was passionate about becoming a teacher, even if her parents wanted her to pursue a career that paid more:

> I feel like I had been running from teaching for a very long time because my parents have always been like, "Oh no, don't teach. Don't teach." But it's like I couldn't run from it anymore. From the experiences and interactions that I've had with all of my kids to, like, any volunteer opportunity that I take is revolving around kids. . . . Like, everything I do is revolved around teaching in some way, shape, or form. And so at that moment, like I said, this lightbulb just went off and it was like, "Jayla, you have to be a teacher."

However, she realized this her junior year, when it was too late to change her field of study to education: "I'm really sad that I'm not [an education major]. I didn't come to this realization until January of last year, and so by that time I wouldn't have been able to declare [an] education major and still graduate on time." While the alternative certification process to becoming a teacher is challenging, Jayla used TFA to simplify the process:

> It was a new idea for me to teach. I didn't know when I should apply, or who should I talk to, or what should I do. . . . And so TFA just was really appealing because I applied to [it] and then [they told] me what to do . . . it was a new process for me and I had noooo idea what I was doing, it was really nice to have something that had a little structure for me so that . . . I know exactly what I need to do.

Likewise, Robert, an upper-middle-class political science major, explained that TFA walked him through every step of the alternative certification process, so that by the end of his senior year, he had already taken the PRAXIS exam necessary to become certified, as well as other steps that made him ready to become a teacher in his mid-western placement state. Thus, through TFA, Jayla and Robert can immediately enter their chosen careers of teaching after being too late to enter the profession in the typical way.

TFA is the only service program in the study that facilitates direct career entry. All other service programs are structured as short-term opportunities with no room for advancement into careers. For instance, participating in the Peace Corps cannot lead directly to a career in nonprofits, as the participants would have to apply for jobs after they return from abroad. However, local school districts hire TFA participants and TFA ensures that the participant becomes certified through the state's alternative certification program. Therefore, by the end of the two-year program, TFA participants can stay at that same school and continue teaching, even when they are no longer part of TFA. TFA is a unique service program that allows direct career entry while all other programs, by nature, are only temporary programs with no opportunity for advancement—making the Professional orientation to service programs unusual. For this reason, I do not draw conclusions about how social class influences this approach with only two students, though based on its extrinsic focus it is likely more common for students from lower social class backgrounds. That being said, most TFA participants do not stay in the same school after they complete the two-year program and many do not remain in the teaching profession at all (Donaldson and Johnson 2011; Heineke et al. 2014). In this study, only two of the seven students who applied for TFA intend to stay in teaching in the long term (the Professionals), supporting prior research that even among TFA participants, the Professional orientation to service program participation is unusual.

Professionals share some similarities with Enthusiasts in that they prioritize intrinsically rewarding work in the short and long term. However, Professionals differ from Enthusiasts because Professionals already have an alignment between their career aspiration and their identity, while Enthusiasts have strongly built identities but have unclear career aspirations to match them. Furthermore, Professionals use service programs to enter their chosen career and gain the necessary credentials—an extrinsic reward for participation that Enthusiasts see as unnecessary at this life stage due to their class privilege. Thus, Professionals are not using this period after college to try out new experiences like emerging adulthood theory would predict. Instead, they already see themselves as full adults entering their long-term careers.

Discussion

This study identified four types of orientations toward service programs: 1) Backup Planners participate for extrinsic reasons, generally to gain experience necessary to begin long-term careers they would prefer to be pursuing immediately, but are unable or fear being unable to do so; 2) Delayed Careerists participate because they see the period immediately after graduation as the right time in their life course to pursue temporary work for intrinsic reasons before they pursue long-term careers that will be more extrinsically oriented; 3) Enthusiasts participate for intrinsic reasons, generally because they have formed an identity project relating to religion or solving a social problem and seek to explore work opportunities that will allow them to follow their passions; and 4) Professionals participate in order to directly enter their long-term careers. Each of these orientations is based in part on the student's social class background and their current financial security/assistance and how these come together to shape their work values during this transition out of college: Backup Planners tend to be from the lowest social class backgrounds and feel the least financial security, Delayed Careerists tend to have moderate financial security from a variety of class backgrounds, and Enthusiasts tend to be from the highest social class backgrounds and feel the most financially secure.

These findings critically challenge emerging adulthood theory in several ways. First, in line with previous sociological literature, I find evidence that emerging adulthood is not a universally experienced development stage across social classes (Côté 2014; Deluca et al. 2016; Edin and Kefalas 2005; Furstenberg 2016). This study goes beyond previous findings to show that even among students who will soon graduate from an elite university, a situation typically assumed to be most consistent with emerging adulthood (Arnett 2016b), the period is not experienced universally as a time for untethered identity exploration. Backup Planners feel constrained by their financial resources and as a result do not see the period after college graduation as time for self-exploration. They already feel like adults (Benson and Furstenberg 2006) who should ambitiously pursue their professional careers and must have responsible backup plans in place in case those initial applications are not successful. Likewise, Professionals also feel like full adults who are pursuing their long-term careers, despite being from more advantaged class backgrounds than the typical Backup Planner.

However, this study also brings a new challenge to emerging adulthood: pursuing intrinsic work because of its alignment with identity is not the same as identity exploration. At first glance, Enthusiasts and Delayed Careerists seem to align well with Arnett's (2004) emerging adulthood framework: Enthusiasts seek fulfilling experiences immediately after college in order to try out potentially rewarding career fields, and Delayed Careerists explicitly talk about the period after college as being distinct from their later careers and as an opportunity to try something exciting and different before beginning more profitable careers. However, neither group fully aligns with his argument about identity exploration. Young adults who do not know their future careers are assumed to be engaging in identity development when they try out different jobs. However, Delayed Careerists and Enthusiasts already had clear identities that they developed during college. Delayed Careerists lack the structural opportunities to pursue long-term careers that matched their identities and instead compromised by allowing themselves to engage in meaningful work short-term that aligned well with their passions. Enthusiasts assume that career opportunities that match their identities exist, but they lack the knowledge of what those careers might be. Given that students from privileged backgrounds at elite colleges often do not consider career when choosing a major (Mullen 2010), it is not surprising that some students do not know how to transfer their newly acquired passions into careers. Thus, when middle-class recent college graduates engage in short-term work, it should not necessarily be assumed that they are engaging in identity development, as they may already have strong identity but may be unsure what jobs correspond to those identities.

The findings of this study suggest that rather than seeing the rise of recent college graduates participating in service programs as a product of their developmental phase, we should understand this trend to be the reaction to conditions that vary based on the student's social class background and financial security. For instance, various labor market constraints seem to be at play in shaping their decisions. Students from more disadvantaged class backgrounds recognize that they are at risk of underemployment after college and have no financial safety net to rely on, and turn to service programs as backup plans for building human capital for future careers and making money in the meantime. Students from more advantaged class backgrounds have been raised to seek intrinsically rewarding work and have developed strong identities in college but, in the case of Delayed Careerists, do not perceive any long-term career opportunities in the labor market to pursue these passions, and so they turn to short-term opportunities to do so. In the case of Enthusiasts, these privileged students believe that intrinsically rewarding jobs that fit their identities do exist, but they are not yet sure what those opportunities are. Finally, Professionals are taking advantage of the changed labor market that allows more people to follow nontraditional pathways into some occupations, in this case teaching. Thus, each group faces a different problem associated with the labor market, based in part on their social class differences in work values, and the successful rise of service programs may be evidence that young adults see these programs as at least partially solving the problems they face.

DISCUSSION QUESTIONS

1. What is the theory of *emerging adulthood* explanation for the rise in popularity of service programs? Does this theory fit with how "typical" college age students (those 18–22) are usually portrayed in popular culture?

2. What are some of the reasons the author suggests for why the theory of emerging adulthood and the assumption that those in their 20s are engaged in identity exploration is NOT a universal phenomenon?

3. Why are short-term service programs ideal for studying whether all typical college-age students engage in identity exploration?
4. What are the four typologies she describes? What characterizes each? What role do social class, work values, and labor market orientation play in each orientation?
5. Does your school offer or promote short-term service programs like the ones described in this reading? If so, what messages about social class, work values, or labor market conditions do those advertising the program use?
6. Social class shapes many features about attending college. Watch the Tedx Talk by sociology Sarah Goldrick-Rab about the challenges faced by many college students and what structural changes can be implemented to help them; available at https://www.youtube.com/watch?v=dSqW43aTuRM.

Strangers in Their Own Land

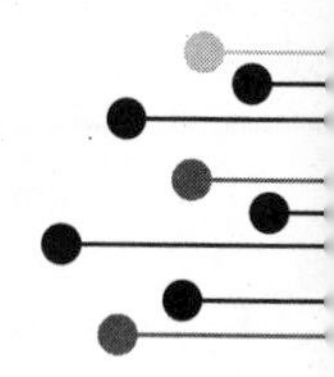

Anger and Mourning on the American Right

Arlie Russell Hochschild

As American politics became more and more divisive, and the gulf between "liberals" and "conservatives" grew wider and wider through the 2010s, self-described "liberal sociologist from Berkeley, California" Arlie Hochschild decided to start spending as much time with Tea Party supporters as she could.

Her goal was not to try to change their minds but to try to understand how they saw the world in ways that were different (or similar) to how she saw it. Hochschild was interested in getting over what she termed an empathy wall—"an obstacle to deep understanding of another person, one that can make us feel indifferent or even hostile to those who hold different beliefs or whose childhood is rooted in different circumstances." She went to Louisiana, in the geographic heart of conservatism, and through a connection with a former student began spending time with Tea Party supporters trying to get to the political and social world on the other side of the empathy wall she hoped to scale.

The resulting book, Strangers in Their Own Land, *from which this excerpt is taken, provides an insightful, empathetic portrait of the beliefs and mindsets of those on the far right that she met. Rather than focusing on being critical or dismissive of the opinions and beliefs of her interviewees, she instead carefully pieces together how their social location (race, class, gender, religion, etc.) explains a great paradox. The Tea Party supporters she talked to would (and do) benefit from government funding and regulations. Louisiana receives far more federal assistance than it pays in tax dollars, and its citizens are among the poorest, sickest, least educated, and most exposed to environmental contamination in the country. Yet those she talked with adamantly supported the Tea Party, whose candidates' stated goals are to remove funding and regulation that would directly benefit those voting for them. She wanted to understand how Tea Party supporters resolved this paradox in their own minds.*

She finds that they do so through a deep story—a story that feels as though it is true (whether it actually is or not). The Tea Party supporters saw the

---

Excerpt from *Strangers in Their Own Land: Anger and Mourning on the American Right* by Arlie Hochschild.

government as helping undeserving people "cut in line" ahead of them on their way to the American Dream, a line that had been at a standstill for most of their lives but that they had never complained about. They had continued to work hard, even under terrible conditions and for diminishing wages, while government workers, minorities, women, immigrants, and others got what they saw as special treatment and were whisked ahead of them in line by liberals. And they saw their best ally in returning fairness to the line for the American Dream as big business, and so they supported deregulation and smaller government because politicians pledging to make those changes also promised to support the free market and big businesses.

Much like Reading 12 about parents who refuse to vaccinate and Reading 13 about how police are socialized to fear all interactions with citizens, this reading provides insight into how an often disliked group sees the world from their point of view. Regardless of your own political orientation, think about how she writes about her subjects in sharing her research and how that differs from social media and news media posts about Tea Party supporters and others to the right of the political spectrum.

Traveling to the Heart

Along the clay road, Mike's red truck cuts slowly between tall rows of sugarcane, sassy, silvery tassels waving in the October sun, extending across an alluvial plain as far as the eye can see. We are on the grounds of the Armelise Plantation, as it was once called. A few miles east lies the mighty Mississippi River, pressing the soils and waste of the Midwest southward, past New Orleans, into the Gulf of Mexico. "We used to walk barefoot between the rows," Mike says. A tall, kindly white man of sixty-four, Mike removes his sunglasses to study an area of the sugarcane, and comes to a near stop.

Mike has passed his boyhood in an era of sugar, cotton, and mule-drawn plows and his adulthood in the era of oil. As a teenager earning money over the summer for college, he had laid wooden boards through mosquito-infested bayous to set up oil-drill platforms. As a grown, college-educated man, he had trained himself as an "estimator"—calculating the size, strength, and cost of materials needed to construct large platforms that held oil-drilling rigs in the Gulf, and to create the giant white spherical tanks that stored vast quantities of chemicals and oil. "When I was a kid, you stuck a thumb out by the side of the road, you got a ride. Or if you had a car, you gave a ride. If someone was hungry, you fed him. You had community. You know what's undercut all that?" He pauses. "Big government."

We climb back in his red truck, take a swig of water (he has brought plastic bottles for us both), and continue edging forward through the cane as our conversation shifts to politics. "Most folks around here are Cajun, Catholic, conservative," he explains, adding with gusto, "I'm for the Tea Party!"

I'd first seen Mike Schaff months earlier standing at the microphone at an environmental rally on the steps of the Louisiana state capital in Baton Rouge, his voice cracking with emotion. He had been a victim of one of the strangest, literally earth-shaking environmental disasters in the nation, one that robbed him of his home and community—a sinkhole that devoured hundred-foot-tall trees and turned forty acres of swamp upside down, as I shall describe. That raised a big question in my mind. The disaster had been caused by a lightly regulated drilling company. But as a Tea Party advocate, Mike had hailed government deregulation of all sorts, as well as drastic cuts in government spending—including that for environmental protection. How could he be both near tears to recall his lost home and also call for a world stripped of most government beyond the military and hurricane relief? I was puzzled. I sensed a wall between us.

Empathy Walls

You might say I'd come to Louisiana with an interest in walls. Not visible, physical walls such as those separating Catholics from Protestants in Belfast, Americans from Mexicans on the Texas border, or, once, residents of East and West Berlin. It was empathy walls that interested me. An empathy wall is an obstacle to deep understanding of another person, one that can make us feel indifferent or even hostile to those who hold different beliefs or whose childhood is rooted in different circumstances. In a period of political tumult, we grasp for quick certainties. We shoehorn new information into ways we already think. We settle for knowing our opposite numbers from the outside. But is it possible, without changing our beliefs, to know others from the inside, to see reality through their eyes, to understand the links between life, feeling, and politics; that is, to cross the empathy wall? I thought it was.

I'd asked Mike Schaff to show me where he'd grown up because I wanted to understand, if I could, how he saw the world. By way of introduction I'd told him, "I'm from Berkeley, California, a sociologist, and I am trying to understand the deepening divide in our country. So I'm trying to get out of my political bubble and get to know people in yours." Mike nodded at the word "divide," then quipped, "Berkeley? So y'all must be *communist*!" He grinned as if to say, "We Cajuns can laugh, hope you can."

We live in what the *New Yorker* has called the "Tea Party era." Some 350,000 people are active members, but, according to another Pew poll, some 20 percent of Americans—45 million people—support it. And the divide cuts through a striking variety of issues. Ninety percent of Democrats believe in the human role in climate change, surveys find, compared with 59 percent of moderate Republicans, 38 percent of conservative Republicans, and only 29 percent of Tea Party advocates. In fact, politics is the single biggest factor determining views on climate change.

And the Tea Party's turn away from government may signal a broader trend. During the depression of the 1930s, Americans turned to the federal government for aid in their economic recovery. But in response to the Great Recession of 2008, a majority of Americans turned away from it. As the political divide widens and opinions harden, the stakes have grown vastly higher. Neither ordinary citizens nor leaders are talking much "across the aisle," damaging the surprisingly delicate process of governance itself. The United States has been divided before, of course. During the Civil War, a difference in belief led to some 750,000 deaths. During the stormy 1960s, too, clashes arose over the war in Vietnam, civil rights, and women's rights. But in the end, a healthy democracy depends on a collective capacity to hash things out. And to get there, we need to figure out what's going on—especially on the more rapidly shifting and ever stronger right.

The Great Paradox

Inspired by Thomas Frank's book *What's the Matter with Kansas?*, I began my five-year journey to the heart of the American right carrying with me, as if it were a backpack, a great paradox. Back in 2004, when Frank's book appeared, there was a paradox underlying the right-left split. Since then the split has become a gulf.

Across the country, red states are poorer and have more teen mothers, more divorce, worse health, more obesity, more trauma-related deaths, more low-birth-weight babies, and lower school enrollment. On average, people in red states die five years earlier than people in blue states. Indeed, the gap in life expectancy between Louisiana (75.7) and Connecticut (80.8) is the same as that between the United States and Nicaragua. Red states suffer more in another highly important but little-known way, one that speaks to the very biological self-interest in health and life: industrial pollution.

Louisiana is an extreme example of this paradox. *The Measure of America*, a report of the Social Science Research Council, ranks every state in the United States on its "human development." Each rank is based on life expectancy, school enrollment, educational degree attainment, and median personal earnings. Out of the 50 states, Louisiana ranked 49th and in overall health ranked last. According to the 2015 National Report Card, Louisiana ranked 48th out of 50 in eighth-grade reading and 49th out of 50 in eighth-grade math. Only eight out of ten Louisianans have graduated from high school, and only 7 percent have graduate or professional degrees. According to the *Kids Count Data Book*, compiled by the Annie E.

Casey Foundation, Louisiana ranked 49th out of 50 states for child well-being. And the problem transcends race; an average black in Maryland lives four years longer, earns twice as much, and is twice as likely to have a college degree as a black in Louisiana. And whites in Louisiana are worse off than whites in Maryland or anywhere else outside Mississippi. Louisiana has suffered many environmental problems too: there are nearly 400 miles of low, flat, subsiding coastline, and the state loses a football field-size patch of wetland every hour. It is threatened by rising sea levels and severe hurricanes, which the world's top scientists connect to climate change.

Given such an array of challenges, one might expect people to welcome federal help. In truth, a very large proportion of the yearly budgets of red states—in the case of Louisiana, 44 percent—do come from federal funds; $2,400 is given by the federal government per Louisianan per year.

But Mike Schaff doesn't welcome that federal money and doubts the science of climate change: "I'll worry about global warming in fifty years," he says. Mike loves his state, and he loves the outdoor life. But instead of looking to government, like others in the Tea Party he turns to the free market. Mike's mother had voted for the Louisiana Democrat Edwin Edwards because he was Cajun and for Jack Kennedy because he was Catholic; "Democrat" wasn't a bad word when he was going up. But it is now. Mike had long worked for a small business and advocates a free market for businesses of all sizes, and from this yet another paradox seemed to unfold. Many Tea Party advocates work in or run small businesses. Yet the politicians they support back laws that consolidate the monopoly power of the very largest companies that are poised to swallow up smaller ones. Small farmers voting with Monsanto? Corner drugstore owners voting with Walmart? The local bookstore owner voting with Amazon? If I were a small business owner, I would welcome lower company taxes, sure, but strengthening the monopolies that could force me out of business? I didn't get it.

Wrapped around these puzzles was a bigger one: how can a system both create pain and deflect blame for that pain? In 2008, reckless and woefully underregulated Wall Street investors led many to lose savings, homes, jobs, and hope. Yet, years later, under the banner of a "free market," many within the growing small-town right defend Wall Street against government "over-regulation." What could be going on?

Maybe the best way to find out, I thought, was to reverse the "Big Sort," to leave my blue neighborhood and state, enter a red state, and try to scale the empathy wall.

What, I wanted to know, do people *want to feel*, what do they think they *should or shouldn't* feel, and what *do they feel* about a range of issues? When we listen to a political leader, we don't simply hear words; we listen predisposed to want to feel certain things. Some broad emotional ideals are shared across the political spectrum but others are not. Some feel proud of a "Give me your tired, your poor, your huddled masses" Statue of Liberty

America, while others yearn to feel proud of a Constitution-abiding, work-your-own-way-up America.

At play are "feeling rules," left ones and right ones. The right seeks release from liberal notions of what they *should feel*—happy for the gay newlywed, sad at the plight of the Syrian refugee, unresentful about paying taxes. The left sees prejudice. Such rules challenge the emotional core of right-wing belief. And it is to this core that a free-wheeling candidate such as the billionaire entrepreneur Donald Trump, Republican candidate for president in 2016, can appeal, saying, as he gazes upon throngs of supporters, "See all the *passion.*"

We can approach that core, I came to see, through what I call a "deep story," a story that *feels as if* it were true. As though I were seeing through Alice's looking glass, the deep story was to lead me to focus on a site of long-simmering social conflict, one ignored by both the "Occupy Wall Street" left—who were looking to the 1 and the 99 percent within the private realm as a site of class conflict—and by the anti-government right, who think of differences of class and race as matters of personal character. The deep story was to take me to the shoulds and shouldn'ts of feeling, to the management of feeling, and to the core feelings stirred by charismatic leaders. And, as we shall see, everyone has a deep story.

"The Spill Makes Us Sad, the Moratorium Makes Us Mad"

The BP oil rig *Deepwater Horizon* exploded in the Gulf of Mexico off the coast of Louisiana. President Obama called it "the worst environmental disaster America has ever faced." The blowout killed eleven workers and injured seventeen. It ruptured an oil pipe 10,000 feet below the surface of the water, from which oil gushed into the Gulf continuously for three months. The spill released the equivalent of one *Exxon Valdez*–sized oil spill every three to four days—for 87 days.

Highly trained engineers were helpless. Anxious experts testified on television. Louisiana's 397-mile Gulf coast was critical, they said, to the life cycle of over 90 percent of all fish and 98 percent of all commercial species in the entire Gulf of Mexico. Eyeless shrimp and infant dolphins washed ashore, and oil balls appeared along an estimated 650 miles of coastline. Pelicans died. Crab traps were soiled and shrimp harvests were decimated. Oil leaked onto oyster plots. After the blowout, carcasses of 6,000 birds, 600 sea turtles, over a hundred bottlenose dolphins, and other marine mammals, including whales, washed ashore. Later studies discovered that embryos of fish, especially tuna, that had been exposed to BP oil showed distorted body shapes, hearts, and eyes.

More bad news followed. Some 90,000 fishermen had lost their livelihood and were offered jobs to clean up the spilled oil, using their own boats, in the Vessels of Opportunity program. However, their protective gear was inadequate against the oil and the dispersant Corexit, and some developed skin lesions, blurred vision, breathing difficulties, and headaches.

In response, President Obama ordered a six-month moratorium on deep-sea drilling until safeguards could be put in place, reasoning that it was better to have one disaster than two or more. No one knew for sure why the accident had occurred. At that time, the blowout preventer BP had used had never before been used at a depth of 10,000 feet. Even the robots used to explore the site of the blowout had never before been used, so no one knew if they would work. Thirty-two other rigs were still drilling in the Gulf using similar technology at such depths. BP itself did not object to the moratorium. Altogether, it seemed to many a wise step.

But months later, a team of Louisiana State University researchers asked some 2,000 residents of the devastated coast, "Do you favor or oppose a moratorium that would halt offshore drilling until new safety requirements are met?" Half opposed it, and only a third favored it. When asked, "Have your views about other environmental issues such as global warming or protecting wildlife changed as a result of the oil spill?" seven out of ten answered "no." The rest—interestingly, the less educated and female—said "yes." The inland Louisianans I spoke with, like Congressmen Boustany and Landry, were also adamantly opposed to Obama's moratorium.

Freedom to, Freedom from, Freedom for Whom?

So how did Louisianans look at government regulation of *any* sort? I thought an answer to that might help me understand the coastal Louisianans who were sad at the spill but mad at the government. Maybe it was government regulations in general they resented, At first glance, Louisiana's own policies seemed flamboyantly opposed to the very idea of regulation. With regard to alcohol, Louisiana is one of the most permissive states in the nation. You can pull into a drive-through frozen daiquiri stand and buy daiquiris in "go-cups"—the only legal proviso being that the plastic lid is pressed on and the straw is not yet inserted. At a Caribbean Hut in Lake Charles, a satisfied customer reported ordering a 32-ounce Long Island Iced Tea with a few extra shots, a piece of Scotch tape placed over the straw hole—so it was "sealed"—and drove on. And only in 2004 did it become illegal to drive with unsealed containers. There is even a late July "Defend the Daiquiri Festival" held in New Orleans—supported, naturally, by an alcohol lobbying group.

An unlicensed vendor can sell handguns, shotguns, rifles, or assault weapons, and large-capacity magazines. A person can buy any number of guns and, except for handguns, need not register them, or report a theft of one, or hesitate to take them into parking lots and state parks. Louisiana also has a "Stand Your Ground" law, permitting a frightened homeowner to shoot first. A person can walk into a bar on Bourbon Street in New Orleans with a loaded gun.

Indeed, a gun vendor in Louisiana can keep no records, perform no background checks, and sell guns to an array of customers forbidden in other states: those with violent and firearms-related misdemeanors, people on terror watch lists or "no fly" lists, abusers of drugs or alcohol, juvenile offenders, and criminals with a history of serious mental illness or domestic violence. In 2010, the governor passed a law that permitted concealed handguns in churches, synagogues, and mosques. The next year, Louisiana had the highest rate of death by gunfire in the country, nearly double the national average.

Still, many I talked to were ardent believers in the right to bear arms. Mike Schaff had four guns. "A .22 rifle, a .22 pistol that I got when Daddy died, a .40 Smith & Wesson Automatic, and a 12-gauge shotgun. These killed varmint or deer," he explained, while "the Smith & Wesson's for self-defense." He went on to describe his first wife's rifle and another long Kentucky rifle, a "show gun" he had assembled from a kit. But he now had four, which he described as "nothing for the South. Most have seven or eight guns." He didn't have a conceal and carry permit, he added, but said he would get it eventually if "things got worse."

Looked at more closely, an overall pattern in state regulation emerges, and the Great Paradox becomes more complicated than it first seemed. Liquor, guns, motorcycle helmets (legislation had gone back and forth on that)—mainly white masculine pursuits—are fairly unregulated. But for women and black men, regulation is greater. Within given parameters, federal law gives women the right to decide whether or not to abort a fetus. But the state of Louisiana has imposed restrictions on clinics offering the procedure, which, if upheld in the U.S. Supreme Court, would prevent all but one clinic, in New Orleans, from offering women access to it. Any adult in the state can also be jailed for transporting a teenager out of state for the purposes of an abortion if the teen has not informed her parents.

Young black males are regulated too. Jefferson Davis Parish passed a bill banning the wearing of pants in public that revealed "skin beneath their waists or their underwear," and newspaper accounts featured images, taken from the back, of two black teenage boys exposing large portions of their undershorts. The parish imposed a $50 fine for a first offense and $100 for a second. A town ordinance in Ville Platte (in which 54 percent of the population is black) requires residents to wear "something reflective" and visible from all directions on an outer garment when walking after dark.

Next to the death sentence, prisons are the ultimate instrument of regulation. The United States incarcerates a higher proportion of its population than does any nation in the world outside the Seychelles Islands—more than Russia or Cuba. Louisiana incarcerates the highest proportion of its population of all the states in the union, and those inmates are disproportionately black. It also houses Angola, the nation's largest maximum security prison, in which rules are notoriously harsh. The prison is the site of the longest-standing case of solitary confinement in the nation—a black man, Albert Woodfox, who had been locked up for twenty-three out of every twenty-four hours a day for forty-three years before finally being released on February 19, 2016. So while the state boasts a reputation of an almost cowboy-style "don't-fence-me-in" freedom, that is probably not how a female rape victim who wants an abortion, or a young black boy in Jefferson Davis Parish, or Albert Woodfox see the matter.

Yet when people spoke indignantly of regulation, it was not abortion clinics and prisons that came to mind, but rather what the government was telling them to buy in stores. At a meeting of the Republican Women of Southwest Louisiana, across-the-table talk of regulation focused on the promotion of fluorescent or LED light bulbs: "The government has no right to regulate the light bulbs we buy," one woman declared. "I made my husband change all my light bulbs *back* to the *old* ones." Others complained of all the "forced" salads on the menus in fast food restaurants now. "I don't need the government telling me what to eat," one woman complained. "You remember that apron that says 'If the cook ain't fat, I ain't eatin' it?'" one woman asked to a round of happy laughter. Others were irritated by a local ban on driving on sidewalks, or on having more than one RV in your yard, and still others by child-protection devices. One woman recalled an age without child-proof lids on medicine bottles or car seat belts. "We let them throw lawn darts, smoked alongside them," she said. "And *they survived*. Now it's like your kid needs a helmet, knee pads, and elbow pads to go down the kiddy slide." Laughter rippled around the table.

Media as Anxiety Producer

We are still drinking sweet teas at the cafeteria, and Madonna pokes at her cell phone to show me her Twitter feed, which reflects the list of sources of information she relies on: the Republican National Committee, Jeb Bush, Michael Reagan, Michelle Malkin, the *National Review,* the *Drudge Report,* Donald Trump. Then it continues with motivational quotes, Fox News, Debbie Phelps (the mother of Olympic swimmer Michael Phelps), and various Christian leaders. Madonna's car radio is tuned to Rush Limbaugh, her "brave heart."

As a powerful influence over the views of the people I came to know, Fox News stands next to industry, state government, church, and the regular media as an extra pillar of political culture all its own. Madonna tunes into Fox on the radio, television, and Internet. Up in Longville, where few subscribe to cable, Mike Tritico told me he could tell who was watching Fox News by the tilt of rooftop aerials. "It's nearly all Fox," he said. Fox gives Madonna and others the news. It suggests what the issues are. It tells her what to feel afraid, angry, and anxious about.

To some, Fox is family. One woman, a great reader who is highly attuned to world news, tells me she listens to Fox throughout the day. When she turns the ignition in her SUV, Fox News comes on. When she sits at her computer in her study at home, she tunes in to Fox via a small television to the right of her monitor. At the end of the day, sitting in a soft chair next to her husband, before a large screen, she watches the five o'clock news on Fox. "Fox is like family to me," she explains. "Bill O'Reilly is like a steady, reliable dad. Sean Hannity is like a difficult uncle who rises to anger too quickly. Megyn Kelly is like a smart sister. Then there's Greta Van Susteren. And Juan Williams, who came over from NPR, which was too left for him, the adoptee. They're all different, just like in a Family."

Fox offers news and opinions on matters of politics, of course, but it often strikes a note of alarm on issues—diseases, stock market plunges—with little direct bearing on politics. All news programs address our emotional alarm systems, of course. But with talk of a "terror mosque" at Ground Zero, of the "left's secret immigration plan" to wipe traditional America off the face of the earth, of Obama's supposed release of the ISIS leader Abu Bakr al-Baghdadi, of his supposed masterminding the massacre at Fort Hood, Fox News stokes fear. And the fear seems to reflect that of the audience it most serves—white middle- and working-class people.

We all intuitively filter the news ourselves. One well-read, enthusiastic member of the Tea Party relied mainly on Fox News to watch and the *Drudge Report* to read online. But she sometimes dipped into the liberal media, occasionally purchasing the Sunday *New York Times* "just for the arts section." The rest of the *Times,* she said, "I throw away. It's too liberal to read." She was a devotee of Fox News, but, employed as a flight attendant, she sometimes found herself in foreign cities, flipping channels on the TV in her hotel: BBC, CNN, MSNBC. "CNN is not objective at all," she complains. "I turn it on for news and what I get is opinion."

"How can you tell straight news from opinion?" I ask. "By their *tone of voice,*" she explains. "Take Christiane Amanpour. She'll be kneeling by a sick African child, or a bedraggled Indian, looking into the camera, and her voice is saying, 'Something's *wrong.* We have to *fix* it. 'Or worse, *we caused* the problem. She's using that child to say, '*Do* something, America.' But that child's problems aren't our fault." The Tea Party listener felt Christiane Amanpour was implicitly scolding her. She was imposing liberal feeling rules about whom to feel sorry for. The woman didn't want to be told she should feel sorry for, or responsible for, the fate of the child. Amanpour was overstepping her role as commentator by suggesting how to feel. The woman had her feeling guard up. "*No,*" she told herself in so many words, "That's *PC.* That's what liberals want listeners like me to feel. I don't like it. And what's more, I don't want to be told I'm a bad person if I don't feel sorry for that child." The social terrain around her—industry, government, church, media—lifted focus away from such a child's needs and from her own detachment from them. Again, I was backing into her deep story by exploring what it shut out. But all deep stories do that, and we all have deep stories.

The Deep Story

The deep story here, that of the Tea Party, focuses on relationships between social groups within our national borders. I constructed this deep story to represent—in metaphorical form—the hopes, fears, pride, shame, resentment, and anxiety in the lives of those I talked with. Then I tried it out on my Tea Party friends to see if they thought it fit their experience. They did. Like a play, it unfolds in scenes.

Waiting in Line

You are patiently standing in a long line leading up a hill, as in a pilgrimage. You are situated in the middle of this line, along with others who are also white, older, Christian, and predominantly male, some with college degrees, some not.

Just over the brow of the hill is the American Dream, the goal of everyone waiting in line. Many in the back of the line are people of color—poor, young and old, mainly without college degrees. It's scary to look back; there are so many behind you, and in principle you wish them well. Still, you've waited a long time, worked hard, and the line is barely moving. You deserve to move forward a little faster. You're patient but weary. You focus ahead, especially on those at the very top of the hill.

The American Dream is a dream of progress—the idea that you're better off than your forebears just as they superseded their parents before you—and extends beyond money and stuff. You've suffered long hours, layoffs, and exposure to dangerous chemicals at work, and received reduced pensions. You have shown moral character through trial by fire, and the American Dream of prosperity and security is a reward for all of this, showing who you have been and are—a badge of honor.

The source of the American Dream is on the other side of the hill, hidden. Has the economy come to a strange standstill? Is my company doing okay? Will I get a raise this year? Are there good jobs for us all? Or just a few? Will we be waiting in line forever? It's so hard to see over the brow of the hill.

The sun is hot and the line unmoving. In fact, is it moving backward? You haven't gotten a raise in years, and there is no talk of one. Actually, if you are short a high school diploma, or even a BA, your income has dropped over the last twenty years. That has happened to your buddies too; in fact, some of them have stopped looking for good jobs, because they figure for guys like them, good jobs aren't out there.

You've taken the bad news in stride because you're a positive person. You're not a complainer. You count your blessings. You wish you could help your family and church more, because that's where your heart is. You'd like them to feel grateful to you for being so giving to them. But this line isn't moving. And after all your intense effort, all your sacrifice, you're beginning to feel stuck.

You think of things to feel proud of—your Christian morality, for one. You've always stood up for clean-living, monogamous, heterosexual marriage. That hasn't been easy. You've been through a separation yourself, a near—or actual—divorce. Liberals are saying your ideas are outmoded, sexist, homophobic, but it's not clear what *their* values are. And given a climate of secular tolerance, you remember better times, when as a child you said morning prayer and the flag salute—before "under God" became optional— in public school.

The Line Cutters

Look! You see people *cutting in line ahead of you!* You're following the rules. They aren't. As they cut in, it feels like you are being moved back. How can they just do that? Who are they? Some are black. Through affirmative action plans, pushed by the federal government, they are being given preference for places in colleges and universities, apprenticeships, jobs, welfare payments, and free lunches, and they hold a certain secret place in people's minds, as we see below. Women, immigrants, refugees, public sector workers— where will it end? Your money is running through a liberal sympathy sieve you don't control or agree with. These are opportunities you'd have loved to have had in your day—and either you should have had them when you were young or the young shouldn't be getting them now. It's not fair.

And President Obama: how did *he* rise so high? The biracial son of a low-income single mother becomes president of the most powerful country in the world; you didn't see that coming. And if he's there, what kind of a slouch does his rise make you feel like, you who are supposed to be so much more privileged? Or did Obama get there *fairly?* How did he get into an expensive place like *Columbia* University? How did Michelle Obama get enough money to go to *Princeton?* And then *Harvard* Law School, with a father who was a city water plant employee? You've never seen anything like it, not up close. The federal government must have given them money. And Michelle *should feel* grateful for all she has but sometimes she seems mad. She has no right to feel mad.

Women: Another group is cutting ahead of you in line, if you are a man: women demanding the right to the men's jobs. Your dad didn't have to compete with women for scarce positions at the office. Also jumping in line ahead of you are overpaid public sector employees—and a majority of them are women and minorities. It also seems to you that they work shorter hours in more secure and overpaid jobs, enjoying larger pensions than yours. That assistant administrator at the Department of Regulation has cushy hours, a fat pension awaiting her, lifetime tenure—and she's probably sitting at her screen doing online shopping. What has she done to deserve perks that you don't enjoy?

Immigrants: And now Filipinos, Mexicans, Arabs, Indians, and Chinese on special visas or green cards are ahead of you in line. Or maybe they snuck in. You've seen Mexican-looking men building the man camps that are to house Sasol's Filipino pipefitters You see the Mexicans work hard—and you admire that—but they work for less, and lower white American pay.

Refugees: Four million Syrian refugees are fleeing war and chaos, thousands a day, appearing in boats on the shores of Greece. President Obama accepted 10,000 of them, two-thirds women and children, to settle in the United States. But word has it that 90 percent of the refugees are young men, possibly ISIS terrorists, poised to get in line ahead of you and get their hands on your tax money. And what about you? You've suffered floods, oil spills, and chemical leaks. There are days when you feel like a refugee yourself.

The brown pelican: Unbelievably, standing ahead of you in line is a brown pelican, fluttering its long, oil-drenched wings. The Louisiana state bird, pictured on the state flag, nests in mangrove trees on ribbons of sand along the coast. The brown pelican was at one time nearly wiped out by chemical pollution, but in 2009 it was removed from the endangered species list—a year before the 2010 BP oil spill. To keep surviving, it now needs clean fish to eat, clean water to dive in, oil-free marshes, and protection from coastal erosion. That's why it's in line ahead of you. But really, it's just an animal and you're a human being.

Blacks, women, immigrants, refugees, brown pelicans—all have cut ahead of you in line. But it's people like *you* who have made this country great. You feel uneasy. It has to be said: the line cutters irritate you. They are violating rules of fairness. You resent them, and you feel it's right that you do. So do your friends. Fox commentators reflect your feelings, for your deep story is also the Fox News deep story.

You're a compassionate person. But now you've been asked to extend your sympathy to all the people who have cut in front of you. So you have your guard up against requests for sympathy. People complain: Racism. Discrimination. Sexism. You've heard stories of oppressed blacks, dominated women, weary immigrants, closeted gays, desperate refugees, but at some point, you say to yourself, you have to close the borders to human sympathy—especially if there are some among them who might bring you harm. You've suffered a good deal yourself, but you aren't complaining about it.

Betrayal

Then you become suspicious. If people are cutting in line ahead of you, someone must be *helping* them. Who? A man is monitoring the line, walking up and down it, ensuring that the line is orderly and that access to the Dream is fair. His name is President Barack Hussein Obama. But—hey—you see him *waving to* the line cutters. He's helping them. He feels extra sympathy for them that he doesn't feel for you. He's on *their* side. He's telling you that these line cutters *deserve* special treatment, that they've had a harder time than you've had. You don't live near the line cutters or have close friends in most categories of the line cutters, but from what you can see or hear on Fox News, the real story doesn't correspond to his story about the line cutters, which celebrates so many black people, women, and immigrants. The supervisor wants you to sympathize with the line cutters, but you don't want to. It's not fair. In fact, the president and his wife are line cutters themselves.

You feel betrayed. The president is *their* president, not *your* president. Now you have your guard way up. Watch out for lies. Presidents and other officials often wear a small pin showing the American flag—a flag pin. Did you see what a *small* flag pin he is wearing today? Maybe that means he's not proud of America. So the great pride you feel in being an American cannot be conveyed through him. As a source of honor, being an American is more important to you than ever, given the slowness of this line to the American Dream, and given disrespectful talk about whites and men and Bible-believing Christians.

Obama's story seems "fishy." You're not a paranoid type, but it seems to you that either the federal government funded Obama's education or, even worse, secret strings were pulled. A friend of yours asks you whether or not you noticed that Obama took off his wristwatch for Ramadan. (She is referring to a custom of removing jewelry during the Muslim holy month.) "He was brought up on the Koran," a neighbor says.

You may not yet have the biggest house, but you can certainly be proud of being American. And anyone who criticizes America—well, they're criticizing you. If you can no longer feel pride in the United States through its president, you'll have to feel American in some new way—by banding with others who feel as strangers in their own land.

Checking Back With My Friends

I return to my new Louisiana friends and acquaintances to check whether the deep story resonates with them. When I relate the story to him, Mike Schaff writes in an e-mail, "*I live your analogy.* We pay hundreds of millions of dollars in hard-earned taxes for these bureaucrats at the Department of Environmental Quality and the EPA to do their job and they do nothing of the sort. To add insult to injury, these slackers jump the line to retire before the workers who pay their salaries can. When the tax payer finally gets to retire, he sees the bureaucrats in Washington have raided the fund. And the rest of us are wailing in line."

Attitudes toward blacks, immigrants, public sector workers, and others parallel to those I found here.

Behind the Deep Story: Class, the Federal Government, and Free Market as Proxy Allies

For the right today, the main theater of conflict is neither the factory floor nor an Occupy protest. The theater of conflict—at the heart of the deep story—is the local welfare office and the mailbox where undeserved disability checks and SNAP stamps arrive. Government checks for the listless and idle—this seems most unfair. If unfairness in Occupy is expressed in the moral vocabulary of a "fair share" of resources and a properly proportioned society, unfairness in the right's deep story is found in the language of "makers" and "takers." For the left, the flashpoint is up the class ladder (between the very top and the rest); for the right, it is down between the middle class and the poor. For the left, the flashpoint is centered in the private sector; for the right, in the public sector. Ironically, both call for an honest day's pay for an honest day's work.

Left and right also seemed to ally with different sectors of society. It is almost as if those I talked with thought about the government and the market in the same way others think of separate nations. Just as various nations back different sides in a foreign war, fighting each other on a "proxy" battlefront, in the same way those I spoke with seemed to talk about the federal government and the free market. The free market was the unwavering ally of the good citizens waiting in line for the American Dream. The federal government was on the side of those unjustly "cutting in."

Feeling betrayed by the federal government and turning wholeheartedly to the free market, the right is faced with realities the deep story makes it hard to see or focus on. Giant companies have grown vastly larger, more automated, more global, and more powerful. For them, productivity is increasingly based on cheap labor in offshore plants abroad, imported cheap foreign labor, and automation, and less on American labor. The more powerful they've become, the less resistance they have encountered from unions and government. Thus, they have felt more free to allocate more profits to top executives and stockholders, and less to workers. But this is the "wrong" theater to look in for the conflict that absorbs the right—except when a company like Texas Brine causes a sinkhole like the one in Bayou Corne.

And this may explain why much of the right isn't bothered by something else—the unaligned interests between big and small business. Many members of the Tea Party run or work in a small business—oil company suppliers, trailer parks, restaurants, small banks, and shops. Small businesses are vulnerable to the growth of big monopolies. What is transpiring today, Robert Reich argues in *Saving Capitalism,* is that big monopolies support policies that help them compete against smaller businesses by rewriting property bankruptcy and contract laws that favor big business over small. Under recently revised bankruptcy laws, the billionaire Donald Trump can freely declare bankruptcy while insulating himself from risks to investment, while smaller businesses cannot. The choice is not, Reich argues, between a governed and an ungoverned market, but between a market governed by laws favoring monopolistic companies and one governed by those favoring small business. Ironically, the economic sector that stands to suffer most from big monopolies is small business, many of which are run by those who favor the Tea Party. It might not be too much to say that the embrace of the 1 percent by mom-and-pop store owners is a bit like the natural seed–using small farmers' embrace of Monsanto, the corner grocery store's embrace of Walmart, the local bookstore owner's embrace of Amazon. Under the same banner of the "free market," the big are free to dominate the small.

But it is very hard to criticize an ally, and the right sees the free market as its ally against the powerful alliance of the federal government and the takers. Even Lee Sherman, who had greatly suffered at the hands of Pittsburgh Plate Glass, owned stock in it and exclaimed proudly to me, when I asked him how he felt about getting fired, "I was pissed and stunned but, hey, I didn't lose everything. I had $5,000 in stocks!"

In the undeclared class war, expressed through the weary, aggravating, and ultimately enraging wait for the American Dream, those I came to know developed a visceral hate for the ally of the "enemy" cutters in line—the federal government. They hated other people for needing it. They rejected their own need of it—even to help clean up the pollution in their backyard.

DISCUSSION QUESTIONS

1. What other issues have an empathy wall that separates two sides? How can sociology help people get over that wall?
2. What is the great paradox she refers to? How is it resolved?
3. Who or what do Tea Party supporters think will make businesses avoid pollution?

4. What role do emotions play in people's political beliefs? How do emotions shape your political values?
5. She notes that many people she talked to were adamant that government regulation was completely unjustified and uncalled for, but that that view did not seem to apply to all parts of the population in Louisiana. Whose interests/hobbies/bodies are relatively unregulated in Louisiana? Whose are highly regulated?
6. What role does Fox News play in the lives of the people she met? How does Fox play a role in the deep story she describes?
7. Watch Hochschild describe more about her research and how she thinks empathy walls and deep stories can help us bridge the political divide using this link: https://www.youtube.com/watch?v=o2flsUT9_QM. Do her insights about empathy walls help you think differently about those whose political opinions differ from your own? Why or why not?

Uberland

How Algorithms Are Rewriting the Rules of Work

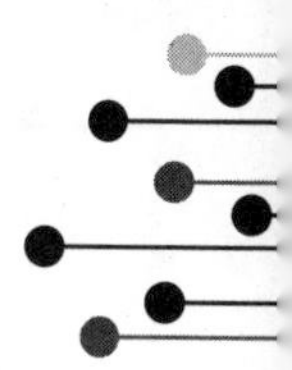

Alex Rosenblat

Uber is one of numerous technology companies whose presence is a routine feature of day-to-day life for many in America. As part of the self-described "sharing economy," companies like Uber, Lyft, and Airbnb describe themselves as technology companies that connect users of their software so they can share services (like rides or a place to stay) with each other. Uber in particular studiously avoids referring to drivers as employees or workers, instead using the term "end user" to refer to drivers and underscoring in its public statements (including in lawsuits against it) that drivers are users of its algorithmic software, not employees.

In this excerpt from her book Uberland, *Alex Rosenblat highlights how this rhetoric of* end users *rather than* workers *underpins Uber's larger narrative of technological exceptionalism, the idea that "the regulations and laws that apply to their industry competitors or precursors do not apply to them for the simply reason that they identify primarily as a technology companies" (see p. 370). This in turn is linked to a standard argument from tech companies, that limited or low regulation is essential to innovation, and that using technology to "disrupt" various segments of society is positive and productive.*

Unfortunately, as Rosenblat shows, much of this disruption comes at the expense of basic protections for workers and without any accountability to the aspects of society that are being disrupted. She shows how Uber and other tech companies trade on the idea that their presence in a community is both a mark of prestige (and also essential to members of a community) to blatantly disregard existing laws in ways that ordinary citizens, and particularly minorities, are often harshly punished for doing.

This reading also demonstrates the importance of language in shaping how we think about the world, and how organizations use language to increase their power. Alongside that, Rosenblat makes the case that companies like Uber are fundamentally changing the way we think about work and employment at a societal level. Her sociological critique of Uber's place in our culture highlights the ways that social class, race, technology, and government collide in the sea of innovation and change that companies like Uber have helped create.

Excerpt from *Uberland: How Algorithms Are Rewriting the Rules of Work* by Alex Rosenblat.

As you read, think about the importance of language in shaping how we think about technology, and how the technologies she talks about are influencing public spaces, resources, and services.

Cole is a part-time Uber driver in Atlanta. On his first week on the job, he finds himself driving a man who has clearly had too many drinks. The passenger, a new arrival to the city, wants to know what to do and where to go, so Cole informs him of several tourist destinations. "Out of nowhere," Cole recounts, "he yells at the top of his lungs and slams his hands on my dashboard. 'Dude, shut the F up. Seriously, just shut the F up or I'm going to have to hurt you.'" Stunned at the sudden outburst, Cole finds his bearings and quietly adjusts his hands on the wheel, careful to keep them loose in case he needs to ward off his aggressive passenger. They ride on in silence. A little while later, Cole's passenger asks if he can smoke in the car. Hoping to appease him, Cole pulls over, so the stench doesn't ruin his car interior—and possibly land him in trouble with a future ride. Each of them smokes a cigarette standing at opposite ends of the car. When they arrive at their destination, Cole's passenger invites him inside to smoke marijuana, and after he declines, suggests another cigarette instead. Feeling agitated and eager to keep the peace, Cole doesn't feel he can easily get out of this one.

"I didn't know the Uber guidelines then," says Cole. Company rules advise that riders who behave disrespectfully can lose access to the Uber platform. But even knowing the guidelines isn't enough to negotiate all the exigencies of a ridehailing job. "If I knew then what I know now, the second he got out of the car I would have driven off. But I didn't know that. I didn't know the kinds of repercussions at the time, having been on it only for a week." His passenger asked for a hug before Cole left, and it lasted too long. Drawing on the customer service skills he had honed at his primary job, Cole brought his hand in front of his chest and gently broke the embrace.

Nearly a year after that first harrowing incident, Cole still drives for Uber, part time. But he also wears another hat: he's a forum administrator, one of many across the globe who put in countless hours managing unofficial online communities where drivers who work for Uber, Lyft, and other ridehail services share advice and warnings, answer questions, and provide a rare sense of camaraderie. Another driver, Doberman, who is also an administrator of a forum group for Uber and Lyft drivers, in Louisiana, says about his own group, "I didn't create the group to learn something from somebody, but to get together with some people." When I interviewed him, he emphasized that he's trying to foster an environment where drivers can coach each other. "I want caring and more sharing when someone has a problem, not just to look over it." Ridehail drivers at Uber and elsewhere have no way to speak with one another through the app.

Instead, the forums—along with journalism, social media, and in-person conversations—are providing a vital source of information for workers trying to navigate a new set of labor practices.

Drivers enjoy the formal freedom to log in or log out of work when they want, but that freedom is constrained in practice. As drivers do their work, they must continually deal with Uber's shifting pay rates, experimental policies, and incentives. An employment relationship like this, which evolves with iterative features, produces instability for drivers as workers, not just as users. Technology companies create products that shape the user's experience of their services; but when the user is a *worker,* these experiments change the nature of work, with mixed effects. Nonetheless, Uber's drivers continue to reap benefits, from the scheduling flexibility to the social connections they make with passengers. As legal scholar V. B. Duval said to me about the growth of insecure work (particularly with regard to the deregulation of the taxi industry), "The good things about this work don't necessarily go away even if you no longer have benefits or security. The affective benefits, like the community you build with other drivers during down periods, continue."

Nevertheless, some of the drawbacks of algorithmic management center on information scarcity, rather than on discussions of employment benefits. Drivers don't have an employee handbook when they start out: instead, they learn what the rules are over time through hundreds of text messages, emails, and in-app notifications. To manage the cognitive load of rapidly shifting terms and conditions in their employment, some drivers turn to information-sharing forums online. On these driver-led forums—on Facebook, on message boards, and on chat apps like WhatsApp, Zello, and WeChat—drivers are forging their own informal information networks, outside the algorithmically proscriptive realm of the ridehail apps. Drivers are always playing catchup to Uber's iterations. Uber may be changing the rules of work, but thanks to digital communications, drivers, too, are creating a workplace culture. These centers of community create an institutional memory that persists even when Uber's practices change. What remains to be seen is how these drivers and their new workplace practices will influence broader culture—including other jobs and other technology companies—because Uber, as the cultural icon of the New Economy, has already left an indelible mark on far more than ridehailing.

The Myth of Technological Exceptionalism

Taxi drivers have protested that Uber violates the laws that regulate their industry by operating without permits, but Uber maintains that it is not a taxi company—it's a technology company that uses neutral algorithms to merely facilitate connections between consumers and drivers. Meanwhile, the growth of Uber has quickly become a threat to the highly regulated taxi industry's monopoly on chauffeur services. Companies like Uber and Airbnb separate themselves from their predecessors, taxis and hotels, by emphasizing the altruistic premise of their "sharing" platforms. Airbnb argues that it is a technology platform, like Facebook, YouTube, or Google, that connects hosts with guests. In conflicts with Airbnb, the hotel industry alleges that the company operates illegal hotels: hosts rent out their spare rooms or homes to traveling guests but do not have to comply with the safety regulations that govern hotels or bed and breakfasts.

Likewise, Facebook, which is in the business of sharing news, resists being categorized as a media company. A media company can be regulated and held to account for journalistic ethics, editorial responsibilities, and news accuracy (rather than "fake news"). A neutral platform that uses algorithms to spread content or to curate newsfeeds is the product of engineering and automation, and these efface the responsibilities a media company might have under the guise of technological innocence. Scholars and journalists have penned marked retorts to Facebook's arguments, but the logic that Facebook uses is similar to what Uber deploys.

Silicon Valley carries the banner of "technological exceptionalism," the idea that the regulations and laws that apply to their industry competitors or predecessors do not apply to them for the simple reason that they identify primarily as technology companies. These tech giants reason that the technology services they offer to achieve a familiar goal (like moving a passenger from A to B in a taxi) are qualitatively different from the actions that these laws were designed to govern. This effectively renders laws archaic, to some degree, and this pattern among Silicon Valley tech companies is often termed "disruption." Law scholar Julia Tomassetti argues that the sharing economy amounts to regulatory arbitrage (an attempt to circumvent unfavorable regulation).

Treating Labor as Consumption: How Uber Justifies Its Management Practices

The vocabulary of technology that Uber deploys to describe its drivers and its own practices has implications for labor: it treats drivers as end users of its software, rather than as workers at all. *End users* is a perfect example of the language of disinformation that distances drivers from employment. The term appears in court documents in lawsuits over Uber's allegedly illegal employment practices and in company communications with the public. The rhetorical impact of that language is clever: as a society, we might be persuaded to care about workers, but who cares about end users? By fudging the terms of employment within its control, such as by potentially misclassifying drivers as independent contractors, and by pivoting to frame drivers as customers or end users, Uber provides us with a template for questioning what we know about employment relationships. And although technology practices and rhetoric have ushered in another way of doing business, older problems, such as harassment, persist under the veneer of technological neutrality.

Using a thin argument about technological exceptionalism, Uber tried to maneuver around legal walls in the case of Douglas O'Connor, Thomas Colopy, Matthew Manahan, and Elie Gurfinkel vs. Uber Technologies. However, Judge Edward M. Chen seemed to find the company's reasoning highly improbable. When presented with the idea that drivers are customers, he said, "The fact that you screen drivers, select them, the fact that you, Uber, sets *[sic]* the fare, not the drivers, the fact that the company could not operate and exist as a company and make money without drivers, you think that does not establish, among other things, that these drivers serve Uber?" Uber's shifts between the language of labor and the language of consumers evoke its earlier tactics of regulatory arbitrage. There's no "sharing" in the sharing economy it has come to represent. In practice, drivers are hardly "entrepreneurs" or true partners with Uber, even though the company calls them "Uber Driver-Partners"; drivers are not suspended or fired, they are "deactivated." This conflation of workers with customers is clearly a cause for disbelief. And yet, the miscategorization has deep roots within Uber's claims about the employment relationship it has with its drivers. Regulators may support that blurring by using language consistent with Uber's own: in 2016, the Federal Trade Commission brought legal action against Uber on the basis that it had misled drivers about their earnings, but the FTC also referred to Uber drivers as "entrepreneurial consumers."

On a cool evening in San Francisco in 2016, I find myself sitting across from a senior Uber employee. Employees had invited me to their offices in the past, but since I've declined to sign a nondisclosure agreement before holding meetings with Uber employees, I'm not able to meet with them inside. Instead, the senior employee and I are meeting at a "non-NDA" café near Uber headquarters. I ask if the company tries to build trust with its drivers, and the answer—that Uber cares about building trust with all of its end users—floors me. The fact that even in an informal interview this person is deploying the language used in the lawsuits gives me pause, and I will return to this moment over and over again in my mind in the months that follow. As our table becomes littered with cappuccino cups, the senior employee persists in asking me how Uber can improve its relationship with drivers. I can't help but think this is roughly akin to asking how to improve your relationship with your girlfriend after she discovers that she is, in fact, the mistress.

The implications are stark: if the problems that Uber drivers experience at work can be reframed as customer satisfaction problems, these drivers lose access to remedies like employment law, which is available to workers in other businesses to redress any harms they suffer as part of their employment. It isn't just Uber using this language—it's echoed by other companies, including Lyft and, across the ocean, a British food-delivery service called Deliveroo. The kind of employment relationship that Uber has with its drivers is not unique: rather, it signals a greater social force that is turning workers into customers through the power of technological tools and narrative. Deliveroo, for example, classifies its food-delivery people as independent contractors in a dozen or so of the countries where it operates, and classifies some, in other countries, as employees, such as in the United Arab Emirates. According to several Deliveroo employees I spoke with in 2017, this boils down largely to the laws that define employment relationships in those respective places. However, the company contorts itself in order to avoid giving the impression that its workers are considered employees. As one media outlet, among many, reported in June 2017, about a leaked doc: "It says bicycle couriers who work for Deliveroo are never to be referred to as workers, employees, or staff, and that the Deliveroo jackets they have to wear on the job are not uniforms but 'branded clothing.' These workers don't have 'contracts,' says the document, but 'supplier agreements.' They don't 'schedule shifts,' but 'indicate their availability.' And they can never get sacked—instead, they're 'terminated.'"

On a different occasion, I meet another senior Uber employee, who makes a comment that reflects the same "drivers-are-customers" sentiment. He arrives a few minutes late to our meeting, overtly casual in a white T-shirt with a matching white towel to wipe away the sweat of an early morning jog from his forehead. His casually authoritative energy on a variety of subjects reminds me of the way women strive to appear effortlessly slim as a practiced way of projecting status. When we hit on the topic of improving customer service for drivers, he explains that, if you count all of the people working in tech in every single function, and then you count all the people working in customer support, the latter is significantly larger. He indicates that there are twice as many customer support agents as employees. Taking it all in, I squint on the inside, and smile on the outside, before observing with a briny smile, "That's because you don't count your drivers as employees." Dipping his head, he concedes that drivers are a much larger group than either of those—about ten times bigger. The central conflict between how to categorize a driver, and how to consider work in the sharing economy more broadly, animates a lot of the conflict between labor advocates and Uber.

By treating labor as consumption, Uber can have its cake and eat it too. When Uber describes its technology as a way to merely (and neutrally) connect two groups of end users—drivers and passengers—it underplays a more pressing reality: Uber's algorithms give the company vast leverage over how drivers do their work. When drivers are misled by algorithmic bosses, it is merely an example of how Silicon Valley companies with power can play us all. Uber's employment conflicts reveal *why* drivers are unfairly treated in a legal framework, but the context of employment merely illustrates how technology platforms can take advantage of all consumers. The context of the workplace provides us with a lens for examining inequities that emerge and multiply in a tech-driven world. The question for us to consider is whether algorithmic management creates a qualitative distinction between work and consumption. Uber's arguments actually articulate dynamic changes in how employment and consumption are negotiated in digital spaces through algorithmic power and transparency.

Gratitude Logic: Move Fast, Break Things, Cite Technology Contributions Later

In its initial rise, from 2009 to 2014 or so, Uber came to represent the sharing economy and was widely celebrated in forums on the future of work, in the media, and across academic and policy circles. Sharing-economy companies argued that they should not be put in the same categories as their industry competitors. In many ways, they successfully evaded preexisting bodies of law regulating taxi services, accommodations, and employment, although some perished by this logic too (e.g., HomeJoy, a housecleaning company, went out of business after employment misclassification suits hampered its fund-raising efforts). Uber banked on the political legacy of Silicon Valley to steamroll local governments that tried to regulate it, too: the technology industry has operated with low regulatory oversight because it successfully persuaded regulators, and society, that low regulation is essential to innovation. This social pact is morally persuasive because of a mainstream belief that the fruits of innovation—specifically, technology services and devices—benefit society. That relationship is characterized by sharing or reciprocity, which implicitly obscures the political power technology companies have over society.

This logic is especially salient because some corners of American technology culture de-emphasize the importance of a social welfare net and are receptive instead to the interventions of private wealth to salve public deficits. One of Uber's Silicon Valley neighbors, Facebook, received serious criticism when it took that attitude abroad. In a program called "Free Basics," Facebook aimed to bring the Internet to underserved populations in India on the premise that this program would bridge the digital divide between those who are connected and those who are not. "Free Basics" wasn't the Internet, though; it was a Facebook portal with some access to

Facebook-curated content and limited access to other digital functions. In effect, Facebook positioned itself as the Internet. In a backlash that continues through 2018, Facebook's efforts have been widely decried as "digital colonialism."

There is a certain receptiveness to tech companies who come in to replace public infrastructure, because they promise certain benefits, like free laptops or, in Uber's case, less road congestion. *New York Times* journalist Natasha Singer identified these dynamics in a multipronged investigation of education-technology adoption in public schools. Her investigation revealed that tech oligarchs were equipping schools with ed-tech programs and devices, and in the process they were changing the nature of the curriculum without any public reckoning of these changes. Microsoft, Facebook, Google, and Salesforce all backed Code.org, the main actor of this story, as the prototype for reform. Its founder, Hadi Partovi, likened Code.org's role to the sharing economy: "Airbnb is disrupting the travel space, but they don't own the hotels," he said, adding, "We are in a similar model, disrupting education. But we are not running the school and we don't hire the teachers." In effect, he said that he is not responsible for the institution of education, stakeholder consultation, or the relationship that schools have with their employees. His digital intervention is capable of disrupting or seriously changing the school model without the responsibilities of ownership.

The *gratitude logic* of "accept our contribution, but don't expect us to submit to governance in this space" was similarly visible in an advertising campaign by Airbnb in San Francisco. A sample ad plastered to a bus stop shelter read, "Dear Public Library System, We hope you use some of the $12 million in hotel taxes to keep the library open later." The condescending ads, which hinted broadly at the city's ingratitude for the taxes that Airbnb's business generates, followed an $8 million lobbying campaign by the company against San Francisco's 2015 ballot measure Proposition F. Voters ultimately rejected the proposition, which would have restricted short-term rentals and thus undermined Airbnb's short-term-rental business model. Gratitude logic is part of how Uber drums up popular support for its regulatory evasions. Even in cities like New York, Chicago, or Toronto, with strict quotas on how many cabs can be in operation, Uber prevails when it insists that it's not a taxi company but rather a technology company; the old rules don't apply to the digital world. For consumers, Uber disrupted a calcified taxi industry that was chiefly known for its inadequate service, while Airbnb undid the monopoly that expensive hotels had on tourism by creating a platform for hosts to rent out their spare bedrooms or homes. The unrepentant politics of disruption became the social standard for assessing the value of technological innovation in society, against the value of entrenched industries.

Despite its reputation, Uber claims to have a cooperative attitude toward governments and regulators. The company wrote to me, "We are actually trying to get governments to update their regulations to use resources and infrastructure more efficiently." Uber is, of course, willing to play nice with regulators as long as they cave in and accommodate the company's perspective. One senior Uber employee shared his theory about Uber's culture clash when we met, and it stuck with me for a while. He mused that Uber's conflicts were about the new world, represented by leaders like Uber cofounder Travis Kalanick, coming into *direct contact* with the old world of compliance, law, hierarchy, and order. The clash is big, public, and polarizing.

In California, where Uber started, the state government took real steps to align itself with advances in technology and society, attempting to be a dance partner in step with ridehail companies. Yet when the Department of Motor Vehicles developed a license for the budding self-driving cars developed by companies like Uber, Google, Lyft, and others, Uber refused to cooperate, contradicting its stated rhetoric. Instead, it debuted its self-driving cars without licenses in the streets of San Francisco. When the DMV and State Attorney General Kamala Harris threatened legal action, Uber initially refused to back down. It offered a flimsy premise, that its particular technology was simply not subject to the rules the DMV had developed.

The most important part of Uber's encounter with the California DMV was the company's rejection of the government's authority on principle. Citing Tesla's autopilot technology as an example of self-driving-car technology that doesn't require a permit, Uber argued that the testing permits the DMV devised for self-driving cars didn't apply to Uber's self-driving cars because they were, in fact, not yet capable of autonomous driving without a human overseer. Anthony Lewandowski, Uber's lead engineer on self-driving cars (who was accused of stealing Google's self-driving Internet protocol when he left and came to Uber), announced, "We cannot in good conscience sign up to regulation for something we're not doing." Uber directly contravened the law with no remorse, and with no real impact. The attorney general's office wrote to Uber in response: "We are asking Uber to adhere to California law and immediately remove its 'self-driving' vehicles from the state's roadways until Uber complies with all applicable statutes and regulations[,] . . . until it obtains the appropriate permit, as 20 other companies have done." Rather than change its approach, Uber packed up its self-driving cars and delivered them to Arizona, with the expectation that regulatory requirements there would be minimal. (In March 2018, Arizona suspended Uber's self-driving car tests after one of them struck and killed a woman as she walked her bicycle across the street in Tempe, Arizona.) Uber's seemingly disingenuous protest against regulations highlights the power of technology companies to ignore the clear intentions of legal authorities.

At the same time, it's disconcerting to watch Uber raise the banner of illegality-as-innovation. Couched in the context of Silicon Valley disruption, however, this illegality-as-innovation can seem like daring entrepreneurial work. But this is a kind of privilege afforded billion-dollar corporations and their (often white) technologist founders that is denied to other segments of the population. Uber was flouting California's rules in 2016, whereas, two years earlier, Eric Garner was choked to death by police—allegedly for selling loose cigarettes. On such a small scale, performed without technology and by a lower-income black man, illegality is not merely punished but punished swiftly and completely out of measure. When law enforcement goes easy on tech entrepreneurs breaking the law but cracks down on racial minorities peacefully living quiet lives, the cultural-privilege dynamics that Uber benefits from become plainly obvious.

What happens to Uber tells us a lot about who may break the law under the guise of innovative disruption with less severe consequences. For some critics, the disruption ethos of technology—often summarized as "move fast, break things" and "don't ask permission; ask forgiveness later"—eerily echoes rape culture, where entitlement and privilege supersede consent.

Travis Kalanick, Uber's most prominent cofounder, has come to represent Silicon Valley warrior-kings. Despite Uber's status as a "decacorn" and its valuation of approximately 70 billion dollars, Kalanick finally resigned in June 2017 because endless scandals were jeopardizing the company's future. Sarah Lacy, longtime Silicon Valley journalist, observed in a keynote speech at Startup Fest in Montreal on July 14, 2017:

> Silicon Valley is a homegrown culture: whoever the highest-value company is, disproportionately impacts the entire culture of that era. Starting with Uber, the highest-valued company in Silicon Valley history from a pre-IPO standpoint, $70 billion—never seen anything to this level before. Total founder control. Founder finally gets ousted because of three years of scandal. Because the disruption and lawbreaking that got them so many billions of dollars, all of those valuations and magazine covers—it turned out they didn't know the difference between breaking taxi laws, breaking labor laws, stealing trade secrets. It was just a lawless organization.

Uber's aggressive disregard for proper adherence to normative restrictions on their behavior is part of the macho attitude of disruption that the sharing economy popularizes in American society.

Yet Uber's reputational roller coaster doesn't necessarily affect its larger legacy: the idea of Uber is important to how we imagine the desirability of technology in society. In its ascent to global heights, Uber has become a shibboleth for technology optimists. For many cities, having Uber is the mark of being on the cutting edge, or at least being part of the global technology-business marketplace. When Uber and Lyft turned swiftly on their heels and left Austin, Texas, in May 2016, in a show of protest against regulatory efforts to impose requirements on them (like data-sharing and fingerprint-based background checks for drivers), the moment was captioned in the press by disdainful headlines such as "By Losing Uber, Austin Is No Longer a Tech Capital." In Vancouver, which has been the least-eager major city in Canada to accept sharing-economy companies, worried University of British Columbia alum and community experts at the university participated in panels such as, in late November 2016, "Why Has Vancouver Been So Slow to Join the Sharing Economy?"

The absence of Uber in metropolitan places is a wrinkle on those cities' reputations, a symbol that they lag behind their more forward peers. The use of Uber has become infrastructural in some cities, a default method of private transit for many. In May 2017, a Painesville, Ohio, municipal judge ordered convicted DUI offenders to download Uber and Lyft onto their phones as part of the conditions of their probation. To consumers, the experience of traveling to an Uber-free zone can feel like culture shock, as disconcerting as when Americans and Canadians go to Europe and learn that they have to pay to use the toilet.

Uber is more than an app you download onto your phone: it changes the way we move around cities, like WhatsApp does in Brazil or Waze does in Israel. Turning off WhatsApp in Brazil would destabilize communications nationwide; likewise, when Waze erroneously advised drivers in Israel to avoid a major roadway, mad traffic jams ensued. The idea of Uber and the logic of its business model have already surpassed Uber itself.

Both as workers and consumers, we have integrated the algorithms of Silicon Valley into our daily lives. The case of Uber shows us that technology has changed work in ways that are unexpected and potentially irreversible. The sharing economy popularized wider changes to work culture by conflating work with altruistic contributions, bringing into question the identity of workers and devaluing work itself. Meanwhile, Uber advanced its own vision of the legal status of its workers, emphasizing that they were closer to technology consumers than workers. This seemingly legalistic nuance is in reality a cultural sea change in how we categorize work.

Uber's employment model, driven by algorithmic practices, represents how technology is permanently altering not only how we define work but also how it is organized. I doubt that Uber set out to undo how work is defined. Rather, as it navigates the challenges to its business, Uber seems to sense the broader cultural undercurrents and know how to effectively mobilize them to defend its practices. The conflicts it raises along the way illustrate how we chafe against those practices, but ultimately, the success of Uber as an idea condones the practices that made it a billion-dollar, global reality. And regardless of what happens to Uber now, the changes are already here.

The conflicted relationship between Uber and its drivers is an example of how labor relations are being shaped in our new, digital age. The rise of algorithmic management of consumers is prominent across Silicon Valley's data-driven technologies. You can't go far in daily life without encountering these systems: GPS navigation apps, like Google Maps, generate route recommendations and crowdsource traffic routes, while Facebook relies on an engine of algorithms to curate the information we digest. We don't imagine Facebook or Google as part of the sharing economy, but Uberland brings to light the power that technology platforms have to disadvantage users even as platforms are shielded by the rhetoric of neutrality.

On the surface, the company's self-serving argument that its drivers are consumers of its technology, like passengers, appears to be just another play to escape regulation. After all, Uber has developed a reputation for changing course whenever the rules catch up with it. But upon closer examination, Uber does treat drivers both like consumers and like workers. By blurring these lines, Uber creates a legacy for how we all identify as workers or consumers. Uber benefits from this strategic ambiguity because it's hard to decide *which* rules apply to its model. If drivers are unpaid for work they perform, should they allege wage theft under labor law, or seek redress for unfair and deceptive practices under consumer protection law? Uber broke norms, not just laws, exposing the fragility of both. It remains an open question whether the new norms Uber ushers in are better or worse for labor and for consumers.

The impact of Uber is profound. Despite the scandals it weathers, and perhaps because of its sustained coverage in the media, Uber is objectified as the future of work in the popular imagination. At the same time, the story of Uber is just one example of how we are all being played by the technologies that have become commonplace, because, simply put, we want to use them. With an unorthodox approach, Uber has changed the playing field in significant ways for a host of stakeholders—from drivers to passengers, from workers to consumers, from the technology industry to the taxi business, and from governments and regulators to civil rights groups. Yet perhaps more importantly, by working the rules of the system to its advantage, Uber used Silicon Valley algorithms to rewrite the rules of work.

DISCUSSION QUESTIONS

1. What role does language play in how Uber shapes its identity?
2. What is algorithmic management?

3. What is regulatory arbitrage? Why is it important?
4. Think about our own experiences with services like Uber, Lyft, or Airbnb. These companies claim that both you and the person providing the service are both merely "end users" of their software, you are not a customer, and the driver or host is not a worker. Is that how it feels when you use these services?
5. What is gratitude logic? What other companies can you think of have used gratitude logic in their dealings with government officials? Do you think that individuals could get away with making the same types of arguments that large technology companies make when they break the law? Why or why not?
6. How is "illegality as innovation" related to race?
7. Watch this interview with Alex Rosenblat to learn more about Uber's business practices and how it affects how we think about work: https://www.youtube.com/watch?v=XESackXDg-4. (Note that the description of this video on YouTube will appear in German when you click on the link, but the actual video and interview are in English.)